Flight Safety

A primer for general aviation pilots

Alexander T. Wells, Ed.D.

This book is dedicated to the memory of Roger Sullivan,
our first flight training coordinator
at Broward Community College, whose life was lost in
the crash of a light airplane on February 14, 1986,
in Dania, Florida.

Roger was a retired air force colonel,
a highly experienced flight instructor, father, friend,
and an inspiration to the many students
with whom he had contact.

Flight Safety

A primer for general aviation pilots

Alexander T. Wells, Ed.D.

TAB | TAB BOOKS
Blue Ridge Summit, PA

FIRST EDITION
FIRST PRINTING

© 1992 by **TAB Books**.
TAB Books is a division of McGraw-Hill, Inc.

Library of Congress Cataloging-in-Publication Data

Wells, Alexander T.
   Flight safety / by Alex Wells.
     p.   cm.
   Includes index.
   ISBN 0-8306-3996-9 (h)
   1. Aeronautics—Safety measures. I. Title.
TL553.W45 1992
629.132′52′0289—dc20   92-6060
                                 CIP

TAB Books offers software for sale. For information and a catalog, please contact TAB Software Department, Blue Ridge Summit, PA 17294-0850.

Acquisitions Editor: Jeff Worsinger
Book Editor: Suzanne L. Cheatle
Director of Production: Katherine G. Brown
Series Design: Jaclyn J. Boone

Photo credits:
Beech Aircraft Corp., 1
Federal Aviation Administration, 19, 61
Broward Community College, Miami, FL, 41
Piper Aircraft Co., 81, 163
Cessna Aircraft Co., 105, 141, 185

Contents

4
CHAPTER

Weather briefings and icing   61

5
CHAPTER

Winter weather operations   81

6
CHAPTER

Takeoffs and landings   105

7
CHAPTER

Midair collisions   141

8 CHAPTER Miscellaneous in-flight hazards 163

9 CHAPTER Ground operations and maintenance 185

Study guide 205
Index 255

Acknowledgments

This textbook would not have been possible without the numerous publications available from the Federal Aviation Administration, including advisory circulars, brochures, and other material used in the FAA Accident Prevention Program. In this regard, I am particularly indebted to the authors of those publications.

I also acknowledge the assistance from the editors at TAB Books, who helped me through the various stages of production.

Thanks are also due to Julie and Joni Williams for the outstanding quality and timeliness of their work in typing the manuscript under the pressure of deadline dates.

Finally, a special recognition to my wife, Mary, for her continuous support through yet another book.

Preface

Total safety of flight is no doubt an unattainable goal. The aerial environment is a hostile one to humans. To remain aloft requires the cooperation of many elements, human and mechanical; it is too much to expect that, over the decades and millions of hours of flights, one or another of those elements will not from time to time fail us. Nevertheless, retrospective examination of aircraft accidents reveals that many occur unnecessarily. The element that failed was within our control. More often than not, it was the pilot who brought about or contributed to the accident. A high percentage are the result of one or a combination of the following factors:

1. a lack of basic knowledge and skills of pilots
2. a complacent attitude toward safety
3. flight hazards associated with the aviation environment

The purpose of *Flight Safety: A Primer for General Aviation Pilots* is to explore accident causes and to promote an understanding of the major factors that affect the general aviation safety record. Once these factors were identified, an attempt was made to review the numerous publications provided by the FAA, such as advisory circulars and other brochures used in its Accident Prevention Program, that address the major causal factors of accidents. This material was categorized under eight chapters, which provides a logical approach, in textbook format, to improving your attitude toward safety, refreshing your aeronautical knowledge, and improving your aeronautical skills.

This book should find a broad spectrum of readers, although its primary value will be to those students enrolled in aviation flight programs. It is at this stage in their career that an attitude toward safety is formed. Nevertheless, the principles and practices covered in this book apply to every category of proficiency.

Characteristics of the text

This text employs a number of features that are designed to facilitate student learning. They are:

Chapter outlines   Each chapter opens with an outline of the major topics to be covered.

Chapter objectives   The broad objectives of the chapter are included so students will know exactly what is to be accomplished after completing the material.

Logical organization and frequent headings   The material covered has been put in a systematic framework so students know where they have been, where they are, and where they are going in the text. The sequence of material generally follows the flight process from planning, takeoff, landing, and ground operations. The first chapter analyzes the major causes and related factors contributing to accidents. It is followed by a thorough discussion of the physiological factors affecting the performance of flight crewmembers. The next three chapters address all of the major problem areas in the flight-planning process, including weather briefings and winter weather operations. Takeoffs and landings are the most crucial phases of flight and are taken up in chapter 6. The subject of midair collisions follows, including ways of avoiding this growing concern. The remaining two chapters cover miscellaneous in-flight hazards and safety during ground operations and maintenance.

Key terms   Each chapter concludes with a list of key terms used in the text.

Review questions   Review questions at the end of each chapter cover all of the important points.

Student study guide   A study guide includes over 400 objective questions that include multiple choice, true/false, fill-in, and matching.

Complete index   A complete index is included to help the student find needed information.

Organization of the text

The following is a brief overview of each chapter.

CHAPTER 1. **General aviation safety analysis.**   This chapter provides a review of NTSB safety data in an attempt to identify the major causes and related factors associated with accidents and incidents. The importance of training and knowing ATC procedures, particularly around airports, is also stressed. The chapter closes with a discussion of the FAA Accident Prevention Program.

CHAPTER 2. **Physiological factors.** The importance of good health is the major focus at the beginning of this chapter. Following is a discussion of the effects of illness and medication on the body. The subjects of hypoxia, hyperventilation, carbon monoxide poisoning, and spatial disorientation are thoroughly explored. The chapter concludes with an in-depth coverage of self-imposed stress resulting from psychological factors, tobacco smoking, alcohol, and drugs.

CHAPTER 3. **Flight planning.** Chapter 3 addresses all the major factors in the flight-planning process, including density altitude, aircraft weight and balance, fuel and runway requirements, and changes to the plan in flight. The importance of a pilot knowing his or her own capabilities and those of the aircraft to be flown is also stressed.

CHAPTER 4. **Weather briefings and icing.** This chapter examines the various types of preflight weather briefings, including the importance of exercising good weather judgment. Thunderstorms and windshear represent two of the worst weather hazards experienced in flight. These subjects are thoroughly explored, including precautions to pilots encountering such conditions. The chapter concludes with a discussion of carburetor icing.

CHAPTER 5. **Winter weather operations.** Some of the most serious accidents occur during winter weather operations. The subject of structural icing is thoroughly covered, followed by a section on flight planning during winter months, including inspection items and precautions. The remainder of the chapter covers all the crucial factors that must be considered while taxiing, during takeoff, climbout, en route, letdown, landing, and postflight, including a final section of surviving a crash during the winter months.

CHAPTER 6. **Takeoffs and landings.** Unquestionably, takeoffs and landings are the most crucial stages of flight and the phases where most accidents occur. This relatively long chapter begins with a discussion on the importance of flying safely at low airspeeds. A thorough discussion of the problem of engine failure at low altitudes is then covered. Other topics included are wake turbulence, traffic advisory practices, and planning safe landings. The remainder of the chapter deals with factors affecting and proper techniques in executing safe landings.

CHAPTER 7. **Midair collisions.** A growing concern in all segments of aviation, midair collisions represent one of the most catastrophic hazards in aviation. Chapter 7 reviews the background of midair collisions and factors affecting safe separation of traffic. A thorough discussion of the air traffic control system follows, including the subject of transponders. The chapter concludes by reviewing ways of avoiding midair collisions.

CHAPTER 8. **Miscellaneous in-flight hazards.** Chapter 8 opens with a discussion of dead reckoning navigation as an important supplement to electronic navigation guidance systems. Then follows a discussion of selected miscellaneous flight hazards, such as fuel selector errors, pneumatic system malfunction, night flying, wire strikes, child restraint systems, and the proper use of shoulder harnesses.

CHAPTER 9. **Ground operations and maintenance.** This chapter concentrates on ground operations, including proper taxiing techniques and basic steps an aircraft owner can take in maintaining his or her aircraft. Other topics covered include airworthiness directives, exhaust system failures, and fuel contamination.

APPENDIX. **Study guide.** The study guide provides approximately 400 objective questions—multiple choice, true/false, fill-in, matching—that students can use to review the material in this book.

General aviation safety analysis

Outline

Learning objectives

After completing this chapter, you should be able to:

△ Recognize the trends in accident statistics for all classes of general aviation operations.

△ Describe the major causes and related factors involving general aviation accidents and fatalities.

△ Define *pilot judgment*.

△ Explain why takeoff and landing are the most crucial phases of flight.

△ Discuss the importance of recurrent training programs.

△ Describe some of the growing concerns regarding changes in the airway system.

△ Recognize the importance of knowing the operating characteristics of your airplane.

△ Understand the purpose of the Accident Prevention Program and the role of its managers.

Introduction

The general aviation aircraft accident rate fell to an all-time low in 1990 as the total number of accidents dropped to the lowest level in more than 50 years, despite an increase in flying hours.

National Transportation Safety Board (NTSB) preliminary figures indicate that the total accident rate fell to 7.01 per 100,000 hours flown in 1990. The fatal NTSB accident rate for all general aviation aircraft remained steady, increasing by a scant 0.01 per 100,000 hours flown.

The 1753 accidents in 1990 involving fixed-wing general aviation aircraft weighing less than 12,500 lbs. continue a steady decline. See TABLE 1-1.

Table 1-1. Accidents, fatalities, and rates for
U.S. General Aviation Aircraft* 1979—1990

| Year | Accidents | | Total fatalities | Accident rates per 100,000 aircraft hours | |
	Total	Fatal		Total	Fatal
1979	3818	631	1221	9.88	1.63
1980	3590	618	1239	9.86	1.69
1981	3500	654	1282	9.51	1.78
1982	3233	591	1187	10.06	1.84
1983	3075	555	1064	9.90	1.79
1984	3011	543	1039	9.55	1.72
1985	2741	497	950	8.95	1.62
1986	2580	473	965	8.80	1.61
1987	2486	433	811	8.45	1.48
1988†	2363	449	781	7.97	1.52
1989*	2167	420	763	7.24	1.38
1990†	1753	362		7.01	1.39

* All operations other than those conducted under 14CFR 121 or 14CFR 135
† Preliminary data

Source: NTSB

Safety review

Since the early postwar days of 1947, when there were 9253 accidents (882 of them fatal), the general aviation safety record has, with few exceptions, been on a steadily improving trend. In 1987, a total of 2486 U.S. registered general aviation aircraft were involved in accidents in the United States and its territories. Since a collision between aircraft is counted as one accident and there were 18 accidents in which 2 general aviation aircraft collided in the air and 9 on the ground, the number of accidents in 1987 was 2459.

In its 1987 *Annual Review of Aircraft Accident Data*, published in December 1989, the NTSB categorizes and cross-references accidents according to type of aircraft, purpose of flight, phase of operation, and causes and contributing factors. Looking at the total profile, the greatest portion of accidents involved pilots between 35 and 39 years of age with between 100 and 499 hours total time who were engaged in personal flying, took place in daylight visual meteorological conditions, were precipitated by a loss of power in the landing or takeoff phases, were complicated by a loss of directional control for which pilot decision making and/ or weather conditions were to blame, ended with a collision with terrain or obstacles, and resulted in no fire or injuries.

Note that 1383 of the total 2459 accidents in 1987 resulted in no injuries. (See TABLE 1-2.) There were 431 fatal accidents (accidents that resulted in death within 30 days). The 289 serious injuries include:

1. hospitalization for more than 48 hours
2. lacerations that caused severe hemorrhages, nerve, muscle, or tendon damage
3. injury to any internal organ
4. second- or third-degree burns

Table 1-2. Summary of losses for all operations 1983 – 1987

	1983	1984	1985	1986	1987
Accidents					
Fatal	555	543	497	473	431
Involved Serious Injury	319	348	307	317	289
Involved Minor Injury	431	445	411	403	356
Involved No Injury	1770	1674	1526	1385	1383
Total	3075	3010	2741	2578	2459
Fatalities					
Passenger	484	469	431	395	345
Crew	573	549	508	481	451
Other Persons	7	21	11	89	14
Total	1064	1039	950	965	810
Aircraft Damaged*					
Destroyed	860	894	795	744	671
Substantial	2204	2085	1931	1827	1782
Minor	12	26	23	18	21
None	30	42	22	22	12
Unknown/Not Reported	0	0	0	0	0
Total	3106	3047	2771	2611	2486

*Number of General Aviation Aircraft

Source: NTSB

Single-engine airplanes were involved in 2001 accidents, which represented 81 percent of the total, 79 percent of the fatal accidents, and 75 percent of the total fatalities aboard aircraft. Fixed-wing single-engine aircraft had total and fatal accident rates of 9.41 and 1.60 per 100,000 hours, respectively. Corporate/executive flying had the lowest rates. (See TABLE 1-3.)

Table 1-3. Accidents, fatal accidents, fatalities aboard,
and rates by type of aircraft and by kind of flying for all operations—1987

Type of aircraft	Accidents	Fatal accidents	Fatalities aboard	Accident rates per 100,000 aircraft hours flown	
				Total	Fatal
Fixed wing	2222	399	748	8.10	1.45
Single recip. engine	2001	341	600	9.41	1.60
Multiple recip. engine	186	46	109	5.50	1.36
Turboprop	31	9	27	2.20	0.64
Turbojet	10	6	12	0.74	0.44
Rotorcraft	171	25	40	12.32	1.80
Recip. engine(s)	114	16	23	17.65	2.48
Turbine powered	57	9	17	7.69	1.21
Gliders	36	4	4	N/A	N/A
Balloons	27	3	3	N/A	N/A
Kind of flying					
Personal	1575	297	558	10.62*	2.07*
Business	180	46	92		
Corporate/executive	19	4	7	0.56	0.12
Aerial application	175	11	10	10.50	0.66
Instructional	337	30	56	6.87	0.61
All aircraft	2459	431	796	8.42	1.47

*The accident rate per 100,000 flying hours is presented for the combination of personal flying and business flying and not for each category separately. The NTSB has previously stated its objections to presenting separate rates until exposure data are available that depict a more credible division of flying hours between the two categories.

Source: NTSB

For the most part, these accident rates reflect the increased level of experience and training required of pilots flying more complex aircraft. They also reflect the advantages of system and powerplant redundancy.

Causes and related factors

In determining probable causes(s) of an accident, all facts, conditions, and circumstances are considered. The objective is to determine those cause-and-effect relationships in the accident sequence about which something can be done to prevent a recurrence of that kind of accident. Accordingly, for statistical purposes, where two or more causes exist in an accident, each is recorded and no attempt is made to establish a primary cause. Therefore, in TABLES 1-4 and 1-5, the figures shown in the columns dealing with cause will exceed the total number of accidents.

Table 1-4. Broad cause/factor assignments for all accidents
1987 and 1982–1986

Broad cause/factor	1987		1982–1986	
	No.	Percent	Mean	Percent
Pilot	2091	84.1	2484.4	83.9
Terrain/runway condition	730	29.4	830.6	28.0
Weather	605	24.3	791.8	26.7
Propulsion system and controls	540	21.7	633.4	21.4
Object (tree, wires, etc.)	534	21.5	587.8	19.8
Light conditions	186	7.5	254.2	8.6
Other person (not aboard)	217	8.7	244.2	8.2
Landing gear	155	6.2	225.2	7.6
Systems/equipment/instruments	104	4.2	141.0	4.8
Airframe	56	2.3	73.8	2.5
Flight control system	37	1.5	51.0	1.7
Other person (aboard)	10	0.4	20.6	0.7
Airport/airways facilities, aids	3	0.1	0.4	0.0
Number of aircraft	2486		2961.4	

Source: NTSB

The term *factor* is used, in general, to denote those elements of an accident that further explain or supplement the probable cause(s). This provides a means for collecting essential items of information that could not be categorized readily elsewhere in the system.

Human factors

Human factors is a blanket term applied to the multitude of variables, from cockpit ergonomics to pilot physiology, that affect flight-crew performance. In determining the probable cause of an accident, NTSB rarely assigns responsibility to a single factor; usually a pattern of events, none critical in itself, emerges. The first event in the pattern that leads to an accident might be found to be a loss of power, an encounter with weather or turbulence, or a loss of control, but because the pilot is ultimately responsible for the flight's safety, something the pilot did or did not do is usually found to be a factor.

In 1987, the pilot was found to be a "broad cause/factor" in 84 percent of all accidents and 89 percent of all fatal accidents; the next most common cause/fac-

Table 1-5. Broad cause/factor assignments for fatal accidents
1987 and 1982–1986

Broad cause/factor	1987		1982–1986	
	No.	**Percent**	**Mean**	**Percent**
Pilot	390	88.6	494.8	89.6
Weather	153	34.8	214.6	38.9
Terrain/runway condition	78	17.7	118.8	21.5
Light conditions	72	16.4	113.2	20.5
Object (tree, wires, etc.)	76	17.3	97.8	17.7
Propulsion system and controls	56	12.7	65.4	11.8
Other person (not aboard)	38	8.6	54.6	9.9
Airframe	20	4.5	29.2	5.3
Systems/equipment/instruments	16	3.6	21.2	3.8
Flight control system	9	2.0	15.2	2.8
Other person (aboard)	1	0.2	7.4	1.3
Landing gear	1	0.2	2.4	0.4
(All other types)	2	0.5	0.0	0.0
Number of aircraft	440		552.2	

Source: NTSB

tor, weather, was cited in 24 percent of all accidents and 35 percent of fatal accidents. (See TABLES 1-4 and 1-5.)

The NTSB's "most prevalent detailed accident causes" for 1987 named the pilot-in-command in all but 159 accidents whose causes went undetermined. (See TABLE 1-6.)

Because the reliability of airframes and powerplants has increased over the years, the onus of responsibility for accidents has fallen increasingly on the human side of the man-machine equation. Although tremendous resources have been mustered to study and reduce mechanical failures, until recently comparatively little research has been performed in the fields constituting human factors.

Although some attention was paid to training pilots in the exercise of good judgment, conventional wisdom generally held that judgment and decision-making skills could not be taught. The pilot was somehow expected to develop these skills on his or her own. In recent years, however, the Department of Transportation (DOT) and the Federal Aviation Administration (FAA) have been engaged in developing training materials and techniques to help improve pilot decision making.

Pilot judgment is the process of recognizing and analyzing all available information about oneself, the aircraft, the flying environment, and the purpose of the flight. This process is followed by a rational evaluation of alternatives to implement a timely decision for the situation that ensures safety. Pilot judgment thus

Table 1-6. Most prevalent detailed accident causes for all accidents—1987

Detailed cause	Number of aircraft	Percent of aircraft
Directional control—not maintained—pilot in command	268	10.8
Undetermined	159	6.4
Fluid, fuel—exhaustion	128	5.1
Airspeed—not maintained—pilot in command	120	4.8
In-flight planning/decision—improper—pilot in command	116	4.7
Stall—inadvertent—pilot in command	111	4.5
Preflight planning/preparation—inadequate—pilot in command	110	4.4
Compensation for wind conditions—inadequate—pilot in command	96	3.9
Visual lookout—inadequate—pilot in command	75	3.0
Fluid, fuel—starvation	66	2.7
In-flight planning/decision—poor—pilot in command	66	2.7
Unsuitable terrain—selected—pilot in command	66	2.7
Total number of aircraft:	2486	

Source: NTSB

involves one's attitudes toward risk taking and one's ability to evaluate risks and make decisions based upon one's knowledge, skills, and experience. A judgmental decision always involves a problem or choice, an unknown element, and usually a time constraint and stress.

Of course, judgment, risk assessment, decision making, and stress reduction are not the only human factors that should be of concern to safety-conscious pilots. Any factor that influences the pilot himself or his interaction with his aircraft, the flight environment, or the nature of a particular mission is ultimately a human factor. However, the traditional reliance on pilot knowledge, skill, and experience has proven to be inadequate in the overall reduction of aviation accidents and incidents. During the 1990s, we can expect to see more research performed on all aspects of human factors in flight and ever-greater emphasis placed on judgment training and the decision-making process as we gain greater knowledge of the variables that affect flight safety.

Weather

Next to faulty pilot judgment, procedures, and decision making, adverse weather has traditionally ranked as the number-two cause of all accidents, in spite of significant advances in weather detection and avoidance technology. It seems clear that no amount of airborne color radar, ground-based weather radar, Stormscopes, or increased educational efforts have had any major effect on the incidence of weather-related accidents.

To a very large extent, a pilot contributes to weather-related accidents. Like so many other categories of accidents, a pilot's faulty judgment, complacency, and experience level are frequently to blame. A pilot who learns of forecast adverse weather along his flight route, but who flies on just the same, certainly cannot blame the weather alone for an accident. NTSB will lump the accident under both adverse weather and several other catch-all categories: improper preflight planning, improper VFR or IFR procedures, or misjudgment of aircraft performance, to name a few.

Takeoff and landing

It should come as no surprise to learn that landing is the most hazardous portion of flight. According to the NTSB, 26 percent of the 2486 general aviation accidents reported in 1987 occurred in the landing phase, specifically in the flare, touchdown, or rollout.

Learning proper landing techniques and using them consistently are the most difficult tasks faced by student pilots. Many of us never really master landings. Some turn out fine. Others suffer from the effects of turbulence, crosswinds, adverse runway surface conditions, distractions, or sloppy technique.

After landings, takeoffs claim the most aircraft. In 1987, 505 accidents—or about 20 percent of the total—occurred in the takeoff phase. (See TABLE 1-7.)

Table 1-7. Most prevalent first phases of operation for all accidents—1987 and 1982–1986

	1987		1982–1986	
Phase of operation	**No.**	**Percent**	**Mean**	**Percent**
Landing	639	25.7	756.0	25.5
Takeoff	505	20.3	612.2	20.7
Cruise	379	15.2	494.4	16.7
Maneuvering	344	13.8	403.4	13.6
Approach	298	12.0	378.6	12.8
Climb	80	3.2	81.4	2.7
Taxi	67	2.7	79.6	2.7
Descent	77	3.1	79.6	2.7
Other	23	0.9	44.0	1.5
Standing	40	1.6	31.6	1.1
Not reported	9	0.4	0.6	0.0
Number of aircraft	2486	100.0	2961.4	100.0

Source: NTSB

The biggest percent of landing accidents occur during the landing roll. The airplane touches down, but the pilot fails to maintain directional control. The advent of the tricycle landing gear helped reduce the number of landing accidents, but problems persist. The ease of steering a tricycle-gear airplane can lull a pilot into complacency. The pilot might not be able to rise to the challenge of adverse wind or runway conditions. Also, each airplane has unique handling characteristics. Failure to identify and compensate for them can have serious consequences.

The initial climb is the most hazardous portion of takeoff. Most can be blamed on loss of power, but even then too many pilots succumb to the fatal temptation to turn back to the runway despite being too low and too slow. Other factors that result in takeoff accidents appear with depressing regularity in NTSB reports: exceeding gross-weight and center-of-gravity limitations, ignoring the effects of high-density altitude conditions, and failure to follow proper short- or soft-field takeoff procedures. A few airplanes crash each year because the pilot becomes distracted by an open baggage or cabin access door. The loud bang heard when a baggage door pops open just after takeoff is easily mistaken for a catastrophic engine failure. The pilot might react instinctively by reducing power, thereby ignoring the first rule in any emergency: Fly the airplane.

Cruise accidents from engine failure, fuel starvation, and weather encounters also claim a large share of airplanes each year.

Greater use of training devices and simulators during private pilot training and for recurrency training might save some pilots who otherwise would be incapable of staying upright in instrument meteorological conditions. The primary task, however, is to impress upon VFR pilots the absolute necessity to avoid such conditions in the first place.

Most accidents involving IFR operations occur in the approach phase, with missed approaches garnering the biggest share.

Each segment of a flight calls for specific planning, organization, and concentration. Pilots must think ahead to the next phase. Training and practice hone techniques, but too often training sessions are treated like pieces in a puzzle. Each piece might be shaped and colored to perfection, but they lack significance until assembled into a complete picture. The test of training is how we apply the lessons learned to our everyday flying.

Training

Mistakes can never be eliminated. Most of us make mistakes, and learn from them, each time we fly. The goal is to avoid committing the big ones, especially at critical times. We are supposed to learn correct techniques and procedures during initial training. We then stay sharp with practice and, when necessary, a little remedial instruction.

The Federal Aviation Regulations (FARs) are much more concerned with the initial training of private-certificate pilots than with recurrency or proficiency standards. FAR Part 61 lays out in detail the prerequisites—schooling, flight proficiency, and aeronautical experience—required to obtain each new certificate and rating. The standards do occasionally change in response to problems and experience. For example, the FAA studied the relationship between flight experience and the acquisition of instrument flight rules skills and found no justification for the existing minimum requirement for 200 hours total time prior to obtaining an instrument rating. As a result, the minimum experience requirement was reduced to 125 hours. Training methods also are subject to change based on new information and theories.

By contrast, the regulations contain few standards related to recurrency. The entire issue is addressed in FAR 61.57, "Recent Flight Experience: Pilot in Command." All pilots must complete a biennial flight review. To carry passengers, a pilot must have completed at least three takeoffs and landings in the preceding 90 days (or nights, if the passenger-carrying trip will take place after sunset). Instrument-rated pilots must log at least six hours of instrument time and shoot six approaches every six months to stay current. If currency lapses, the pilot must pass an instrument competency check.

That is about all the regulations have to say on the subject of pilot proficiency. Few guidelines are offered for conducting a biennial or instrument competency check. In the FAA's view, these are industry-managed programs. Flight instructors are given wide discretion over the content, scope, and direction of these two important proficiency requirements.

Formal training and recurrency programs are now springing up for single-engine pilots. Flight Safety International, Inc., has taken over all pilot and maintenance training for Cessna Aircraft Company's and Beech Aircraft Corporation's piston-engine models and now conducts three-day initial and recurrency programs for Mooney pilots, as well. The American Bonanza Society conducts flight training clinics for its members. Piper Aircraft Corporation offers initial and recurrent training courses for each of its piston-powered models. The AOPA Air Safety Foundation sponsors regular weekend flight-training clinics in various locations around the country. The FAA encourages participation in its Pilot Proficiency Award Program. Pilots are awarded certificates and lapel or tie pins in the shape of wings for completing at least three hours of flight instruction each year covering a specified curriculum and attending FAA aviation safety seminars.

One aspect of aircraft operation that needs to be examined with an eye toward improving training and proficiency standards is avionics usage. Avionics usually are given scant attention as a pilot acquires new certificates and ratings and moves into larger, more sophisticated airplanes. A pilot checking out an unfamiliar aircraft might be instructed in proper airspeeds and emergency procedures, but given a cursory introduction, if any, in the use of the avionics.

No pilot would relinquish the controls to an unpredictable stranger, yet many pilots are strangers to their autopilots. The problem is serious. Airplanes have crashed because pilots have pulled back on the yoke in an attempt to counteract an autopilot that is commanding pitch-down trim. The result is that the autopilot commands even more nose-down trim, eventually overcoming the pilot's efforts to maintain level flight.

An untrained pilot also can lead himself into trouble with weather radar, Stormscopes, horizontal situation indicators, and Loran C receiver/processors. In many cases, state-of-the-art avionics are far easier to use than earlier generations', but today's microprocessor-controlled black boxes have many more functions and far greater capability. The pilot has a lot more opportunity to become confused and make mistakes. Learning how to take full advantage of modern avionics is no small undertaking, but little is available in the way of expert instruction.

Airports and the airway system

More than 50 percent of all general aviation accidents occur at or within five miles of airports. The relationship between the airport/airways system and safety needs attention.

To a pilot not familiar with an area or procedures, dealing with air traffic control (ATC) can be a diversion, and any diversion in the cockpit increases risk. If it is perceived that dealing with ATC has a deleterious impact on safety, then a shortcoming in the training system has been highlighted.

For years pilots were taught to fly in straight lines. Now with more controlled area around airports, arc flying is becoming more prevalent. If VFR traffic concentrates on the edges of regulated airspace and the task of navigating becomes more difficult, then the risk of midair collision surely will increase. Also, when the weather is marginal, restricting the paths a pilot is allowed to follow might increase the risk of an inadvertent entry into clouds.

The ATC system can be used in several ways. The IFR pilot can take full advantage of the system, which links most of the public-use airports and has an excellent safety record. The risk of collision between two airplanes flying under IFR conditions is extremely small.

The pilot who chooses to fly VFR can get traffic advisories, if the controllers have time to give them. The availability of service to VFR users will likely decrease as the amount of regulated airspace increases. Where the changes proposed for Mode C might reduce risk for IFR users, VFR users likely will see a slight increase in risk. See and be seen remains important.

The pilot who chooses to fly completely out of the system, but with Mode C on board, will operate much as he did before any new requirement. Those without Mode C will have to deal with a complicated navigational problem to avoid regulated airspace. Really, for anything other than remote-area or local flying, Mode C might be all but a requirement.

The airport and airway system that is in place is in good shape. In many ways it is getting better, with the only unsolvable problem related to the airports that will never be built, or that will be closed, in and near major metropolitan areas.

Knowing your airplane

Structural failures on airplanes being operated within the airspeed and G-load envelope have never been a big problem in general aviation. In fact, the primary airplane-related accidents have resulted from the interface between the pilot and the airplane. Once a bad relationship is acknowledged, pilots have done a reasonable job of eliminating the problem.

For example, the first light-twin-engine aircraft spin accident during training occurred in July 1958. The flight involved a Beech Travel Air with an FAA inspector on board giving a checkride. At the time, the FAA wanted engine-out minimum control speed demonstrated as low as possible, "but not below 500 feet." Trouble was, stalling speed and minimum control speed were close. If both happened at the same time, at low altitude, a crash was inevitable. Even at higher altitudes, some types of light twins would not recover from a spin that developed with one engine at full power and the other at idle. A tragic lot of similar accidents followed the one in the Travel Air, especially in other Travel Airs, as well as in Twin Comanches and Barons. After several years and more accidents, the problem in the airplane/pilot interface was finally acknowledged and the teaching of engine-out minimum control speed was modified.

Another problem came in the three-way relationship among pilots, partial-panel flying, and vacuum pumps. The pumps were failing. The FAA had deemphasized partial-panel flying, and pilots were losing control of airplanes after the failure of the primary instrument power source. A lot of people died before vacuum systems were made more reliable, stand-by systems were developed, and the FAA and pilots realized that handling an airplane on partial panel remains important.

It has to be acknowledged that FAA requirements are bare minimums for basic airplanes. Certainly it is reasonable to operate a Cessna Skyhawk or Piper Warrior to most of these minimums. Only an annual inspection is required for maintenance; three takeoffs and landings in the past 90 days is okay; and six hours of instrument time and six approaches in six months might be adequate. While the FAA minimums remain the same, the piloting skills needed to fly a Piper Malibu or Beech Bonanza have increased significantly. These airplanes and engines are now far more complex, and the consequences of a failure are more serious. The environment in which the airplane operates is also more complex.

A new consideration in flying during the 1990s will be aircraft age. Since fewer aircraft were produced during the 1980s, the average age of the general aviation airplane is getting older.

Age can be a serious safety factor, depending on maintenance. If an older airplane is maintained properly, it is likely to be as reliable as a newer airplane that is maintained properly. The difficulty arises when the plane ages and it becomes worth less money. An owner is more likely to cut back on maintenance when the cost becomes an ever-higher percentage of the value. For example, on an older twin-engine aircraft, a top-quality overhaul or exchange of both engines might equal the value of the airplane. As a result, a number of airplanes are being taken out of service and sold for parts when time runs out on the engines. The safety implication comes into play if the airplane is kept in service with the old engines, or if a minimum-standard overhaul is done.

Accident Prevention Program

The material in the subsequent chapters was adapted largely from the FAA accident prevention program booklets and advisory circulars. These excellent materials are used by Accident Prevention Program managers (APPMs), formerly Accident Prevention specialists, and volunteer accident prevention counselors (APCs) in conducting safety clinics and seminars. The material is available for pilots at local Flight Standards District Offices (FSDOs).

The *Accident Prevention Program* is based on the fact that general aviation accidents can be prevented or the accident rate reduced through airman education. The concept for the program was developed about 25 years ago because of the FAA's concern about the increasing general aviation accident rate during the 1950s and 1960s.

Starting in 1968, the new safety concept was tested for two years in the FAA's Central and Southwest regions. Through the combined efforts of the aviation public, aviation industry, and various governmental agencies, the test program sought to improve airmen's attitudes toward aviation safety through a better understanding of airmen knowledge, proficiency, and judgment. The program also sought to reduce the hazards in the general aviation environment.

The reduction in the general aviation accident rate in the two regions during the test program proved the validity of the concept: Accidents could be prevented through education. Because of the test program's success, the Accident Prevention Program was adopted nationally in 1971. Today, the program continues to result in a steady decrease in the national general aviation accident figures.

Structure of the APP

The National Accident Prevention Program consists of a national Accident Prevention Program manager and staff in FAA Headquarters in Washington, D.C., to oversee the program. Nine regional Accident Prevention Program managers coordinate the activities of about 80 Accident Prevention Program managers assigned to FSDOs within their regions.

Normally, one APPM is assigned to each FSDO to manage its accident prevention program. Each Accident Prevention Program manager is a qualified FAA aviation safety inspector selected for his or her interest in the Accident Prevention Program and for his or her ability to work with the local aviation community to promote aviation safety.

Assisting the APPMs are about 3500 volunteer accident prevention counselors located throughout the country. The APCs are highly respected individuals active in the aviation community. Appointed annually by their local APPMs, they support the program by providing advice and safety information to their fellow airmen, by arranging and participating in safety seminars, and by promoting aviation safety in many other ways in their local communities. A few have even been appointed as accident prevention counselors-at-large because of their long-term dedication to the program and aviation safety.

Role of the APPM

The role of the APPMs in managing and coordinating the FAA's safety efforts in their local communities is the reason for the title change from accident prevention specialist. Working under the direction of the FSDO manager, the APPM plans, organizes, and conducts aviation safety seminars, workshops, and clinics. They manage the FAA's new Remedial Training Program, work closely with aviation organizations and individuals to identify potential safety problems, and counsel individual airmen as appropriate. They also work with operators of executive aircraft; managers of flying schools, repair stations, and maintenance facilities; and managers of flying clubs, military aero clubs, Civil Air Patrol squadrons, and many other aviation groups to establish accident prevention programs within the various groups. The APPMs' dedication to a safer flying environment is evidenced by their weekend appearances at local airports to promote safety. They actively seek out suggestions and ideas to improve aviation safety, and either implement them or forward the suggestions through the appropriate channels to those who can.

Some of the ways they manage the FSDO safety program include reviewing accident/incident reports to identify airmen deficiencies; participating in aircraft accident investigations to the extent necessary to develop preventive measures; promoting the Pilot Proficiency Award "Wings" program; analyzing related statistics to identify adverse safety trends and causal factors; and working closely with other FAA sections such as Air Traffic, Airports, Medical, Security, and others in developing aviation safety materials and programs. Identifying and resolving safety problems noted during routine surveillance or reported on Safety Improvement Reports also is an important part of their daily job. They work closely with their respective state and local aeronautic commissions to develop aviation safety programs within their areas.

In many cases, an APPM's dedication and interest in aviation goes beyond the job. Many APPMs participate in many different areas of aviation off duty. They are pilots, aircraft owners, maintenance technicians, aeronauts, ultralight pilots, military reservists and National Guard volunteers, and flight and ground instructors. Many are active community workers. The community involvement of many APPMs is typical of many who have been with the program since its beginning.

The Accident Prevention Program managers and the Accident Prevention Program are general aviation's keys to safety. Pilots are encouraged to visit their local FSDO, introduce themselves to the APPM, and be ready to talk about flight safety programs in their area.

Key terms

Human factors
Pilot judgment
Accident Prevention Program managers (APPMs)
Accident prevention counselors (APCs)
Accident Prevention Program

Review questions

1. What is a serious injury?
   What kind of general aviation flying has the lowest total and fatal accident rates per 100,000 aircraft hours flown? The highest?

2. What is a *broad cause factor*?
   What are the leading two broad cause factors for all fatal accidents?
   What is pilot judgment?
   Can training materials and techniques be devised to improve pilot decision making?
   How does the pilot actually contribute to weather-related accidents?

3. Why are landings and takeoffs the most hazardous portions of flight?
   When do most of the landing accidents occur?
   What are some of the causes of takeoff accidents?

4. Why are FARs more concerned with initial training than recurrency or proficiency training?
   What is being done to correct this situation?
   Why is more training needed in the use of avionics equipment?

5. How have improvements in the airway system affected safety positively and negatively?
   Discuss the FAA minimums as they apply to various types of aircraft.
   Why is it important that a pilot recognize his own capabilities and those of his aircraft?
   How can the age of an aircraft affect safety?

6. What is the purpose of the Accident Prevention Program?
   How did it get started?
   Discuss the role of the Accident Prevention Program managers and the accident prevention counselors.

Physiological factors

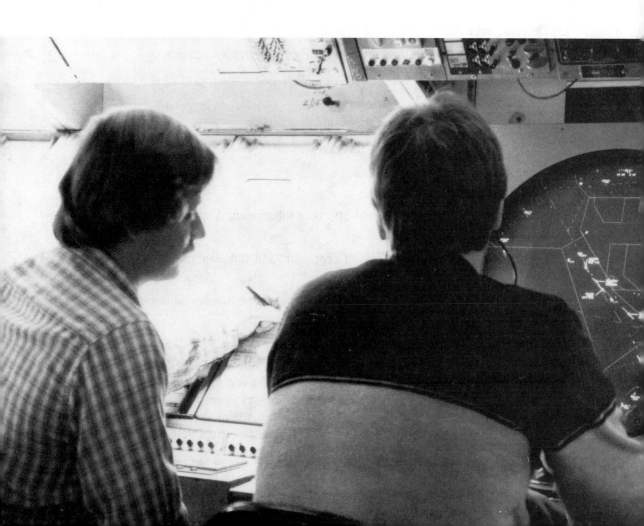

Outline

Learning objectives

After completing this chapter, you should be able to:

△ Discuss the importance of maintaining good health as a prerequisite to flying.

△ Recognize some of the problems that can be encountered when flying with a cold.

△ Describe the initial symptoms of hypoxia.

△ Distinguish between the three oxygen systems used in civil aircraft.

△ Identify and briefly describe the FAA's recommendations regarding the use of supplemental oxygen.

△ Describe the effects of carbon monoxide on the body.

△ Identify some of the basic steps that can be taken by a pilot to prevent spatial disorientation.

△ Define *psychological stresses*.

△ Discuss some of the physiological effects of tobacco smoking and alcohol consumption.

△ Compare and contrast the effects of depressant and stimulant drugs on the central nervous system.

△ Discuss the importance of proper eating habits and physical conditioning to pilots.

Introduction

Just as an aircraft is required to undergo regular checks and maintenance, a pilot is also required to undergo regular medical examinations to ensure fitness to fly. The physical standards established by the FAA are minimum requirements. Many defects can be compensated for, e.g., wearing glasses for visual defects. A pilot might be required to demonstrate by a medical flight test that he or she can compensate for any other defects of potential significance to flight safety.

Student pilots should visit a Designated Aviation Medical Examiner and determine if they meet the standards before spending much money taking flying lessons.

Recall that humans are essentially earth-bound creatures. However, if we are aware of certain aeromedical factors, and pay attention to them, we can leave the earth and fly safely. This chapter includes some of the more important factors a pilot should be aware of prior to flying.

Modern industry's record in providing reliable equipment is very good. When the pilot enters the aircraft, he or she becomes an integral part of the man-machine system. The pilot is just as essential to a successful flight as the control surfaces. To ignore the pilot in preflight planning would be as senseless as failing to inspect the integrity of the control surfaces or any other vital part of the machine. The pilot has the sole responsibility for determining his or here reliability prior to entering the cockpit for flight.

General health

The person who, for whatever reason, does not feel well should not attempt to participate as a pilot in flying activities. General discomfort, whether from a cold, indigestion, nausea, overwork, lack of sleep, worry, or any other bodily weakness is not conducive to safe flying. Perhaps the most insidious and common of all conditions that can result in dangerous inattentiveness, slow reactions, and confused mental processes is excessive fatigue. Marked fatigue is as valid a reason for canceling or postponing a flight as an engine that is found unacceptable during an operations check.

Self-medication can be a very hazardous undertaking for pilots. Probably the best general recommendation for pilots is abstinence from all drugs when flying is anticipated. In some instances, the need for a particular drug or medication is an indication that the pilot's health is such that flying is precluded automatically. In other cases, it is unlikely that a pilot who is ill enough to require a drug would be well enough to fly by the time the chance of toxicity from the drug has disappeared.

Antihistamines, tranquilizers, reducing pills, barbiturates, nerve tonics, and many other over-the-counter drugs can be lethal to a pilot in flight. It is best for those in doubt about such medication to consult a doctor.

Colds

A person with a cold is likely to feel tired, worn out, drowsy, or irritable. Discomfort and possibly pain also can occur. All of these conditions, individually or together, can work to make an unsafe pilot.

Colds can cause even greater problems to the pilot. Swollen lymph tissue and mucous membranes are apt to block the sinuses, as well as the ears. This blockage can cause disabling pain and pressure vertigo during descent, which in turn can result in loss of control of the aircraft. Additionally, infection of the inner ear by various cold and flulike viruses can produce severe vertigo, which could easily make straight-and-level flight impossible.

Flying an unpressurized aircraft can cause ear discomfort during ascent or descent. As an aircraft gains altitude, the atmospheric pressure decreases and so does the pressure in the external ear canal. The middle ear, being a closed cavity, stays at ground-level pressure. When the pressure in the middle ear exceeds that of the external ear canal, a person's eardrum starts to bulge out somewhat. The middle ear is sensitive to this change and requires only a slight excess of pressure to open the eustachian tube, so that gas can pass by this route through the nose or mouth. In this way, pressure is equalized on both sides of the eardrum. A pilot may be aware of this pressure change by alternating sensations of ear fullness or "clearing."

During descent, however, conditions within the ear are reversed. As the surrounding air pressure increases, the middle ear—which has adjusted itself to the reduced pressure at altitude—is at a lower pressure than the external ear canal. Consequently, the outside air forces the eardrum to bulge inward.

This condition is more difficult to relieve, since air must be introduced back up the eustachian tube to equalize the pressure. The partial vacuum in the middle ear also tends to collapse, rather than inflate, the walls of the eustachian tube.

If a person has a cold, the tissue around the nasal end of the eustachian tube probably will be swollen, and he or she can expect ear problems to be aggravated in flight. The best advice is to stay on the ground.

If the flight must be made, it is better to do so at a lower altitude. This precaution may prevent a perforated or painful eardrum. A perforated eardrum generally does not heal rapidly. In some cases, hearing is impaired permanently, or the middle ear becomes infected and causes prolonged disability. It is also best not to rely on cold remedies and prescriptions. Some medicines specifically state on the label that usage will cause drowsiness. Others caution the user to refrain from operating any kind of machinery or equipment. Medications such as aspirin, cold tablets, cough mixtures, and laxatives can jeopardize safe flight by their subtle or unpredictable effects on the pilot.

Effects of medications

Dangers that can accompany pill-taking include drug allergies, which could disable the pilot, and unexpected side reactions, such as nausea or vertigo, even if the pilot has never before suffered such side effects.

High-altitude flying or "G" forces have been observed to change the effect of some medications. Also, two drugs taken at the same time occasionally cancel each other, render each other more potent, or cause a side reaction not experienced with either medication alone.

Remember, too, that the pilot who flies while ill, or while taking disqualifying medication, is in violation of the Federal Aviation Regulations. When in doubt, it is best to check with a local FAA medical examiner.

Hypoxia and hyperventilation

Lack of sufficient oxygen is one of the greatest dangers to pilots at high altitudes. The shortage of oxygen in the human body results in a condition known as *hypoxia*, which simply means oxygen starvation. Hypoxia can be a killer.

When a pilot inhales air at high altitudes, there isn't enough oxygen pressure to force adequate amounts of this vital gas through the membranes of the lung into the blood stream, so that it can be carried to the tissues of the body. The function of various organs, including the brain, is then impaired.

Unfortunately, the nature of hypoxia makes the pilot the poorest judge of when he is its victim. The first symptoms of oxygen deficiency are misleadingly pleasant, resembling mild intoxication from alcohol.

Because oxygen starvation strikes first at the brain, a pilot's higher faculties are dulled. His normal self-critical ability is out of order. His mind no longer functions properly; his hands and feet become clumsy without him being aware of it; he might feel drowsy, languid, and nonchalant; he might have a false sense of security, and the last thing in the world he thinks he needs is oxygen.

As the hypoxia gets worse, the pilot can become dizzy or feel a tingling of the skin. He might have a dull headache, if only half aware of it.

Oxygen starvation gets worse the longer the pilot remains at a given altitude, or if he climbs higher. His heart races; his lips and the skin under his fingernails begin to turn blue; his field of vision narrows; and the instruments start to look fuzzy.

But hypoxia—by its nature, a grim deceiver—makes the pilot feel confident that he is doing a better job of flying than he has ever done before. He is in about the same condition as the person who insists on driving a car home from a New Year's party when he can hardly walk. Regardless of his acclimatization, endurance, or other attributes, every pilot will suffer the consequences of hypoxia when exposed to inadequate oxygen pressure.

Some people believe that breathing faster and deeper at high altitudes can compensate for oxygen lack, but this is only partially true. Such abnormal breathing, known as *hyperventilation*, also causes them to flush from their lungs and bleed much of the carbon dioxide their systems need to maintain the proper degree of blood acidity.

The chemical imbalance in the body then produces dizziness, tingling of the fingers and toes, sensation of body heat, rapid heart rate, blurring of vision, muscle spasm, and finally, unconsciousness. The symptoms resemble the effects of hypoxia, and the brain becomes equally impaired.

Altitude hypoxia

Although some forms of hypoxia are caused by reduced oxygen-carrying capacity of blood, poor circulation of the blood, and the inability of body cells to use oxygen, the most frequent type of hypoxia encountered in aviation is that caused by the decreased partial pressure of oxygen in the atmosphere as a result of the decrease in barometric pressure at altitude. This type is commonly referred to as *altitude hypoxia* and is the greatest potential physiological hazard to the pilot in the high-altitude environment.

In exposure to altitudes below 10,000 feet, the effects of hypoxia on the pilot are mild and considered acceptable. From 12,000 to 15,000 feet, though, impairment of judgment, memory alertness, and coordination are affected; and headache, drowsiness and either a sense of well-being or of irritability may occur.

At cabin-pressure altitudes above 15,000 feet, peripheral vision deteriorates to a point where only central vision remains and cyanosis (blueness) of the fingernails and lips develops. The ability to take corrective action is lost in 20 to 30 minutes at 18,000 feet, and in 5 to 12 minutes at 20,000 feet, followed soon thereafter by unconsciousness.

FAR Part 91 states that exposure to altitudes above 12,500 feet up to and including 14,000 feet for periods of more than 30 minutes requires the use of supplementary oxygen by the pilot.

FAR Parts 121 and 135 require the flightcrew to use supplementary oxygen at cabin altitudes above 10,000 feet up to and including 12,000 feet for more than 30 minutes. The breathing of supplementary oxygen is necessary to increase the concentration of oxygen in the inspired air in order to maintain the oxygen partial pressure in the lungs at a safe level.

Above an altitude of 33,000 feet, the oxygen tension in the lungs falls progressively, even when breathing 100 percent oxygen, and at about 40,000 feet, the oxygen must be delivered under "positive pressure" if the effects of hypoxia are to be prevented.

Special consideration must be given passengers with circulatory disorders (heart disease, anemia, etc.) or with lung disease (asthma, emphysema, etc.). Such passengers might require supplemental oxygen to prevent significant hypoxia at lower altitudes than normally expected.

This situation is true also at cabin altitudes in the normal operation of pressurized cabin aircraft. Experience has indicated that some passengers assume that pressurized aircraft have cabin altitudes equivalent to sea level, and many are not aware that their disease might increase their susceptibility to problems related to changes in atmospheric pressure associated with flight.

Types of oxygen systems

Oxygen systems for civil aircraft are designed to deliver the concentration of oxygen necessary to maintain a partial pressure of oxygen in the lungs sufficient to prevent effects of hypoxia with increasing altitude.

Those systems in general use today consist of three main components: a mask, a regulator, and a source to store the oxygen, all appropriately integrated. The type of oxygen system required to protect the individual depends on the maximum altitude to be used.

There are three distinct types of oxygen systems in use in civil aircraft. The *continuous-flow system* is the most commonly used in piston-engine general aviation aircraft and in passenger oxygen systems in other aircraft. Simply stated, a valve or switch in the aircraft is activated and produces a continuous flow of oxygen into a "bag," as it is commonly called. The oxygen then mixes with the ambient and exhaled air in the bag. The oxygen portion of this mixture remains the same and the flow is constant regardless of the altitude. This system is reported to be an adequate supplemental oxygen system for flightcrews at altitudes up to 25,000 feet, and for passengers up to 40,000 feet.

The *demand system* delivers a mixture of oxygen and air when the user inhales, automatically matching the oxygen in the mixture to the demand or requirement. This system provides flight crewmembers with the protection required up to 40,000 feet.

Above 40,000 feet, the *pressure demand system* is necessary. At lower altitudes, this system functions in the same manner as the demand system, but delivers oxygen under pressure when required. Pressure breathing is intended only for short periods of use: for example, to allow safe descent in emergencies.

Aircraft oxygen systems are potentially dangerous if not properly installed or maintained. These systems should be serviced only by an appropriately qualified person. Only aviation oxygen should be used to refill the oxygen system. The other two types of oxygen available are medical and industrial oxygen.

In medical oxygen, water vapor has been added. The addition of this "moisture" to the medical oxygen makes it unsatisfactory for aviation use because of the possibility of moisture freezing the regulator. Industrial oxygen is not intended to be used in breathing and, therefore, impurities might not have been eliminated.

When supplemental oxygen is required because of the decreased partial pressure of oxygen in the atmosphere, it is imperative that the oxygen equipment be used appropriately.

Oxygen masks are available in many styles, varying in complexity from lightweight plastic disposable masks to units incorporating the regulator, inhalation and exhalation valves, microphone, and special harnessers to achieve rapid donning.

Regardless of the style, the purpose of the mask is to cover the nose and mouth and to deliver oxygen in sufficient quantity to maintain the partial pressure of the oxygen in the lungs necessary to prevent hypoxia.

To be efficient, the masks must fit and form a "seal" with the face. An inward leak will cause excessive dilution of the oxygen, and an outward leak will waste oxygen and reduce mask pressure during pressure breathing. Improper adjustment of the mask's retaining straps impairs the mask-to-face seal.

Performance testing by the industry, as well as by various governmental agencies, has revealed that the oxygen mask-to-face seal also can be seriously compromised by the presence of facial hair (beard and/or mustache) in both the continuous-flow "passenger masks," as well as the demand-type masks. The presence of beards and/or mustaches that affect the mask-to-face seal in crewmembers required to perform at optimum levels during flight at altitudes where supplemental oxygen is required is not compatible with aviation safety.

The FAA has issued a number of suggestions concerning the use of supplemental oxygen:

- Pilots who fly to altitudes that require or may require the use of supplemental oxygen should be thoroughly familiar with the operation of the aircraft oxygen systems. A preflight inspection of the system should be performed, including proper fit of the mask. The passengers should be briefed on the proper use of their oxygen system before flight.

- The FARs related to the use of supplemental oxygen by flightcrew and passengers must be adhered to if flight to higher altitudes is to be accomplished safely. Passengers with significant circulatory or lung disease might need to use supplemental oxygen at lower altitudes than specified by these regulations.

- Pilots of pressurized aircraft should receive physiological training with emphasis on hypoxia and the use of oxygen and oxygen systems. Pilots of aircraft with pressure-demand oxygen systems should undergo training, experience altitude chamber decompression, and be familiar with pressure breathing before flying at high altitudes. Information regarding this training, which is available through the government at nominal cost, can be obtained by writing:

  Chief, Civil Aeromedical Institute
  Attn: Aeromedical Education Branch, AAC-140
  Mike Monroney Aeronautical Center
  P.O. Box 25082
  Oklahoma City, OK 73125.

- Pilots should always have available the type of oxygen system required for the highest altitude planned.

- Pilots of pressurized aircraft should periodically include training exercises with simulated decompression and the emergency use of oxygen equipment in the manner recommended by the aircraft or oxygen system manufacturer.

- Pilots and other crewmembers operating at altitudes in which supplemental oxygen might be required should not have a beard or mustache that will interfere with the proper mask-to-face seal.

- Pilots should understand that although hypoxia is the major problem associated with high-altitude flight, it is not the only one. Pilots should be familiar with decompression sickness, or *bends*, as well as with problems secondary to the expansion of entrapped gases and to ear and sinus blocks.

Carbon monoxide

Carbon monoxide, always present in fumes from the internal combustion engine, is a colorless, tasteless, and odorless gas. This gas has the ability to saturate the blood's hemoglobin and prevent the absorption of oxygen. The brain and body tissue must have oxygen to function and survive. Even minute quantities breathed over a long period of time can have serious consequences. Its effects can be cumulative and are not easily corrected. A breath of fresh air will not bring early relief—several days might be required to completely rid the body of carbon monoxide.

Aircraft heaters designed to use the heat of engine exhaust gases are the usual source for this insidious danger. Be wary if there is a smell of exhaust fumes, especially if mental confusion, dizziness, uneasiness, or headaches follow. If such symptoms develop, shut off the cabin heater, ventilate the cabin to the maximum extent possible, descend to lower altitudes where need for heat is less crucial, and land as soon as possible for a thorough check of the source of the trouble. It is wise to then consult a doctor. Remember it might take several days to rid the body of carbon monoxide.

Although there are several types of relatively inexpensive detectors available today which can warn of unsafe conditions with respect to carbon monoxide in the cabin, they might not always be completely reliable, and their use should not lull one into a sense of false security.

The presence of carbon monoxide results in hypoxia, which will affect night vision in the same manner and extent as hypoxia from high altitudes. Even small levels of carbon monoxide have the same effect as an altitude increase of 8000 to 10,000 feet. Smoking several cigarettes can result in a carbon monoxide saturation sufficient to effect visual sensitivity equal to an increase of 8000 feet in altitude.

Spatial disorientation (vertigo)

Spatial disorientation can exist when an individual does not correctly perceive his position, attitude, and motion relative to the center of the earth. Sensory illusions might lead to spatial disorientation in flight when the pilot is unable to see, believe, interpret, process, or rely on the information presented to him by his flight instruments, but relies instead on the false information provided by his body senses. *Vertigo* is an illusion originally defined as a sensation of rotation occurring during flight. Most pilots refer to all forms of spatial disorientation, with or without subjective rotation, as pilot's vertigo.

The flight attitude of an airplane is generally determined by reference to the natural horizon. When the natural horizon is obscured, attitude can sometimes be maintained by reference to the surface below. If neither horizon nor surface references exist, the airplane's attitude must be determined by artificial means—an attitude indicator or other flight instruments. Sight, supported by other senses such as the inner ear and muscle sense, is used to maintain spatial orientation. However, during periods of low visibility, the supporting senses sometimes conflict with what is seen. When this happens, a pilot is particularly vulnerable to spatial disorientation. The degree of disorientation can vary considerably with individual pilots, as do the conditions that induce the problem. Spatial disorientation to a pilot means simply the inability to tell "which way is up."

Surface references or the natural horizon at times might become obscured by smoke, fog, smog, haze, dust, ice particles, or other phenomena, although visibility might be above Visual Flight Rule (VFR) minimums. This situation can occur especially at airports located adjacent to large bodies of water or sparsely populated areas, where few, if any, surface references are available. Lack of horizon or surface reference is common on over-water flights, at night, or in low-visibility conditions. Other contributors to disorientation are reflections from outside lights, sunlight shining through clouds, and light beams from the airplane's anticollision rotating beacon.

Following are certain basic steps that should assist materially in preventing spatial disorientation:

1. Before flying with less than 3 miles visibility, obtain training and maintain proficiency in airplane control by reference to instruments.
2. When flying at night or in reduced visibility, use the flight instruments.
3. Maintain night currency if intending to fly at night. Include cross-country and local operations at different airports.
4. Study and become familiar with unique geographical conditions in the areas in which the flight is intended.

5. Check weather forecasts before departure, en route, and at destination. Be alert for weather deterioration.

6. Do not attempt visual flight when there is a possibility of getting trapped in deteriorating weather.

7. Rely on instrument indications unless the natural horizon or surface reference is clearly visible.

Motion sickness

Although motion sickness is uncommon among experienced pilots, it does occur occasionally. A person who has been its victim knows how uncomfortable it is. Most important, it jeopardizes the pilot's flying efficiency—particularly in turbulent weather and in instrument conditions when peak skill is required. Student pilots frequently are surprised by an uneasiness usually described as motion sickness. It is probably a result of combining anxiety, unfamiliarity, and the vibration or jogging received from the airplane, and usually is overcome with experience.

Motion sickness is caused by continued stimulation of the tiny portion of the inner ear that controls the pilot's sense of balance. The symptoms are progressive. First, the desire for food is lost. Then saliva collects in the mouth, and the person begins to perspire freely. Eventually, he or she becomes nauseated and disoriented. The head aches and there might be a tendency to vomit. If the air sickness becomes severe enough, the pilot may become completely incapacitated.

Pilots who are susceptible to airsickness should not take the preventive drugs available over the counter or by prescription. These medications might make a person drowsy or depress his or her brain function in other ways. Careful research has shown that most motion sickness drugs cause a temporary deterioration of navigational skills or other tasks demanding keen judgment.

If suffering from airsickness while piloting an aircraft, it is best to open up the air vents, loosen the clothing, use supplemental oxygen, and keep the eyes on a point outside the airplane. Avoid unnecessary head movements then cancel the flight and land as soon as possible.

Self-imposed stress

Stress is an encompassing term that includes anything and everything that places a strain on an individual's ability to perform at his or her very best. The effects of stresses grow, and must be overcome by the body's compensatory mechanisms with the aid of protective equipment. If they are not overcome, the individual will suffer physiologic decompensation, which eventually can lead to incapacitation.

The pilot whose health is impaired is often unable to adjust to stresses or to cope with the demands of flying. When the demands of flight exceed the pilot's capabilities, an aircraft incident or accident can occur. The stresses imposed on the body by the design criteria of the aircraft are unavoidable, and must be accepted in the interest of improved aircraft performance. Any stresses imposed on the pilot by his or her lack of knowledge or inattention to healthy living habits are unacceptable because they might decrease his or her capabilities below the necessary level for the safe operation of the aircraft. Of the many psycho-physiological factors contributing to aircraft accidents, several self-imposed stress areas repeatedly appear in accident investigations and require special attention.

Psychological stress

Psychological stresses cause anxiety, which can lead to mental confusion and difficulty in concentrating. Common causes in this problem area arise from marital, financial, and personal problems. Recognition and prevention of emotional stress in any area is essential for safety. Resolution of conflicts prior to flight is necessary to keep the psychological stress from building up and interfering with, or dominating, the thought process.

Tobacco smoking

Cigarette smoking has particular significance to the flyer, since there are long-term harmful effects from cigarette smoking. In a report by the United States Public Health Service, it was stated that cigarette smokers are 20 times as likely to die of lung cancer as nonsmokers, and 6 to 10 times as likely to die of cancer of the larynx. The report indicated that cigarette smoking might be the cause of cancer of the esophagus and bladder, and is strongly suspected of causing cancer of the pancreas.

Cigarette smoking causes a relative deprivation of oxygen to the heart muscle and contributes to circulatory problems by constricting arteries; thus, it affects the cardiovascular system and is a significant factor in the development of coronary heart disease. Cigarette smoking causes irritation to the lining of the respiratory tree, and thus edema and swelling, preventing air from passing in and out freely. This and other factors lead to emphysema and permanent damage in many individuals.

Tar Tar is a catch-all term for the viscous residue left from cigarette smoke after the gases and water vapor have been eliminated. It is also one of the primary constituents causing long-term harmful effects. In addition to the cancer potential of this substance, it causes swelling and tends to prevent the natural cleansing action of the lungs.

Nicotine Nicotine primarily affects the nerves and muscle tissue. Even in extremely small doses, the pure agent is very poisonous. If the nicotine contained in two cigarettes were extracted from the tobacco and injected into the blood stream, it could have a fatal effect. Fortunately, nicotine in cigarette smoke is not completely absorbed from the respiratory tree.

Nicotine can, however, cause weakness and twitching of skeletal muscles, and can result in abdominal cramping, nausea, and vomiting, particularly in those not habituated to its effects. In addition to altering nerve impulses and the circulation of the blood, it also alters the heart and respiratory rates. There is also evidence that nicotine in small amounts will decrease the body's ability to adapt to stress.

Carbon Monoxide Carbon monoxide produced in cigarette smoking probably presents the most immediate harmful effects in tobacco smoking. Carbon monoxide is a colorless, tasteless, and odorless gas produced by incomplete combustion of any carbon-containing material. It combines with hemoglobin 250 times more readily than oxygen. The hemoglobin involved in this combination is not available for transporting oxygen to the tissues and produces a degree of hypemic hypoxia.

The pilot who smokes will normally have 5 to 10 percent total hemoglobin involved as carboxyhemoglobin. The result is hypemic hypoxia and a lowering of the pilot's altitude tolerance. Flying at a cabin altitude of 10,000 feet with 10 percent carboxyhemoglobin is physiologically equivalent to 15,000 feet. It would take approximately 40 minutes breathing 100 percent oxygen to lose one-half of the carbon monoxide in the hemoglobin. The chronic smoker who is breathing ambient air carries this additional hazard for several hours after his last cigarette.

Without proper pressurization and filtering systems in aircraft, carbon monoxide can present a situation that could lead to an aircraft accident. The number of cigarettes an individual ignites is not crucial; rather, the important questions are: How many times is a cigarette inhaled? How deeply is it inhaled? How many are inhaled in a given period of time? This information will determine the amount of impairment the individual will suffer.

Cigars and pipes have the same effect on the body. As a rule, persons smoking cigars and pipes do not inhale the tobacco smoke as often or as deeply as cigarette smokers, and their impairment is generally less than the cigarette smoker.

Alcohol

The ingestion of alcohol, liquor, wine, or beer is common in most social cultures. Ethyl alcohol is the active ingredient in these beverages and acts as an anesthetic drug, which depresses the brain. Also present are volatile substances that slow down the rate at which the body disposes of ethyl alcohol. Alcohols are poisonous to the body; ethyl alcohol is the least poisonous and most tolerated by the body.

The intoxicating effects of alcohol are brought about in two major actions on the brain; one effect is a change in the proportion of two chemicals called *neurohormones*, which affect the brain. These neurohormones—serotonin and norepinephrine—are believed to control mood and alertness. After consumption of small amounts of alcohol, a crewmember might lose normal cautionary attitudes and become reckless, possibly before he even notes a change in skill or performance.

Another effect of alcohol is a reduction in the ability of the brain cells to use oxygen. Hypoxia enters the mental picture, causing judgment and performance to be impaired. Alcohol also acts as a relaxant and anesthetic, removing a person's inhibitions and lessening his worries. In larger amounts, this relaxation progresses to actual unconsciousness, and eventually leads to death due to respiratory paralysis.

The concentration of alcohol in the blood and brain depends on three factors: the amount consumed, the rate of absorption from the stomach and small intestine; and the rate of its metabolism by the body.

The rate of absorption depends on many factors:

- the type and quantity of food in the stomach
- the degree of hydration of the body
- the concentration of alcohol in the beverage and the type of beverage with which it is mixed
- the rate at which the alcohol is consumed
- body weight
- the individual variation in the absorptive characteristics of the stomach

The rate of metabolism or digestion of alcohol in the body is relatively constant. Two to ten percent of the alcohol is excreted through the lungs and kidney, and the remainder is oxidized by the liver. It takes about one hour to eliminate 0.33 ounce of pure ethyl alcohol from the body. This is the amount of ethyl alcohol in 0.67 ounce of 100-proof liquor or in 6 ounces of beer. The metabolism of alcohol cannot be expedited by any readily available method or remedy. Walking, drinking black coffee, breathing 100 percent oxygen, or taking cold showers are common folklore methods that do not eliminate alcohol from the body.

The physiological effects of alcohol depend on the level of alcohol in the blood. With 0.05 to 0.10 percent of alcohol in the blood, mild intoxication is present, which will lower altitude tolerance even if symptoms are not observed. With 0.10 to 0.15 percent alcohol in the blood, everyone is affected to some degree. In most states, an automobile driver with this level would be considered intoxicated. At a blood alcohol level of 0.15 to 0.20 percent, performance deteriorates, and there are marked symptoms. At 0.30 percent, there is acute intoxication and lack of coordination, and consciousness is lost.

Unconsciousness and possible death may result at levels of 0.40 to 0.50 percent. For an average 160-pound man, 2 ounces of 100-proof whiskey consumed in 1 hour will produce 0.05 percent alcohol in the blood. If a person weighing 160 pounds were to consume approximately four-fifths of a quart of whiskey in 1 hour, it would be fatal. Since the effects of alcohol are compounded by altitude, 10,000 feet of altitude doubles the effects of alcohol on the body.

Hangover effects

Of the many chronic effects of alcohol, those usually having long-term effects on health are found in people suffering from alcoholism. Chronic effects such as vitamin, mineral, and protein deficiency and a fatty liver are caused by improper diet and the direct effect of alcohol. Excess of body carbohydrates, cirrhosis of the liver, and alcoholic psychosis are other effects the heavy drinker may suffer.

The effect of a hangover probably constitutes a more significant flight safety hazard than does the mild intoxication state of alcohol ingestion. Although it may be unlikely that a pilot would attempt to fly an aircraft while intoxicated, the same individual with a hangover, 8 to 18 hours later, might take off although he or she is less efficient and less physically capable than normal.

The symptoms of a hangover are not entirely the result of alcohol ingestion. Many are due to the activities that often accompany overindulgence in alcohol: excessive tobacco smoking, loss of sleep, improper diet, etc. Alcohol is a known cause of dehydration, resulting in many of the hangover symptoms. Alcohol takes moisture from the cerebral spinal fluid that surrounds the brain. Loss of fluid causes tension of the supporting structure of the brain, producing a headache. Dehydration can be increased by exposure to low atmospheric pressures, breathing dry oxygen, and thermal stress. In the early stages of dehydration, judgment and emotional changes are observed, and each can seriously interfere with the flyer's ability to carry out tasks safely and efficiently.

Alcohol also causes disorientation because of its combined effect on the lower brain and inner ear. The effect on the inner ear can be identified by involuntary reflex eye muscle movement 36 to 48 hours after heavy drinking.

Time is the only factor that will alleviate a hangover. Other symptomatic relief can come from eating a well-balanced meal, which provides nonalcoholic carbohydrates to the liver, and by consuming large qualities of nonalcoholic fluids to reduce dehydration. Breathing 100 percent oxygen has no direct effect on a hangover.

Drugs and self-medication

Self-medication or taking medicine in any form when you are flying can be extremely hazardous. Even simple home or over-the-counter remedies and drugs such as aspirin, laxatives, tranquilizers, and appetite suppressors may seriously impair the judgment and coordination needed while flying. The safest rule is to take no medicine while flying, except on the advice of an Aviation Medical Examiner. Also remember that the condition for which the drug is required may of itself be very hazardous to flying, even when the symptoms are suppressed by the drug.

Central nervous system depressants Depressant drugs inhibit the central nervous system (CNS) and slow down normal body functions. There are five general types: narcotics, barbiturates, ethyl alcohol, antihistamines, and tranquilizers.

Ethyl alcohol Although largely replaced by other agents, ethyl alcohol has been used internally as a tranquilizer and sedative. Alcohol is a CNS depressant, which elicits a wide individual variation in response to the drug.

Barbiturates Barbiturates are among the most versatile depressant drugs. Clinical uses include treatment for epilepsy, high blood pressure, insomnia, and certain mental disorders. All barbiturates have depressant effects on the CNS, varying from mild sedation to coma, depending on the dosage level. Certain barbiturates may cause excitement, rather than sedation, especially in the young and the elderly. Other people may react with dizziness, nausea, or vomiting following a period of sedation or sleep. An additional concern is that an individual might react differently at different times and at different dosage levels.

Barbiturates are definitely incompatible with flying because they reduce perception, produce drowsiness, staggering, slurred speech, etc. Small amounts of barbiturates combined with alcohol produce a synergistic combination and can cause severe respiratory depression and death. Barbiturate intoxication is considered the most dangerous of the CNS depressants.

Tranquilizers The term *tranquilizer* is somewhat idealized and carries the implication of mental calm. It applies to a large number of compounds of varying chemistry and mechanisms of action. Unlike barbiturate-type sedatives, tranquilizers generally are used to relieve tension and anxiety, hopefully without significantly impairing mental and physical functions. Many tranquilizers are useful as skeletal muscle relaxants.

Some undesirable effects for this group of drugs are: stuffy nose, constipation, blurred vision, dry mouth, hypertension, and drowsiness. Even the nonsedating tranquilizers usually have measurable effects on alertness, judgment, efficiency, and overall performance. In most cases, you should not fly with a medical condition that requires tranquilizers. Whether the individual is aware of it or not, some tranquilizers have pharmacologic effects that last for a number of days, instead of a matter of hours.

Narcotics Narcotics have a variety of uses: morphine and codeine are pain relievers; codeine is a cough suppressant found in common cough syrups; and other opiates are constipating agents found in diarrhea mixtures such as paregoric (camphorated tincture of opium). Narcotics have the undesirable effects of producing drowsiness, constipation, tension, hunger, thirst, nausea and/or vomiting, constriction of the pupils, and respiratory depression.

Some preparations containing small amounts of narcotics are exempt from prescription requirements in certain states, and are frequently free from controls in other countries. These products include certain cough medicines containing codeine and paregoric-type preparations for diarrhea.

Antihistamines Antihistamines are present in most common cold compounds and are probably the most frequently used depressant drugs. Undesirable effects in aviation include drowsiness, dizziness, dry mouth, headaches, nausea, muscular twitching, and impaired depth perception. The drowsiness produced can be a hazard because it might not be recognized by the flyer, and it might recur after a period of apparent alertness.

Central nervous system stimulants Some stimulants have the effect of stimulating the CNS and accelerating the normal body functions. Some examples of common stimulants are caffeine, amphetamines, and cocaine.

Caffeine The most widely used stimulant is caffeine, an ingredient found in coffee, tea, cola, and other beverages. Consumed in large amounts, caffeine has the undesirable effects of indigestion, nervousness, insomnia, increased heart rate, and elevated blood pressure. Also a problem is the fact that many people become "hooked" on caffeine-containing beverages, and when suddenly deprived of them, have multiple problems, especially diminished alertness.

Cocaine Cocaine is a stimulant obtained from the leaves of the coca bush found in South America. It was once used as a local anesthetic, but has been largely replaced by newer, less toxic drugs. Cocaine can produce a sense of euphoria, a sense of increased muscle strength, anxiety, fear, hallucinations, etc. It dilates the pupils and increases the heart rate and blood pressure. Following the stimulation and excitement produced by the drug, there is a period of depression.

Amphetamines First used in the 1930s as a nasal vasoconstrictor in the treatment of colds and hay fever, amphetamines were later found to stimulate the CNS. They produce an elevation of mood and a feeling of well-being. They delay onset of fatigue and tend to force the body's normal limits, resulting in the popular name "pep pill."

Clinically, amphetamines are used in the treatment of obesity, narcolepsy (overwhelming attacks of sleep, which cannot easily be inhibited), depression, and certain behavioral disorders. Some common undesirable side effects are palpitations, dry mouth, sweating, headache, diarrhea, and dilation of the pupils.

Dexedrine and Benzedrine are trade names for popularly used amphetamines that are often taken to prolong periods of wakefulness for driving and studying, and also in dieting. Nervousness, impaired judgment, and euphoria are some of the undesirable side effects, and addiction is not uncommon. When diet pills containing amphetamines are taken, hypoglycemia also might be present. Amphetamines should not be used during flight except when prescribed by a physician.

Diet and hypoglycemia

Improper diet and malnutrition problems encountered by pilots are usually short-term problems or long-term obesity problems.

Short-term effects   Missing meals or substituting a quick snack and coffee for a balanced meal, eaten in comparative leisure, can contribute to fatigue. The body requires periodic refueling if it is to function properly.

The liver provides a source of reserve energy that gives us leeway in the frequency of food intake, and often the busy pilot depends on this reserve source, rather than ingesting a balanced diet at regular mealtimes. The liver is one of the body organs that controls the blood sugar level, storing energy in the form of glycogen. It can readily convert this storage form of sugar into glucose, which is released into the bloodstream to maintain the required level of blood sugar. Unless food is consumed at regular intervals, the stored glycogen becomes exhausted, and the liver can no longer fill the blood sugar gap that occurs when a meal is deleted.

The body must have an adequate concentration of glucose in the bloodstream to serve as an energy source for the body. If the level of sugar falls too low, the body's efficiency decreases, or in severe cases, weakness and fainting can occur, a condition called *hypoglycemia*.

The effect of low blood sugar and hypoxia are closely related. Hypoglycemia is easily prevented by eating a well-balanced diet of protein, fats, and carbohydrates.

Long-term effects   Obesity is often the long-term effect of improper eating habits. Too much food and inadequate exercise usually lead to obesity. Insurance statistics reveal that the obese person is likely to suffer from the degenerative diseases of old age sooner than a normal individual. The overweight pilot carries an additional hazard because of the additive effects of obesity and the stresses he is exposed to in flight.

A pilot suffering from obesity might decide on a crash diet to lose weight fast. To do so without consulting a physician might cause symptoms of hypoglycemia. Diet pills (usually amphetamines) are a hazard to flight and should not be taken. An obese person should consult a physician when contemplating a diet to lose weight. Exercise will increase the energy needs of the body, but energy expenditures are not going to help weight loss at a greatly accelerated rate. A good weight-loss program is a combination of exercise, balanced food, and a restricted calorie intake.

Exhaustion and fatigue

Exhaustion and fatigue remain as two of the most treacherous hazards to flight safety because they might not be apparent to the pilot until he or she makes serious errors. Part of the fatigue might be actual muscle-tiredness from prolonged use of a given set of muscles; however, psychological and mental fatigue are often the most serious aspects of fatigue.

Acute skill fatigue The term *acute skill fatigue* refers to the loss of strength, coordination, or attention to details that occur during prolonged operation or procedure. Monotony, immobility, repetition, and psychological stress are causes of acute skill fatigue. Short test periods or other tasks will attenuate the effects brought by acute skill fatigue.

Chronic skill fatigue Exhaustion occurs when there is insufficient time for full recovery between episodes of acute skill fatigue. It manifests itself by decreased attention to detail, a lack of interest, an increase in minor physical complaints, unwarranted risks, substandard performance, and lowered morale. Chronic skill fatigue is often seen when the job requires frequent, repetitious, demanding performance over a prolonged period of time. Assembly-line operations often produce chronic skill fatigue.

Chronic skill fatigue can be delayed with observance of rest regulations, adequate recreation, good living conditions, and attention to morale factors. Individual capabilities for prolonged work and individual variations in the need for rest prevent generalizing on just how much rest might be needed.

Circadian rhythm The term *circadian rhythm* is derived from the Latin *Circa dies*, meaning about a day. It refers to a time period that imprecisely approximates 24 hours in duration, ranging from 20 to 28 hours. It is commonly applied to rhythmic biologic functions, which are geared to an internal "biologic clock," the intrinsic sleep-wake cycle and/or other influences (the solar day-night cycle, temperature, social environment, etc.).

Examples of circadian rhythms are changes in body temperature, heart rate, performance, and evaporative water loss. Man is influenced by inherited characteristics and environment, and he tends to gauge his activities on a day-night cycle.

An individual often requires hours or days to adjust to the effects of time-zone changes. For instance, east and west flights cause more difficulty than north and south flights. Also, recovery times were noted to be somewhat longer after eastward flights when compared with westward flights. But the fact that biological and temporal time are desynchronized is more important than the direction of travel. Studies have indicated that complex body functions—those measured by tests of decision time, reaction time, and efficiency—are affected by rapid shifts through several time zones. This phenomenon has often been called *jet lag* or *jet fatigue*.

Little is known about the means for speeding recovery or overcoming the varied unwanted effects associated with changes in the normal circadian rhythms.

Individuals often adjust fast when given time for rest immediately after travel is completed.

Physical conditioning   Physical fitness means more than mere muscle conditioning. Every pilot should participate in a variety of conditioning programs, among them fast walking and aerobics, one of the well-known physical conditioning programs. The key to aerobic exercises and walking is oxygen consumption. The effect increases maximal oxygen consumption by increasing the efficiency of the means of supply and delivery, thereby improving the overall condition of the body. The lungs begin processing more air and with less effort; the heart becomes stronger, pumping more blood with fewer strokes; the blood supply to the muscles improves, and the total blood volume increases.

Most authorities feel that physical exercise on a regular basis tends to lessen the risk of heart attacks. The endurance type of exercise, with regularity, encourages the development and enlargement of anatomic channels that become functional channels useful in coronary circulation if a main artery is blocked. Evidence suggests proper conditioning might be effective in arresting the progress of coronary heart disease, particularly arteriosclerosis.

Key terms

Hypoxia
Hyperventilation
Altitude hypoxia
Continuous flow oxygen system
Demand oxygen system
Pressure demand oxygen system
Carbon monoxide (fuel exhaust)
Spatial disorientation
Vertigo
Motion sickness
Stress
Psychological stresses
Tar
Nicotine
Carbon monoxide (smoking)
Ethyl alcohol
Barbiturates
Tranquilizers
Narcotics

Antihistamine
Caffeine
Cocaine
Amphetamine
Hypoglycemia
Acute skill fatigue
Chronic skill fatigue
Circadian rhythm

Review questions

1. What are some of the medical problems a pilot can experience when flying
    with a cold or flu?
   Why are these problems exacerbated at higher altitudes?

2. Describe the cause and effects of altitude hypoxia.
   What is hyperventilation?
   Describe the three types of oxygen systems used in civil aircraft.
   What is the difference between aviation oxygen and medical oxygen?

3. List some of the FAA's recommendations to pilots concerning the use of
    supplemental oxygen.
   What are some of the effects of carbon monoxide inhalation over a long
    period of time?
   How can the presence of carbon monoxide affect night vision?

4. What are some of the causes of spatial disorientation (vertigo)?
   Describe several steps that can be taken to prevent spatial disorientation.
   What is the cause of motion sickness?

5. What is meant by *psychological stresses*?
   Explain the effects of cigarette smoking on the cardiovascular system.
   What are *tar* and *nicotine*?
   How do they affect the body?

6. How does alcohol affect the brain?
   Describe the effects of varying amounts of alcohol in the blood.
   Why is the effect of a hangover just as significant to flight safety as alcohol
    ingestion?

7. List and briefly describe the effect of several depressant drugs on the central nervous system.
   Do the same for several stimulant drugs.

8. Discuss the importance of proper eating habits.
   What is hypoglycemia?
   What is the difference between *acute skill fatigue* and *chronic skill fatigue*?
   Define *circadian rhythm*.
   Why is physical conditioning so important?

Flight planning

Outline

Learning objectives

After you finish this chapter, you should be able to:

△ Recognize the importance of periodically reviewing the owner's manual and/or operating handbook for the aircraft you fly.

△ Describe the factors that must be considered in reviewing your own capabilities to perform a particular flight.

△ Define *density altitude* and describe its effect on takeoff and landing.

△ Describe your responsibility in seeing that your aircraft's weight and balance are within the prescribed limits for each flight.

△ Identify several aircraft performance characteristics that are adversely affected by overweight.

△ List some of the factors under control of the pilot that affect the location of an aircraft's c.g.

△ Discuss some of the problems encountered in planning fuel requirements for a flight.

△ Define *ground effect* and its significance on takeoff.

△ Discuss some of the important factors that must be considered in reviewing runway requirements.

△ Explain the steps that should be taken in the event of power loss during takeoff or on climbout.

△ Summarize all the crucial elements that must be considered in the preflight planning process.

Introduction

The Federal Aviation Regulations clearly indicate that "Each pilot in command shall, before beginning a flight, familiarize himself with all available information concerning that flight" (FAR 91.3). Unfortunately, no pilot could possibly be familiar with all information about a flight, and no matter how much preparation, there is no way to know when he or she has done all that can be done. However, the rule stands and pilots must determine how to live with it in the real world. This chapter examines the major factors you should consider in the flight-planning process.

Knowing your aircraft

You should periodically reread the owner's manual and/or operating handbook for the aircraft you fly. Know the aircraft systems—how to operate them and what to do in the event of a system malfunction or failure. Know how to conserve fuel. Review the procedures to follow after an engine failure. Above all, know and remember how your aircraft performs in high temperatures and when loaded to maximum allowable gross weight.

When an emergency occurs in flight, there is little time to decide the proper action to be taken. You must have an established plan of action and a thorough knowledge of your aircraft before an actual incident occurs.

The owner's manual, by federal regulation, must be on board the aircraft for flight. These manuals can be purchased from any local flight center and can be a great investment. The manual includes all pertinent information concerning the aircraft, for example, an explanation of flight maneuvers. It might have been some time since you have flown these maneuvers, and this chapter will refresh your memory to ensure you are following procedures correctly.

An important section to read over more than a few times is the one on landing irregularities. Information on crosswind landings might help you get out of a tight situation and back on the ground safely. Additionally, more detailed information on flight maneuvers can be obtained from special training manuals, also available at the flight center.

There is a section on the stall characteristics of the aircraft, including stall speeds for various aircraft configurations and angles of bank. Notice particularly the configurations most used when you fly traffic patterns and approach to landings. It would be advisable to commit the speeds (maybe two or three at the most) to memory. If you are not the type who has a good memory for those things, write them down on a 3-×-5-inch card so you can have a ready reference while you fly. You can review them just prior to entering the traffic area. Stalling can be extremely hazardous at the low altitudes of the traffic pattern and place you in a situation from which you cannot recover before hitting the ground.

Foremost, you should read and thoroughly understand the chapter on emergency procedures and operating limitations of the aircraft. These are items the aircraft manufacturer has decided are important enough to warrant your special attention. The manufacturer thoroughly tested the aircraft and its capabilities before it was delivered. The procedures are designed to help you recover the aircraft safely when it performs less than advertised.

This section has only highlighted some of the more important things to review. Do not stop here. The owner's manual can be a pilot's best friend. It allows you the freedom to ponder the manufacturer's recommendations while your body is safe and sound on the ground. If questions arise, it is much better that they arise there than in the air.

In an accident prevention program publication prepared by the FAA entitled "Meet Your Aircraft," there is a quiz designed to aid a pilot in understanding the aircraft he or she flies (see TABLE 3-1). This quiz is designed to aid pilots in better understanding the systems of the specific aircraft they fly. Although no attempt is made to cover in depth everything in the information contained in the typical pilot's owner's manual or operating handbook, the quiz will, nonetheless, provide a review of the basic information you should know about your aircraft.

Since the questions are designed to be answered in "open book" fashion (wherein you may use any sources to provide the correct answer), no minimum passing score is set. It is assumed, however, that pilot's possessing at least a private pilot's certificate will score high.

Table 3-1. Aircraft checklist quiz

Aircraft model & type _____

1. What is the normal climb-out speed?___

_____
2. What is the best rate-of-climb speed?

_____
3. What is the best angle-of-climb speed?___

_____
4. What is the maximum flaps-down speed?

_____
5. What is the maximum gear-down speed?

_____
6. What is the stall speed in a normal landing configuration?_____

7. What is the "clean" (flaps, gear up) stall speed?_____
8. What is the approach-to-landing speed?

_____
9. What is the maneuvering speed?_____
10. What is the never-exceed speed?_____
11. What engine-out glide speed will give you the maximum range?

_____
12. What is the VMC? (multi-engine only)

_____
13. What is the make and horsepower of the engine(s)?_____
14. What is the estimated true airspeed at 5000 feet and 65% power?

_____

Table 3-1. Continued.

15. What rpm or combination of rpm and manifold pressure yields 65% power at 5000 feet MSL?
_____rpm_____MP

16. How many gallons of fuel are consumed per hour at 65% power at 5000 feet MSL?_____

17. How many usable gallons of fuel can your aircraft carry?

_____

18. Where are the fuel tanks located and what are their capacities?
Main tank_____ gallons_____
Left tank_____ gallons_____
Right tank_____ gallons_____
Rear tank_____ gallons_____
Auxiliary tank #1_____ gallons_____
Auxiliary tank #2_____ gallons_____

19. (Multi-engine only) in the event an engine fails, can all on-board fuel be fed to the running engine?_____
If yes, explain how_____

_____

20. With full fuel, 65% power, at 5000 feet, allowing a 45-minute reserve, what is the maximum duration (in hours)?_____

21. What speed will give you the best glide ratio?_____

22. What is the octane rating of the fuel used by the aircraft?_____

23. How do you drain the fuel sumps?_____

_____

24. What weight of oil is being used?_____

25. Is the landing gear fixed, manual, hydraulic, or electric?_____. If retractable, what is the back-up system for lowering the gear?_____

_____

26. What is the maximum allowable crosswind component for the aircraft?

_____

27. How many persons will the aircraft safely carry with full fuel?_____

28. What is the maximum allowable weight the aircraft can carry in the baggage compartments?
Rear_____pounds
Front_____pounds
Belly_____pounds
Left engine nacelle _____pounds
Right engine nacelle_____pounds
Total_____pounds

29. What take-off distance is required to clear a 50-foot obstacle at maximum gross weight at a pressure altitude of 5000 feet and 75 °F (assume no wind and a hard-surfaced runway)?_____feet

30. What would be the answer to number 29 if the takeoff were made from a sea-level pressure altitude?_____feet

31. Would high humidity increase or decrease this distance?_____

32. How do you determine pressure altitude?

_____

33. What is your maximum allowable useful load?_____pounds

34. Solve the weight and balance problem for the flight you plan to make. If you plan to fly solo also solve the problem for a 170-pound passenger in each seat. Does your load fall within the weight and balance envelope:_____ What is your gross weight?_____ If you solved the problem contemplating 170-pound passengers in each seat, how much fuel could you carry?_____
Where?_____ If you carry full fuel, how much baggage could you carry_____ Where?_____

35. List two frequencies you can use to contact a flight service station:
Transmit   Receive
1_____   _____
2_____   _____

36. What is the emergency frequency?

_____

Source: FAA

Knowing your own capabilities

Flying safely involves a good dose of common sense. Applying common sense to our flying isn't necessarily difficult. It does, however, require a willingness on the part of the pilot to sharpen his or her flight sense and then create a disciplined program for making the whole thing work.

How many pilots have operated an aircraft rarely or not at all during the winter months? There are probably quite a few. Preparing to fly on those first warm, balmy spring days after a long layoff can be a very trying experience for pilot and aircraft alike. Common sense dictates that you are rusty and that a couple of hours of dual with an instructor might be in order.

Get out your logbook. When was the last time you flew? What maneuvers did you accomplish? Are you embarking on a journey with passengers? Even a few trips around the pattern with a fight instructor might be well worth it. A flight instructor will ensure that you are doing everything correctly. That is tough to do solo.

Maybe an instructor flight is not necessary, and you decide a solo flight is more appropriate. Instead of just droning around doing area reconnaissance, take a little time out to practice a few stalls and a steep turn. You will be surprised at how little time it takes. When you come back to the traffic pattern, instead of flying normal traffic patterns and landings, practice those short and soft field patterns and landings instead. Try to get in some crosswind practice. Maybe there are some airfields in your area where a crosswind prevails. This will be beneficial when that cold front moves a little faster than you thought and the winds kick up. And it is great practice for going cross-country to a strange field when you are not exactly familiar with the surroundings or wind patterns.

Cross-country flying introduces a number of variables that can go wrong. Preflight planning is the best method of preparation. The longer it has been since you flew cross-country, the more preparation you need. Make sure you know everything there is to know about your airplane, the route of flight, and the enroute weather.

Weather is such an important factor it will be treated separately in the next chapter. It is the primary cause of many general aviation accidents—accidents that would have been prevented if the pilot had just turned around and returned home. Many times, the pilot did not have the instrument rating to fly in weather, but continued anyway.

Clouds make it tough to see mountains and other obstructions. They also contribute to carburetor icing and reduced performance.

Some weather phenomena are always in season, so take a good hard look at the weather while you are still on the ground. Consider alternative routes of flight or delay the trip a day or two until the weather gets better.

Density altitude

Density altitude represents the combined effect of pressure altitude and temperature on the performance of an aircraft. Hot, high, and humid weather conditions can change a routine takeoff or landing into an accident. Three important factors that affect air density:

1. *Altitude*   The higher the altitude, the less dense the air.
2. *Temperature*   The warmer air, the less dense it is.
3. *Humidity*   Humidity is not generally considered a major factor in density altitude computations because the effect of humidity is related to engine power, rather than aerodynamic efficiency. At high ambient temperatures, the atmosphere can retain a high water vapor content. For example, at 96 °F, the water vapor content of the air can be eight times as great as at 42 °F. High-density altitude and high humidity do not often go hand in hand. However, if high humidity does exist, it would be wise to add 10 percent to your computed takeoff distance and anticipate a reduced climb rate.

The Pilot's Operating Handbook or owner's manual prepared by the airframe manufacturer provide good information regarding the aircraft performance under standard conditions (sea level at 59 °F). However, if a pilot becomes complacent regarding aircraft performance or is careless in using the charts, density altitude effects might provide an unexpected element of suspense during takeoff and climb.

Density altitude effects are not confined to mountain areas. They also apply at elevations near sea level when temperatures go above standard 50 °F (15 °C). It's just that the effects are increasingly dramatic at the higher elevations. Takeoff distance, power available (in normally aspirated engines), and climb rate are all adversely affected, and although the indicated airspeed remains the same, the true airspeed increases. Too often, a pilot who is flying in high density-altitude conditions for the first time in an aircraft with a normally aspirated engine becomes painfully aware of the retarded effect on the aircraft's performance capabilities.

Additionally, at power settings of less than 75 percent, or at density altitudes above 5000 feet, it is essential that normally aspirated engines be leaned for maximum power on takeoff unless equipped with an automatic altitude mixture control. Otherwise, the excessively rich mixture adds another detriment to overall performance. Turbocharged engines, on the other hand, need not be leaned for takeoff in high density-altitude conditions because they are capable of producing manifold pressure equal to or higher than sea-level pressure.

Density altitude is not be confused with pressure altitude, indicated altitude, true altitude, or absolute altitude, and is not to be used as a height reference, but will be used as determining criteria for the performance capabilities of the aircraft. The published performance criteria in the Pilot's Operating Handbook is generally based on standard atmospheric conditions at sea level (50 °F or 15 °C and 29.92 inches of mercury).

When the temperature rises above the standard temperature for the locality, the density of the air in that locality is reduced and the density altitude increases. This increase affects the aircraft's aerodynamic performance and decreases the horsepower output of the engine. Pilots should make a practice of checking their aircraft performance charts during preflight preparation, especially when temperatures are above normal, regardless of airport elevation.

From the pilot's point of view, an increase in density altitude results in:

- Increased takeoff distance.
- Reduced rate of climb.
- Increased true airspeed on approach and landing (same IAS).
- Increased landing roll distance.

At airports of higher elevations, such as those in the western United States, high temperatures sometimes have such an effect on density altitude that safe operations are impossible. In such conditions, operations between midmorning and midafternoon can become extremely hazardous. Even at lower elevations, aircraft performance can become marginal, and it might be necessary to reduce aircraft gross weight for safe operations. Therefore, it is advisable, when performance is in question, to schedule operations during the cool hours of the day—early morning or late afternoon—when forecast temperatures are expected to rise above normal. Early morning and late evening are sometimes more ideal for both departure and arrival.

A pilot's first reference for aircraft performance information should be the operational data section of the Aircraft Owner's Manual for the Pilot's Operating Handbook developed by the aircraft manufacturer. When these references are not available, the *Koch Chart* (FIG. 3-1) can be used to figure the approximate temperature and altitude adjustments for aircraft takeoff distance and rate of climb.

Like most potentially threatening aviation hazards, the effects of density altitude can be handled through pilot awareness of and respect for the phenomenon. How well you plan your flight at times of high density altitude could mean whether or not it is safe to fly.

Aircraft weight and balance

Aircraft performance and handling characteristics are affected by the gross weight and center-of-gravity (c.g.) limits. If every pilot were to understand and respect this fact, general aviation accidents could be reduced dramatically. An overloaded

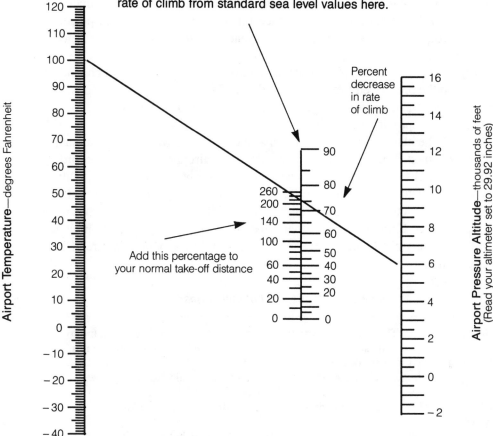

1. To find the effect of altitude and temperature connect the temperature and airport altitude by a straight line.

2. Read the increase in take-off distance and the decrease in rate of climb from standard sea level values here.

Example: The diagonal line shows that 230% must be added for a temperature of 100° and a pressure altitude of 6000 feet. Therefore, if your standard temperature sea level take-off distance, in order to climb to 50 feet, normally requires 1000 feet of runway, it would become 3300 feet under the conditions shown. In addition, the rate of climb would be decreased 76%. Also, if your normal sea level rate of climb is 500 feet per minute, it would become 120 feet per minute.

This chart indicates typical representative values for "personal" airplanes. For exact values consult your airplane flight manual. The chart may be conservative for airplanes with supercharged engines. *Also remember* that long grass, sand, mud or deep snow can easily double your take-off distance.

Source: FAA

Fig. 3-1. The Koch Chart for altitude and temperature effects.

or improperly balanced aircraft will require more power and greater fuel consumption to maintain flight, and the stability and controllability will be seriously affected. Lack of appreciation for the effects of weight and balance on the performance of aircraft—particularly in combination with such performance-reducing factors as high density altitude, frost or ice on the wings, low engine power, severe or uncoordinated maneuvers, and emergency situations—is a prime factor in many accidents.

Every pilot is responsible for ensuring that his or her plane's weight and balance is within the prescribed limits for each flight. Each aircraft is delivered with its empty weight and center of gravity data entered into and remaining with records that are kept with the plane.

It is up to the plane's owner to ensure that the mechanic who does the annual inspection or modifications makes entry into the aircraft's logbook record, amending as necessary when the plane's empty weight or center of gravity changes. Without these updated entries, the pilot has no accurate baseline for making loading calculations and decisions. The pilot should check weight and balance prior to each flight, ensuring that gross weight and c.g. are within limits. See TABLE 3-2 for weight and balance terms that all pilots should be aware of in planning a flight.

Table 3-2. Weight and balance terms

arm (moment arm)   The horizontal distance, in inches, from the reference datum to the item. The algebraic sign is plus (+) if measured aft of the datum, and minus (−) if measured forward of the datum.

center of gravity (c.g.)   The point about which an aircraft would balance if it were possible to suspend it at that point. It is the mass center of the aircraft or the theoretical point at which the entire weight of the aircraft is assumed to be concentrated.

center of gravity limits   'The specified forward and aft points beyond which the c.g. must not be located during flight. The c.g. moment envelope is contained in the aircraft flight manual and FAA Aircraft Specifications of Data Sheets.

center of gravity range   The distance between the forward and aft c.g. limits.

datum line   An imaginary vertical plane or line from which all measurements of arm are taken. The datum is established by the manufacturer. After the datum is selected, all moment arms and the c.g. range must be computed with reference to that point.

fuel load   The expendable part of the aircraft load; includes only usable fuel and not the fuel required to fill the lines or that which remains trapped in the tank sumps.

moment   The produce of the weight of an item multiplied by its arm. Expressed in inch pound (in.-lb.).

total moment   The weight of the aircraft multiplied by the distance between the datum and the c.g.

moment index   The moment divided by a constant, such as 100, 1,000, or 10,000. The purpose of using a moment index is to simplify computations of weight and balance on large aircraft where heavy items and long arms result in large,

Table 3-2. Continued.

unmanageable numbers. It is simply a matter of reduction to the least common denominator.

mean aerodynamic chord (MAC)   The average distance from the leading edge to the trailing edge of the wing. The MAC is specified for the aircraft by determining the average chord of an imaginary wing that has the same aerodynamic characteristics of the actual wing. Center of gravity is usually located at or near the forward 25 percent of the chord.

station   A location in the aircraft that is identified by a number designating its distance in inches from the datum. The datum, is therefore, identified as zero and the station and arm are usually identical.

useful load   The weight of the pilot, copilot, passengers, baggage, usable fuel, and drainable oil.

empty weight   The airframe, engines, and all items of operating equipment that have fixed locations and are permanently installed in the aircraft. Includes optional and special equipment, fixed ballast, hydraulic fluid, unusable (residual) fuel, and undrainable (residual) oil.

Source: FAA

Aircraft weight

The lifting capability of an aircraft depends upon the airfoil design of the wing, the speed at which the wing moves through the air, and the density of the air. It is the design of the aircraft wing that limits the amount of available lift, and it is the available power from the engine(s) that likewise limits the speed at which the wing can be made to move through the air. The efficiency of the engine/wing combination is reduced when air is less dense than the established *standard day* (barometric sea-level pressure of 29.92 inches of mercury at a temperature of 59 °F). Therefore, every pilot should ascertain during preflight preparation that the aircraft gross weight is within safe limits for the intended flight, considering the aircraft performance capabilities. The total weight of baggage, cargo, and fuel load should be adjusted accordingly to provide an adequate margin of safety.

Pilots must understand that in many general aviation aircraft it is not possible to fill all seats, load the baggage compartment to capacity, carry full fuel, and remain within approved weight and balance c.g. limits. In many four- and six-place airplanes, the fuel tanks cannot be filled to capacity when a full complement of passengers and their baggage is carried. It is necessary to reduce the number of passengers or baggage weight if the proposed flight distance requires a full fuel load.

The aircraft performance characteristics adversely affected by overweight are:

- Increased takeoff speed
- Increased takeoff runway length

- Rate of climb
- Maximum altitude capability
- Operational range
- Maneuverability
- Controllability
- Stall speed
- Approach speed
- Landing distance

Every pilot must consider how these characteristics would affect the aircraft in an emergency situation.

Aircraft balance

Balance refers to the location of the c.g. along the longitudinal axis of the aircraft. It is of primary importance to safety of flight. There are forward and aft limits beyond which the c.g. should not be located for flight. These limits are established by the aircraft design engineers to ensure proper, predictable aircraft control about the horizontal, vertical, and lateral axes. The operational weight and balance limits for each aircraft are contained in the aircraft owner's or flight manual. This information also can be obtained from the FAA Aircraft Specification or Data Sheets available at most aircraft maintenance facilities.

The weight and balance information for each aircraft must be amended when repairs or alterations have been made that affect a change in the aircraft empty weight or c.g. location. To ensure aircraft controllability during flight, the aircraft must be loaded within the design weight and c.g. limits.

A forward c.g. limit is specified to ensure that sufficient elevator deflection is available at minimum speed, as for landing. The aft c.g. limit is the most crucial during flight maneuvers or operation of the aircraft. Aircraft stability decreases as the c.g. moves aft, and the ability of the aircraft to right itself after maneuvering will be decreased correspondingly. The aircraft will be highly unstable in gusting or turbulent air, making attitude and directional control extremely difficult.

If, after the aircraft is loaded, the c.g. does not fall within the allowable limits, it will be necessary to shift loads before attempting flight. The actual location of the c.g. is determined by a number of factors under the control of the pilot:

- Placement of baggage and cargo.
- Assignment of seats to passengers according to each individual's weight.
- Fuel load—selective use of fuel from various tank locations during flight may aid in maintaining safe balance conditions.

Weight and balance control

You should always make a simple and fundamental weight check before flight to ensure that the aircraft *useful load* is not exceeded. If there is the slightest doubt about the loading, you should calculate it by using actual weights and *moment arms* to determine that the aircraft is loaded within safe limits:

$$\text{Aircraft Empty WT} \times \text{c.g. (ARM)} = \text{Moment}$$

$$\text{Oil WT} \times \text{ARM} = \text{Moment}$$

$$\text{Pilot and Passenger WT} \times \text{SEAT (ARM)} = \text{Moment}$$

$$\text{Passengers WT} \times \text{Seat (ARM)} = \text{Moment}$$

$$\text{Baggage WT} \times \text{Compartment (ARM)} = \text{Moment}$$

$$\text{Fuel WT} \times \text{Tank (ARM)} = \text{Moment}$$

$$\text{Aux. Fuel WT} \times \text{Tank (ARM)} = \text{Moment}$$

Add total weight and check against maximum takeoff weight. If it is within limits, add the total moment and divide by the total weight to determine loaded c.g. The loaded c.g. should be within the fore and aft c.g. limits shown in the aircraft flight manual weight and balance information. If not, a few minor load adjustments may correct the problem.

For your safety and the safety of your passengers, check the weight and balance of your aircraft before each flight. Keep the aircraft gross weight and center of gravity within prescribed limits.

An in-depth explanation of the subject of weight and balance is provided in several FAA advisory circulars available from the Superintendent of Documents, U.S. Government Printing Office, Washington, DC 20402. They are:

- AC 91−23A, Pilot's Weight and Balance Handbook
  SN 050−007−00405−2

- AC 61−23A, Pilot's Handbook of Aeronautical Knowledge
  SN 050−011−00051−8

- AC 43.13−1A, Acceptable Methods, Techniques, and Practices—Aircraft Inspection and Repair
  SN 050−011−00058−5

Fuel requirements

Fuel load affects runway length requirements and the extent of air traffic and weather detours a pilot can expect en route. It also determines which airports can be used as alternates.

The slower the airplane, the more difficult it is to calculate time en route because wind will be a greater percentage of the true airspeed and thus have greater impact on groundspeed. For example, a light single-engine aircraft flying at 100 kts with 50 kts of wind is having its groundspeed altered by 50 percent. A jet flying at 450 kts with 100 kts of wind is experiencing a change of 22 percent in its groundspeed. To make the contrast worse, the winds-aloft forecasts are least accurate at low altitudes.

When you are flying a slow airplane into a headwind, small errors in the winds-aloft forecast can render impossible a trip that was supposed to be easy. For example, suppose you have fuel to fly for 4¹/₂ hours at 120 kts true airspeed; the trip is 300 nm and the headwind is forecast to be 30 kts. Calculations indicate that the trip will take 3 hours and 20 minutes, leaving you with a comfortable 1 hour and 10 minutes reserve. Now, suppose the wind forecast is off by 20 kts, which is actually more accurate than usual. With a 50-kts headwind, the 300-nm trip now requires 4 hours and 17 minutes. That hour-plus reserve has vanished.

The only way out of this flight-planning trap is to assume the worst: headwinds are always stronger than forecast and tailwinds never as beneficial. Whether or not the forecast is correct, you land with more fuel in the tanks than expected. Although this conservative approach usually works, some days the forecasts are so far off that landing short of the destination is the only option.

The minimum fuel required by regulation is stipulated as time at normal cruising speed. The minimum fuel required under VFR is 30 minutes, or 45 minutes for night VFR or IFR. Most experienced pilots, however, think of minimum landing fuel in terms of a specific amount that seldom varies. Because an airplane can cruise at a wide variety of fuel flows, the time-reserve requirement is almost meaningless. For example, a high-performance single-engine aircraft can cruise at a high speed on 20 gph or on 10 gph at long-range cruise speed. If the pilot elects to use 45 minutes at 10 gph as a reserve, he will land with only eight gallons in the tanks. That's just not enough for safety, even though it is legal.

One way to avoid these problems is to simply subtract one hour of average block fuel from the total fuel available for the trip. For example, suppose your fuel tanks hold 74 gallons, and the average block fuel burn is 14 gph. For flight-planning purposes, assume that the tanks only hold 60 gallons, which must cover taxi, take-off, climb, cruise, and legal minimums.

Many pilot's operating handbooks contain fuel-endurance charts for various power settings that include a 45-minute reserve. Look closely at the chart because the fuel reserve is often calculated at a 45-percent power setting, even though the chart itself is labeled for endurance at a higher power setting. Other charts say the 45-minute reserve is calculated at maximum-range power, which is just another way of saying the lowest usable cruise power. Either way, a 45-minute reserve at a low power setting leaves very little fuel in the tanks.

Range charts can be misleading because there is always some wind aloft, while the chart is based on still air. A listing of fuel-flow rates at all possible power settings probably would make more sense.

Planning IFR fuel reserves for marginal weather conditions can be difficult. IFR alternate minimums at most ILS-equipped airports are a 600-foot ceiling and 2 miles visibility. That means the forecast for such an airport must be at least that good before you can file it as an alternate. But the forecasters often predict something such as 1000 overcast and 5 miles visibility with a chance of 500 overcast and 1 mile in rain. The chance of lower weather minimums takes that airport out of the legal alternate flight-planning category.

Runway requirements

Takeoff and landing distances in pilot's operating handbooks are predicated on paved, dry, level runway conditions. A rough, dirt, or grass landing strip will considerably lengthen your overall takeoff distance. Likewise, standing water, snow, or slush on a paved runway, or an uphill sloping runway, also will significantly increase your takeoff roll. Wind direction and velocity will also have a significant effect upon your takeoff roll. A headwind will reduce your overall takeoff distance because the airplane will reach its takeoff velocity more quickly and, hence, will become airborne sooner than in calm air. Conversely, a tailwind will increase your takeoff distance since the aircraft will take longer to accelerate to its takeoff speed. Remember, though, your airspeed indicator will, in both cases, read the same indicated airspeed.

The effects of a crosswind on takeoff performance will vary, depending upon the wind's direction. A 90-degree crosswind will have a negligible effect on takeoff distance. A gusting wind will require that you keep the airplane on the ground for a slightly longer period of time, thereby increasing your overall takeoff roll.

Ground effect

When you are flying close to the ground, drag is reduced because of the restricted air flow patterns around the wing. This occurrence is called *ground effect*. This effect makes it possible to lift off at too high a pitch angle, or too soon with a heavy load. However, taking off too soon, at possibly too steep an attitude, will cause the airplane's angle of attack to be at or near that of a stall, with drag and thrust nearly equal. If you leave ground effect under these conditions, the airplane might not be able to accelerate to its proper climb speed, unless you first lower the nose momentarily.

Do not force your airplane to become airborne too soon. Let it lift off when it's ready to fly. Then, hold it in ground effect momentarily before climbing out. This is especially important when departing from a short, soft field with obstacles. In such cases, the only way to regain your normal climb attitude is to lower the nose, accelerate, and then climb, assuming that there are no obstacles and it is not too late to sacrifice altitude for speed.

Clearing a 50-foot obstacle

Pilot operating handbooks for light aircraft include required takeoff and landing runway length, but they are determined using a new airplane flown by a competent pilot under good conditions. To be on the safe side, double the published length needed to climb to 50 feet. For example, a Cessna 182 fixed-gear Skylane, using short-field techniques, can take off and clear a 50-foot barrier at maximum weight under standard atmosphere conditions in about 1500 feet. That doesn't leave much room for error. If even a small problem in airplane performance or pilot technique develops, the airplane will not make it. Double that distance to 3000 feet and you have a chance.

Of course, it is impossible to determine a balanced field length for a single-engine aircraft because the airplane cannot continue to fly after an engine failure. However, if you use a runway that is twice the length required to climb to 50 feet, you also double the options should the engine fail on takeoff. Landing straight ahead on the runway would be an option for a longer period of time, and when that was no longer possible you would have enough altitude for at least some maneuvering before landing off the airport.

Emergency planning

It is essential to prepare for the possibility of an emergency during takeoff. Most power losses occur at the first application or reduction of power. The best way to check your engine for a possible malfunction is during your engine runup, before takeoff. Use your checklist. Listen for any abnormalities that might signal impending power loss or other problem. In the event of a power loss during takeoff or on climbout, take the following steps:

1. If power loss occurs during your takeoff roll, stop straight ahead on the runway. If insufficient runway remains, continue straight ahead, turning only to avoid obstacles.

2. If you experience a power loss after liftoff, do not attempt to return to the airport. You should, instead, lower the nose to maintain proper airspeed, then land straight ahead with your gear down to lessen impact forces. Make only slight turns to avoid obstacles.

3. Remember, the cardinal rule in the event of any power loss is to maintain airspeed and control at all times.

4. If you experience a power loss after sufficient altitude has been gained, you have the option of either selecting an open field in which to land or, possibly, doing a 180-degree turn and returning to the airport from which you departed. But, do not be trapped because you have a little extra altitude. Maintain your best glide speed until you are sure you can reach the area of intended landing. Then, you can lower the flaps or

extend the landing gear. In the meantime, make use of this valuable time to troubleshoot the problem. Maybe the cause of the power loss is as simple as letting the fuel tank go dry, placing the fuel selector in an "off" or intermediate position, or moving the mixture control to idle cut-off.

Changes to the plan in flight

In flight it is essential to remember that the flight plan is just that—nothing more than a plan. The crucial calculations are based on forecasts, not facts. Once en route, the plan must be modified using the winds as they exist, not as forecast. Unforecast conditions also can necessitate a change in cruise altitude, which in turn changes the fuel flow and true airspeed. The plan you made on the ground satisfied the rules; the plan you make en route compensates for reality.

When the headwinds are stronger than forecast, you must decide where to stop for fuel. When you continue toward the destination in the hope that conditions will improve, your need to land at the destination becomes more urgent. Because it is disconcerting to stop just a few miles short, it becomes easy to violate minimum landing-fuel requirements.

You also must monitor weather at the destination while you are en route. Ceiling and visibility forecasts are generally more accurate than winds-aloft predictions, but they, too, can be totally wrong. When an airport is fogged in early in the morning, the forecast is usually for rapid improvement, but there are days when the field doesn't come up to minimums until late afternoon, if at all. An overcast above the fog, a delayed wind shift, or many other factors can hold the fog in place, giving no real clue to the forecasters, who are working with nothing more than probabilities.

No matter how thorough the flight plan, it is nothing more than the sum of many predictions concerning weather and aircraft performance. All that really matters are the conditions that you encounter, so you must remain flexible in your flight-planning options after takeoff.

Closing comments

Preflight planning goes a long way toward helping develop common sense into common practice. A few moments spent prior to each flight affords the pilot an excellent opportunity for a thorough preflight inspection that includes an equally thorough preflight weather briefing.

Carelessly performed or disregarded preflight inspections have been the contributing cause of many accidents. Flights have been started, but sometimes not completed, because fuel or oil tanks were not checked, fuel caps were left off or loose, pilot systems were covered or blocked, gust locks were left on, wheel skirts were jammed with mud, engine coolers were blocked by bird nests, or wings and other surfaces were covered by frost, snow, and ice.

However, there are other preflight considerations, too. Be sure to consider your aircraft's fuel capacity, consumption rate, and range vs. wind conditions of each flight, and give careful thought to endurance and fuel reserves well above the minimum required by the FAR's.

Review routing, minimum altitudes along the flight path, navigation aids, notices to airmen, alternate airports in the area, destination airport runway lengths, and the like. Learn as much as you can about your destination airport before you depart.

Performance and flight characteristics of your aircraft are determined, to a large degree, by the plane's maximum weight. Never exceed your aircraft's maximum weight. An aircraft loaded beyond gross weight might be uncontrollable, or might not even fly at all.

Know your *useful load*—the difference between empty weight and maximum gross weight—and remember that this weight includes the weight of the oil and fuel, baggage, and passengers. Do not forget that some aircraft will exceed their gross weight limits if all seats are occupied and full fuel is carried.

Just as important as not exceeding the aircraft gross weight is to load the aircraft properly. Center of gravity limits are becoming more crucial with larger-capacity aircraft. Know how to determine the c.g. location for various loads and configurations of your aircraft.

Required runway lengths for landing and taking off might vary considerably with changes in field elevation, outside air temperature, aircraft load, and runway surface. To avoid running out of runway, consult your pilot's operating handbook for the distances required to make a takeoff or landing under the conditions that exist at the time of the operation. Many pilots add a safety factor of 50 percent or more just to be sure.

Remember that mixture, power, and rpm settings vary fuel consumption considerably. Fuel gauges might be inaccurate. Think of your aircraft's endurance in terms of the actual fuel used versus the flight time. Remember a headwind or a tailwind can significantly shorten or lengthen the actual fuel range. Always provide for fuel reserves. Hundreds of aircraft have run out of fuel in the traffic pattern or in sight of the airport.

According to the NTSB, many other accidents caused by pilot error involve pilots who do not know their aircraft's operational numbers. Too fast, too slow, stall/spin, below engine-out speed, exceeded structural limit speed, loss of control in turbulence, out of c.g. limits, field too short for aircraft load and conditions, landed fast, or stalled on approach are just a few of the accident causes attributed to pilots who just didn't know "the numbers" for their aircraft.

To examine more closely just one of those factors, remember that controlling speed and using the correct speeds directly affect both your longevity and that of your aircraft. High speeds in turbulence or rough air might damage or destroy the aircraft structure. Too slow a speed might cause a stall, spin, or undershoot on landing. Knowing your best engine out-glide speed and best climb speed might mean the difference between you making the airport or ending up in the trees.

Among the more important speeds to memorize include the various stall speeds, recommended approach speed, best rate and angle of climb speed, best glide speed, maneuvering (rough air) speed, maximum never-exceed speed, and gear and flap extension speeds. Remember, stall speeds increase measurably with angle of bank and weight increases.

Of course, one of the most important elements in developing good flight safety is you. Establish a set of safe standards and limitations to which you can confidently adhere. Then stick to them, modifying the limitations only as you gain confidence and experience.

Key terms

Density altitude
Koch Chart
Empty weight
Center of gravity
Balance
Useful load
Moment arms
Ground effect

Review questions

1. Why is it important to review your owner's manual and/or operating handbook periodically?

   What are some of the areas of particular concern?

   What is the purpose of the aircraft checklist quiz?

   Discuss the importance of knowing your own capabilities prior to making a flight.

2. What are the three factors that affect air density?

   How can density altitude affect takeoff and climbout?

   What is the Koch Chart and how can it be used to adjust aircraft takeoff distance and rate of climb?

3. What are the effects of an overloaded or improperly balanced aircraft?

   Define the following terms: *arm* (moment arm), *center of gravity* (c.g.), *datum line*, *moment*, *useful load*, and *empty weight*.

   List ten aircraft performance characteristics adversely affected by overweight.

Who determines the forward and aft limits of balance which the c.g. should
not be located for flight?
What are the factors under control of the pilot that affect the actual location of
the c.g.?
How do you determine the useful load?

4. Discuss the importance of fuel requirements in flight planning.
How can winds-aloft adversely affect fuel reserves?
How can this problem be avoided?
What is the problem with fuel-range endurance charts?

5. How can runway requirements be affected by condition of the runway and
wind direction?
What is *ground effect* and how can it affect takeoff?
Pilot's operating handbooks for light aircraft include takeoff and landing runway length required under ideal conditions. Explain.

6. Describe the steps to be taken in the event of power loss during takeoff or on
climbout.
"The flight plan you made on the ground satisfied the rules; the plan you make
en route compensates for reality." Do you agree with this statement? Why?
Summarize the crucial factors that must be taken into consideration in preflight
planning.

Weather briefings and icing

Outline

Learning objectives

When you are finished with this chapter, you should be able to:

△ Understand the importance of a good weather briefing.

△ List the information needed by a weather briefer in order to tailor a briefing to meet your needs.

△ Describe the basic elements included in a preflight briefing.

△ Compare and contrast the following briefings: Abbreviated preflight, outlook preflight, and in-flight.

△ Explain how you can improve your "go or no-go" weather judgment by setting personal weather minimums.

△ Distinguish between: area forecasts; sequence (hourly) weather reports; terminal forecasts; wind and temperature aloft forecasts; and in-flight advisories.

△ Define *SIGMETs*, *AIRMETs*, and *PIREPs*.

△ Recognize the serious nature of thunderstorms and windshear.

△ Describe the different types of carburetor icing conditions and the precautions pilots should take during all phases of taxiing and flight.

Introduction

Every flight must be viewed with prevailing weather conditions in mind. Whether the flight is local or extended cross country, a determination of weather conditions must be an integral part of total preflight planning.

A good weather briefing starts with developing an awareness of the overall big picture before looking at the details. At many locations, you can learn about the big picture by listening to the Transcribed Weather Broadcast (TWEB); the Telephone Information Briefing Service (TIBS), for automated FSSs; or the

Pilot's Automatic Telephone Weather Answering Service (PATWAS), for non-automated FSSs; or the Interim Voice Response System (IVRS); or by watching a good television weather report. The *Airport Facility Directory* and other aviation reference materials list the sources of weather information. When you are ready to call for a weather briefing, you can use these sources to obtain the telephone number for the Federal Aviation Administration.

In a telephone book, look under "United States Government/Department of Transportation/Federal Aviation Administration/Flight Service Station." Make sure your planned route of flight is worked out and your flight plan *partially* completed *before* you make the telephone call.

A universal toll-free number for Flight Service Stations has been established in conjunction with the FSS Modernization Program. In the areas of the country where this system is operational, you can dial 1−800 WX BRIEF (1−800−992−7433) and you will be switched automatically to the FSS or automated flight service station that serves the area from which you are calling. When you reach the FSS, you will be answered by a briefer.

If you are connected to one of the automated FSSs, you will be answered by a recorded announcement, which includes the name of the facility, followed by instructions for both touch-tone and rotary-dial telephone users. Touch-tone users can elect to talk to a briefer for any of the direct-access services, or can select a menu that identifies those services and the associated codes for each. The direct-access services available from an automated FSS are recorded weather and aeronautical information and "fast-file" flight plan filing. If you are using a rotary dial or pulse -tone telephone, you will be switched automatically to a briefer, who will provide the information desired; or, if requested, can connect you to one of the direct-access services.

So that your preflight briefing can be tailored to your needs, give the briefer the following information:

1. Your qualifications, i.e., student, private, commercial, and whether instrument rated.
2. The type of flight contemplated, either VFR or IFR.
3. The aircraft's N-number identification. If you do not know the N-number, give the pilot's name.
4. The aircraft type.
5. Your departure point.
6. Your proposed route of flight.
7. Your destination.
8. Your proposed flight altitude(s).
9. Your estimated time of departure (ETD).
10. Your estimated time en route.

Request that the briefer provide you with a standard weather briefing. Then listen to the briefer. The briefer will be following procedures and phraseology used by FAA personnel providing flight services. The briefer will advise you of any adverse conditions along your proposed route of flight. When a VFR flight is proposed and actual or forecast conditions make VFR flight questionable, the briefer will describe the conditions and may advise you that "VFR flight (is) not recommended." If this occurs, or if you feel that the weather conditions are clearly beyond your capabilities (or that of your aircraft or equipment), you should consider terminating the briefing. This will free the briefer to handle other incoming calls.

The briefer will summarize weather reports and forecasts. After he or she concludes the briefing, if there is anything that you do not understand about the weather briefing, let the briefer know. If terminology is used that you do not understand, ask the briefer to explain it. A briefer who talks too fast should be asked to speak more slowly. The amount of detail in your weather briefing will depend upon how complicated the weather situation really is. Remember, if the weather situation really is questionable, expect—and insist upon—a standard weather briefing. It is both your legal responsibility and your prerogative as a pilot to do so.

Standard preflight briefing

At a minimum, your standard preflight briefing should include the following elements:

1. *Adverse conditions*   Significant meterological and aeronautical information that might influence you, the pilot, to alter your proposed route of flight, or even cancel your flight entirely (e.g., thunderstorms, icing, turbulence, low ceilings or visibilities, airport closures). Expect the briefer to emphasize conditions that are particularly significant, such as low-level windshear, embedded thunderstorms, reported icing, or frontal zones.

2. *Synopsis*   A brief statement as to the cause of the weather (e.g., fronts or pressure systems), which might affect your proposed route of flight.

3. *Current conditions*   When your proposed time of departure is within two hours, a summary of the current weather, including PIREPs, applicable to your flight will be given.

4. *Enroute forecast*   Expect the briefer to summarize forecast conditions along your proposed route in a logical order; i.e., climbout, en route, and descent.

5. *Destination forecast*   The destination forecast for your planned ETA will be provided, including any significant changes within one hour before and after your planned time of arrival.

6. *Winds aloft*   The briefer will summarize forecast winds aloft for the proposed route. Temperature information will be provided on request.

7. *Notice to airmen*   "Current" Notice to Airmen (NOTAMs) pertinent to your proposed route of flight will be provided. However, information on military training routes and areas (MTR and MOA), along with Published NOTAMs and Special Notices, must be specifically requested.

Abbreviated preflight briefing

Request an abbreviated briefing when you need information to supplement mass disseminated data or update a previous briefing, or when you need only one or two specific items. Provide the briefer with appropriate background information, the time you received the previous information, and/or the specific items needed. You should indicate the source of the information already received so that the briefer can limit the briefing to the information that you have not received and appreciable changes in meterological conditions since your previous briefing. To the extent possible, the briefer will provide the information in the sequence shown for a standard briefing. If you request only one or two specific items, the briefer will advise you if adverse conditions are present or forecast. Details on these conditions will be provided at your request.

Outlook preflight briefing

You should request an outlook briefing whenever your proposed time of departure is 6 or more hours from the time of the briefing. The briefer will provide available forecast data applicable to the proposed flight. This type of briefing is provided for planning purposes only. You should obtain a standard briefing prior to departure in order to obtain such items as current conditions, updated forecasts, winds aloft, and NOTAMs.

In-flight briefing

You are encouraged to obtain your preflight briefing by telephone or in person before departure. In those cases where you need to obtain a preflight briefing or an update to a previous briefing by radio, you should contact the nearest FSS to obtain this information. After communications have been established, advise the specialist of the type of briefing you require and provide appropriate background information. You will be provided information as specified previously, depending on the type of briefing requested. In addition, the specialist will recommend shifting to the FLIGHT WATCH frequency when conditions along the intended route indicate that it would be advantageous to do so. (See TABLE 4-1 for a summary of sources of inflight weather updates.)

Following any briefing, feel free to ask for any information that you or the briefer might have missed. It is best to save your questions until the briefing has

Table 4-1. Sources of inflight weather updates

---

* Via VHF radio:

  ~ EFAS (FLIGHT WATCH on 122.0 MHz below FL 180 and as published at FL 180 and above for "real-time" weather.
  ~ FSS.
  ~ Centers and terminal area facilities will broadcast a SIGMET or CWA alert once on all frequences upon receipt.
  ~ To the extent possible, centers and terminal area facilities will issue pertinent information on weather and assist pilots in avoiding hazardous weather areas, when requested.

* Transcribed radio broadcasts:
  ~ Transcribed Weather Broadcasts (TWEBs).
  ~ Hazardous Inflight Weather Advisory Service (HIWAS).

Destination/arrival weather can be obtained from the following sources as available:

* Via VHF radio from:
  ~ En Route Flight Advisory Service (EFAS).
  ~ FSSs or other air traffic control facilities.
  ~ Unicom.

* Transcribed VHF radio broadcasts:
  ~ Automatic Terminal Information Service (ATIS).
  ~ On-site automated weather observation.

Source: FAA

---

been completed so the briefer can present the information in a logical sequence. Waiting until the briefing is completed also reduces the chance of important items being overlooked.

Weather judgment

Judgment, which can be defined as the power of arriving at a wise decision, is the combined result of knowledge, skills, and experience. You can improve your "go or no-go" weather judgment by setting personal weather minimums that are higher than the legal minimums. For instance, use a 2000-foot ceiling and 5 miles visibility, instead of the legal 1000 and 3, until you are familiar with flight under those conditions. You can then gradually reduce your personal minimums to whatever limits you find comfortable, at or above the legal limits.

Following are some obvious "DO NOTS" for every pilot:

• Do not fly in or near thunderstorms. Scattered thunderstorms can be circumnavigated safely, but do not try to fly through or under one.

- Do not continue VFR into IFR weather conditions at any time unless you are IFR rated and have the appropriate ATC clearance. Wait it out or turn around if you find enroute weather lowering to IFR conditions. Do not forget there will be areas en route, or even near airports, that are below VFR minimums, whenever reporting stations are at or near VFR minimums. Be especially cautious when the temperature and dewpoint spread is 5° or less—fog may result.

- Do not proceed "on-top," hoping to find a hole at the other end or hoping to get ATC to "talk you down" if you get caught on top.

- Allow more margin for weather at night. Scud and lower clouds do not show up very far ahead, particularly when it is a really dark night.

- Do not fly into areas of rain when the air temperature is near freezing. Ice on the windshield and on the wings make for poor VFR flying conditions. Remember, too, flight into known icing conditions is prohibited for all aircraft not properly equipped.

Finally, if you do get caught in weather, tell an FSS or another ATC facility. They will do their utmost to help you.

Weather information sources used by briefers

The weather information sources that briefers use are explained in this section.

Area forecasts

Area forecasts (FAs) are 12-hour aviation forecasts plus a 6-hour categorical outlook giving general descriptions of cloud cover, weather conditions, and potentially hazardous weather that could affect aircraft operations.

Heights of cloud bases, tops, freezing level, icing, and turbulence are referenced to mean sea level (MSL). Ceilings, however, are given in heights above ground level (AGL). SIGMET-type information affecting a particular area is included in the area forecast, and a separate SIGMET is always issued. AIRMETs are issued only when hazardous conditions not adequately covered in the original forecast develop or are expected to develop.

Categorical outlook terms, describing general ceiling and visibility conditions for advanced planning purposes, are defined as follows:

- LIFR (Low IFR) Ceiling less than 500 feet and/or visibility less than 1 statute mile.

- IFR Ceiling 500 feet to less than 1000 feet and/or visibility 1 to less than 3 statute miles.

- MVFR (Marginal VFR) Ceiling 1000 to 3000 feet and/or visibility 3 to 5 statute miles, inclusive.

- VFR   Ceiling greater than 3000 feet and visibility greater than 5 statute miles; includes sky "clear."

The causes of LIFR, IFR, or MVFR are indicated by either ceiling or restrictions to visibility, or both. The contraction *CIG* (for ceiling) and/or weather and obstruction to visibility symbols are used. If winds (or gusts) of 25 kts (kts) or greater are forecast for the outlook period, the word *wind* is also included for all categories, including VFR.

Example: LIFR CIG   Low IFR due to a low ceiling.

Example: IFR F   IFR due to visibility restricted by fog.

Example: MVFR CIG H K   Marginal VFR due both to ceiling and to visibility restricted by haze and smoke.

   Example: IFR CIG R WIND   IFR due to both low ceiling and visibility restricted by rain; the wind is expected to be 25 kts or greater.

Area forecasts, each covering a broad geographical area, are issued three times a day in the contiguous United States and Alaska, and four times a day in Hawaii.

The dissemination time differs from area to area. You can obtain specific schedule times for your location by calling the nearest FSS. These forecasts are amended as required.

Sequence (hourly) weather reports

Sequence (hourly) weather reports (SA) are specific aviation weather observations taken at designated reporting sites throughout the United States. Usually, but not always, these sites are located on airports.

Observations are usually made hourly at about 50 minutes past each hour. These observations are transmitted between 55 minutes past each hour and 3 minutes past the hour, and are generally available at all FSSs within 10 minutes of transmission time. Of course, special observations are taken whenever changing weather conditions warrant.

Example: RDU SA 0150 M50 OVC 10RW – 094/74/59/1009/982/RB 40/OCNL
                 LTG DSNT SW

Translation: Raleigh-Durham, observation at 0150 ZULU, measured ceiling 5000 feet overcast, visibility 10 statute miles; light rain showers; sea-level pressure 1009.4 millibars; temperature 74 °F; dewpoint 59 °F; wind from 100 degrees true at 9 kts; altimeter 29.82 inches.

Remarks: Rain began at 40 minutes past the hour; occasional lightning to the distant southwest.

Note: When providing advisories to departing or arriving aircraft, air traffic control will give current winds relative to magnetic north.)

Terminal forecasts

Terminal forecasts (FT) are issued for specific airports and generally cover a 5-nautical-mile radius from the center of the runway complex. They contain information on the expected ceilings, cloud heights and coverage, visibility, weather, obstructions to vision, and surface winds. They are valid for a 24-hour period. The last 6 hours of each forecast contains a categorical outlook statement indicating whether VFR, MVFR, IFR, or LIFR conditions are expected.

Terminal forecasts are written in the following format:

- Station identifier.
- Date/time group.
- Ceilings   Identified by the letter "C."
- Cloud heights in terminal forecasts   Always reported in hundreds of feet above ground level (AGL). This differs from area forecasts where, except for ceilings, the bases of clouds are reported in feet above mean sea level (MSL).
- Cloud layers   Stated in ascending order of height.
- Visibility   Reported in statute miles (or fractions thereof up to 2 statute miles), but omitted if the visibility is greater than 6 statute miles.
- Weather and obstructions to vision   Displayed in standard weather and obstructions to visibility symbols.
- Surface winds   Reported in tens of degrees from true north and in knots; omitted when less than 10 kts. (*Note*: Wind direction indicates the direction from which the wind is blowing.)
- Remarks.

Terminal forecasts are issued three times a day, based on the time zone in which the forecast office is located, and they are disseminated within 20 minutes after release. Each forecast is amended according to prescribed criteria when required. For specific issuance times, contact your local FSS.

Example: BOS FT 221010 10 SCT C18 BKN 5SW – 3415G25
OCNL C8X1/2SW 12Z C50 BKN 3312G22
04Z MVFR CIG

Translation: Boston terminal forecast for the 22nd day of the month, valid time 10Z – 10Z. Scattered clouds at 1000 feet (AGL); ceiling 1800 feet broken (AGL), visibility 5 statute miles; light snow showers; surface wind from 340 degrees at 15 kts with peak gusts to 25 kts; occasionally, ceiling 800 feet obscured; visibility one-half mile in moderate snow showers. After 12Z, becoming ceiling 5000 feet broken (AGL); surface wind from 330 degrees at 12 kts with gusts to 22 kts. After 04Z and for the last 6 hours of the terminal forecast, becoming marginal VFR due to ceiling.

Wind and temperatures aloft forecasts

Wind and temperatures aloft forecasts (FDs) contain upper air velocity and temperature forecasts for some 160 locations in 48 states. Winds for in-between points can be calculated by interpolation. Winds and temperatures aloft forecasts are 6-hour, 12-hour, and 24-hour forecasts of wind direction to the nearest 10 degrees relative to true north, along with wind speed, in knots, for selected altitudes.

Temperatures aloft, always in degrees Celsius, are given for all but the lowest forecast level (with the possible exception of mountainous areas, where temperatures for the lowest level might also be available, depending upon the elevation of the reporting station).

Prepared twice daily from 0000Z and 1200Z radiosonde upper air observations, these forecasts are available about 4 hours after each observation.

Example:
Altitude 3000, 6000, 9000, etc.
JFK 2925 2833 00 2930-04, etc.

Partial translation   Kennedy Airport, at 6000 feet MSL, the forecast wind is from 280 degrees true north at 33 kts with a temperature of 0 °C.

Inflight advisories

SIGMETs and AIRMETs (WS) warn pilots of potentially hazardous weather. SIGMETs warn of severe and extreme conditions of importance to all aircraft, e.g., icing, turbulence, dust storms, sandstorms, etc. Convective SIGMETs (WST) are issued by the National Severe Storms Forecast Center in Kansas City for the continental United States and warn of tornadoes, thunderstorms, and hail. Appended hourly to convective SIGMETs is a 2- to 6-hour outlook that describes the area where and why expected convective conditions may meet issuance criteria. AIRMETs (WA) concern weather of less severity than SIGMETs or convective SIGMETs that might be hazardous to aircraft having limited capability because of lack of equipment, instrumentation, or pilot qualifications.

SIGMETs and convective SIGMETs are produced whenever conditions dictate. Convective SIGMETs are updated on an hourly basis. AIRMETs are issued only when the conditions were not adequately described in the area forecast.

A center weather advisory (CWA) is an unscheduled in-flight flow-control air traffic and aircrew advisory. CWAs are considered as "nowcast," rather than a flight planning product. They normally provide a narration of conditions existing at the time of issuance and a forecast for the next two hours.

Example: "Attention all aircraft, a line of thunderstorms exists from Williamsport, PA, southeast to Norfolk, VA. Line moving east at one five knots, maximum tops to flight level four five zero. Possibility of strong winds, hail, and heavy rain. Expected to continue beyond two three zero zero ZULU."

PIREPs

The best way to eliminate (or at least reduce) enroute weather surprises is to give—and obtain—pilot-reported in-flight weather observations, or *PIREPs* (UA). A PIREP gives a pilot valuable information on weather conditions actually being experienced in flight by other pilots. This information supplements data reported by ground stations.

Pilot reports are used in the receiving facility immediately, and are disseminated to other FAA facilities, the NWS, and pilots as soon as possible after receipt. They remain in the system for approximately 3 hours.

Example:

LYH UA /OV RIC-LYH 180010/TM 1415/FL065/ TP
C152/SK 030 SCT-BKN 040 100 OVC/WX FV5 H/ TA 06
/TB LGT/RM MDT TURBC SFC-045 DURGC RIC

Translation   Pilot report; from Richmond, VA, to 10 nautical miles south of Lynchburg, VA; time-1415 UTC; altitude 6500 feet MSL; type aircraft, Cessna 152; cloud bases 3000 feet MSL, coverage scattered to broken, tops 4000 feet MSL, higher cloud bases 10,000 feet MSL, coverage overcast; flight visibility 5 statute miles, haze; temperature 6 °C; light turbulence; remarks—moderate turbulence from the surface to 4500 feet MSL during climb from Richmond.

The best way to get PIREPs into the system is via Flight Watch, FAA's real-time weather service to pilots. Contact Flight Watch and give (or ask for) PIREPs along your route of flight. If you are unable to reach Flight Watch, report PIREP information to the nearest FSS, approach or departure control, or the Air Route Traffic Control Center (ARTCC) controller. Remember, by providing real-time weather input to the system, you will be improving the quality of the weather information available to pilots following you over the same area or route. A good PIREP consists of the following:

- Your type of aircraft, altitude, and location (ideally, in reference to a VOR or significant geographical landmark).
- Cloud cover, including base and top reports.
- Turbulence and icing
- Visibility restrictions
- Outside air temperature (OAT)
- Other significant weather data

Thunderstorms

Thunderstorms often encompass some of the worst weather hazards known to flight. The basic requirements for formation of a thunderstorm are:

1. unstable air

2. An initial updraft

3. high moisture content of the air

The general aviation pilot must contend with thunderstorms of varying intensities in virtually all parts of the country and should be aware that all thunderstorm cells progress through three distinct stages which are more commonly called the *lifecycle*. These stages are:

1. cumulus

2. mature

3. dissipating.

The severity of any thunderstorm is governed by the makeup of the mature stage. While most cumulus clouds do not become thunderstorms, the initial stage is always the cumulus cloud. The main feature of the cumulus cloud that will develop into a thunderstorm is the predominate updraft. This updraft may extend from the earth's surface to several thousand feet above the visible cloud tops. During the cumulus stage, tiny cloud droplets grow into raindrops as the cloud builds upward.

When these droplets become so large they can no longer be supported by the existing updraft, they begin to fall. This marks the beginning of the mature stage and usually occurs some ten to fifteen minutes after the cumulus cloud has built upward beyond the freezing level. Thunderstorm cells that progress rapidly through the mature stage are called *limited-state* thunderstorms.

In the limited-state thunderstorm, the mature stage is self-destructive until the updraft will no longer support the raindrops and precipitation begins to fall through the updraft. The buoyancy of the air is decreased until the updraft becomes a downdraft. The cool precipitation tends to cool the lower portion of the cloud, and thus its fuel supply is cut off, the cell loses its energy, and the storm dissipates. When all water droplets have fallen from the cloud, the dissipating stage is complete.

If, in the mature stage, the updraft and downdraft areas remain equally balanced, the mature stage might then become a *steady-state* thunderstorm cell, in which extreme turbulence and large hail can predominate. The limited-state thunderstorm cell can last from 20 minutes to $1^{1}/2$ hours, while the steady-state thunderstorm can last as long as 24 hours and travel for 1000 miles.

Many pilots have flown through limited-state thunderstorms with little or no damage to the aircraft or passengers. They can only consider themselves extremely fortunate, for any thunderstorm is an uncontrolled "heat engine" and might produce any or all of the most violent weather hazards—such as hail, ice, and turbulence—a pilot will ever encounter.

Pilots should avoid all thunderstorms and never venture closer than 5 miles to any visible storm cloud with overhanging areas because of the possibility of encountering hail. Hail and violent turbulence can be encountered within 20 miles of very strong thunderstorms.

Pilots also should be extremely cautious in attempting flight beneath all thunderstorms, even when visibility is good, because of the destructive potential of shear turbulence in these areas. Pilots should reduce airspeed to the manufacturer's recommended airspeed at the first sign of turbulence. Finally, pilots should fly a straight and level attitude on a heading that will take them through the storm area in a minimum time. Figure 4-1 shows the average number of thunderstorm days per year throughout the continental United States.

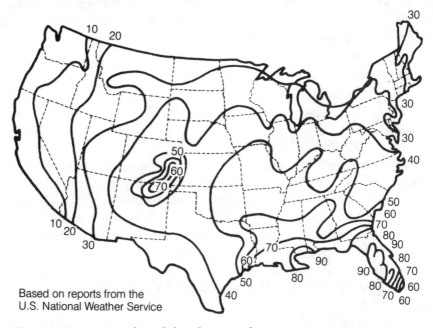

Based on reports from the
U.S. National Weather Service

Fig. 4-1. Average number of thunderstorm days per year.

Windshear

Windshear is a change in wind speed and/or direction over a short distance. It can occur either horizontally or vertically and is most often associated with strong temperature inversions or density gradients. Windshear can occur at high or low altitude. This section will discuss only low-altitude windshear.

There are four common sources of low-level windshear:

1. Frontal activity
2. Thunderstorms
3. Temperature inversions
4. Surface obstructions

Frontal windshear

Not all fronts have associated windshear. In fact, shear is normally a problem only in those fronts with steep wind gradients. Like so many things in weather, there is no absolute rule, but there are a couple of clues:

1. The temperature difference across the front at the surface is 10 °F (5 °C) or more.
2. The front is moving at a speed of at least 30 kts.

You can get clues to the presence of windshear during the weather briefing by checking these two factors. Ask the briefer, and if these factors are present, be prepared for the possibility of shear on approach.

Thunderstorms

Windshear is just one of the many unpleasant aspects of thunderstorms. The violence of these storms and their winds are well documented. The two worst problems outside actual storm penetration—the first gust and the downburst—are shear-related.

Almost everyone has seen the rapid shift and increase in wind just before a thunderstorm hits. This phenomenon is called the *first gust*.

The gusty winds are associated with mature thunderstorms and are the result of large downdrafts striking the ground and spreading out horizontally. These winds can change direction by as much as 180 degrees and reach velocities of 100 kts as far as 10 miles ahead of the storm. The gust wind speed can increase as much as 50 percent between the surface and 1500 feet, with most of the increase occurring in the first 150 feet. The implications for a shear on approach in such a case are obvious.

The other wind problem mentioned earlier, *the downburst*, is also downdraft related. It is an extremely intense localized downdraft from a thunderstorm. This downdraft exceeds 720 feet per minute vertical velocity at 300 feet AGL. The power of the downburst can actually exceed aircraft climb capabilities, not only those of light aircraft but even, as documented in one case, a high-performance Air Force jet.

The downburst is usually much closer to the thunderstorm than the first gust, but there is no absolutely reliable way to predict the occurrence. One clue is the presence of dust clouds, roll clouds, or intense rainfall. It would be best to avoid such areas.

Temperature inversions

Pilots who have flown in the Southwest or in southern California or Colorado are familiar with temperature inversions. Overnight cooling creates a temperature inversion a few hundred feet above the ground. This phenomenon coupled with high winds from what is known as the *low-level jet*, can produce significant wind-shears close to the ground.

One particularly bothersome aspect of temperature-inversion shears is that, as the inversion dissipates, the shear plane and gusty winds move closer to the ground. In some areas of the Southwest, a 90-degree change in direction and 20- to 30-kt increases in surface winds in a few minutes are not uncommon. Obviously, such a shift would make an approach difficult, at best.

Surface obstructions

Surface obstructions are usually thought of in terms of hangars or other buildings near the runway. The sudden change in wind velocity can seriously affect a landing. (Large hangars are a good example.) But there is another type of obstruction.

Some airfields are close to mountain ranges, and mountain passes are close to the final approach paths. Strong surface winds blowing through these passes can cause serious localized windshears during approach. The real problem with such shear is that it is almost totally unpredictable in terms of magnitude of severity. A pilot can expect such shears whenever strong surface winds are present.

Kinds of windshear

Windshear can be divided into horizontal and vertical shears. Although both components can affect an aircraft simultaneously, it is easier to discuss each separately.

Horizontal shear occurs when the flight path of an airplane passes through a wind-shift plane. The other kind is the one most often associated with an approach. The *vertical shear* is normal near the ground and can have the most serious effect on an aircraft. The change in velocity or direction can alter lift, indicated airspeed (IAs), and thrust requirements drastically and can exceed the pilot's capability to recover.

Windshear, in its many forms, can change a routine approach into an emergency recovery in a matter of seconds.

This has been a brief look at the kinds of windshear and their sources. Now let's look at the effects of windshear on an aircraft, pilot techniques for coping with shear, and new developments in forecasting windshear.

Windshear is an abrupt change in direction and/or velocity of wind. The shear can be horizontal or vertical and is associated with frontal activity, thunderstorms, temperature inversions, or surface obstructions.

An aircraft is affected by the change in wind direction/velocity because the aircraft motion relative to the ground is also changed by the wind. Suppose the aircraft is stabilized on an instrument landing system (ILS) approach and encounters a shear that results from a decreasing headwind. In such a case, there is transient loss of airspeed and lift, causing the aircraft to descend. The pilot must compensate for this loss of lift. The crucial factor is whether there is sufficient altitude to complete a recovery. In FIG. 4-2, the shear occurs at an altitude high enough for the pilot to complete the recovery (just past the final approach fix, for example).

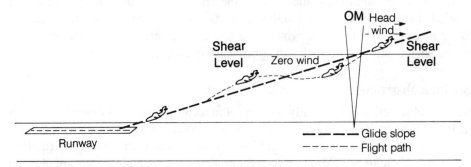

Fig. 4-2. Moderate shear—altitude sufficient to effect recovery.

As the aircraft passes through the shear level, airspeed and lift are lost. The aircraft starts to sink and drops below the glide path. The pilot sees this as a deviation and corrects with increased pitch and power. Very often the correction is too large, and the aircraft overshoots the desired airspeed and glide path. However, since there is sufficient altitude to correct, the pilot is able to land safely.

Figure 4-3 illustrates the situation where the shear encounter is farther down the glide path. Reaction time is more critical. Again, the initial reaction of the aircraft to the shear and the pilot's correction are the same. In this case, however, if the pilot overcorrects, causing the aircraft to go above the glide slope and airspeed to increase sufficiently, there is insufficient altitude to recover, and the aircraft could land long and hot.

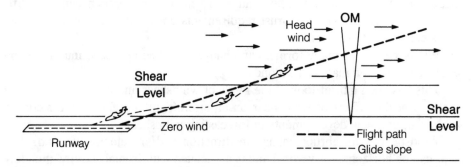

Fig. 4-3. Moderate shear—at altitude where overcorrection results in long landing or overshoot.

The case in FIG. 4-4 is the most serious. When the altitude of the encounter is too low to effect a recovery or the shear itself is sufficiently strong to overcome the aircraft performance, the aircraft lands short.

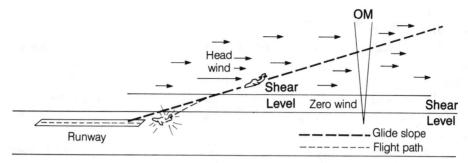

Fig. 4-4. Shear of sufficient magnitude and at an altitude too low to effect recovery.

A decreasing tailwind has the opposite effect. When the aircraft crosses the shear plane and loses the tailwind, lift increases and the aircraft climbs above the glide path. As in the headwind case, the pilot's reaction can mean an overcorrection. The worst case here is the one similar to FIG. 4-3. There the overcorrection leads to a transition to below the glide path, but without enough altitude to correct. This is the classic high sink rate, hard landing.

The most hazardous form of windshear is that encountered in thunderstorms. The severe, sudden wind changes can exceed the performance capabilities of many sophisticated aircraft. There have been numerous documented cases of aircraft mishaps directly related to encounters with thunderstorm windshear.

The best way a pilot can cope with a shear is to:

1. Know it is there
2. Know the magnitude of the change
3. Be prepared to correct or go around

Carburetor icing

Another subject, closely related to weather planning and a significant cause of accidents, is carburetor icing. Most carburetor- or induction-icing accidents occur during climbout or cruising and are attributable to the pilot.

Kinds of icing

Impact induction ice, which can affect an engine with injection-type pressure carburetors as well as one with float-bowl carburetors, forms when moisture-laden air, at temperatures below freezing, strikes air scoops, heat or alternate air valves, intake screens, and protrusions in the carburetor. Flying in snow, sleet, rain, or clouds is conducive to the formation of this type of icing.

Fuel ice forms at and downstream from the point where fuel is mixed with the incoming air. It occurs when the moisture in the air is cooled by the vaporization of the fuel. If ice is allowed to build up in the walls of the induction passages, it can throttle the engine.

Visible moisture in the air is not necessary to cause fuel icing, which can occur at temperatures from 32° to 100°F, and with a relative humidity of 50 percent or more. Note, however, that the likelihood of icing increases as the temperature decreases (down to 32°F) and as the humidity increases. Fuel icing is most likely to occur with temperature below 70°F and relative humidity above 80 percent.

Throttle ice is formed at or near a partially closed throttle, as in a cruise power setting. In engines with float-type carburetors, throttle icing usually occurs along with fuel icing, compounding the problem.

All three kinds of icing can cause loss of power because the flow of the fuel-air mixture to the engine is restricted. The FAA Advisory Circular points out that pilots should use carburetor heat or alternate air when icing conditions are present to prevent ice buildup. Fast-forming ice can reduce the amount of heat available, and the use of partial heat might be worse than not using it at all.

In aircraft with smaller engines, and no carburetor air or mixture temperature instrumentation, apply full carburetor heat as necessary. Shut off carburetor heat for full-power operations such as takeoffs and emergency go-arounds. Leaving the heat on could seriously reduce the amount of power available and could damage the engine.

Just as carburetor heat is automatically applied before throttling back for descent, you should automatically turn off carburetor heat before applying full power for a go-around or a touch-and-go.

Carburetor heat should be on the pretakeoff checklist to test its effectiveness. Note how the power drops on runup when carb heat is applied. If the relative humidity is above 50 percent and the temperature is below 70°F, apply carburetor heat immediately before takeoff, since ice might have accumulated during taxi. Do not leave it on, however.

If you observe a power loss, apply full heat or alternate air before disturbing the throttle. If the ice remains, gradually advance the throttle to full power and climb at maximum rate to produce as much heat as possible.*

Carburetor ice need not be the catalyst of disastrous events. Avoiding carburetor ice problems simply means knowing the conditions, the telltale signs, and ways to render carburetor ice harmless.

Key terms

Preflight briefings
Adverse conditions
Synopsis

*Refer to the operator's manual for the airplane you fly for specific operating instructions and/or procedures pertaining to its operation.

Current conditions
Enroute forecast
Destination forecast
Winds aloft
Notice to Airmen (NOTAMs)
Abbreviated briefing
Outlook briefing
Area forecasts (FAs)
Sequence (or hourly) weather reports (SAs)
Terminal forecasts (FTs)
Winds and temperatures aloft forecasts (FDs)
SIGMETs (WSs)
Convective SIGMETs (WSTs)
AIRMETs (WA)
Center Weather Advisory (CWA)
PIREPs
Flight Watch
Windshear
Horizontal shear
Vertical shear
Impact induction ice
Fuel ice
Throttle ice

Review questions

1. How can a pilot develop a broad understanding of weather conditions before
    attempting to get a detailed weather briefing?
    What specific information should a pilot give to a weather briefer in order to
    tailor the briefing to his or her specific needs?
    A standard preflight briefing should include what basic elements?
    What is the difference between the following briefings: abbreviated
    preflight, outlook preflight, and in-flight?

2. What are some of the "Do Nots" in exercising weather judgment?
    Define: *area forecasts*; *Sequence* (hourly) *weather reports*; *terminal
    forecasts*; *wind and temperatures aloft forecasts*; and *inflight advisories*.
    What is the difference between SIGMETs and AIRMETs?
    What information is included in a PIREP?

3. Discuss some of the cautions that pilots should exercise when flying in and
    around thunderstorms.

What is vertical windshear and why is it so dangerous when an aircraft experiences its effects at a low altitude?

4. What is the difference between fuel ice and throttle ice? When should carburetor heat be applied?

Winter
weather operations

Outline

Learning objectives

After you have completed this chapter, you should be able to:

△ Recognize the conditions under which icing can take place.

△ Describe the various types of structural icing.

△ List the effects of structural icing on airfoils and control surfaces.

△ Identify the rates of ice accumulation for pilot reporting purposes.

△ Discuss some of the items you should check in preparing your aircraft for winter operations.

△ Identify several items that are particularly important to check prior to the operation of your aircraft in cold weather.

△ Describe some of the precautions you should take during taxiing and takeoff in winter weather.

△ Describe some of the problems that can arise during climbout and while en route in winter weather.

△ Discuss the problem of hydroplaning during landing.

△ Identify some important items to consider following a flight during the winter months.

△ List the essential items that should be included in a survival kit.

Introduction

Most pilots are familiar with winter conditions in their particular area; however, often a distance of a few miles can change the environment enough to present new problems to an inexperienced pilot. Weather conditions during the winter months can present some of the most treacherous hazards faced by a pilot: snow, ice, freezing rain, contaminated runways, slush, hydroplaning, supercooled clouds, in-flight icing, frigid temperatures, and more.

Physical principles of aircraft icing

Aircraft structural icing is the accretion of ice on leading-edge surfaces caused by the impingement of supercooled water droplets during flight. This adhesion normally involves liquid moisture and subfreezing temperatures.

Icing will occur in flight when the following four conditions are present:

1. The air temperature is below freezing by a certain amount.
2. Some liquid water is present.
3. The sizes of the droplets are large enough to strike an aircraft component.
4. The exposure time to these conditions along the flight path is long enough for a discernible amount of ice to form.

The temperature of the clouds or liquid water must be below freezing by an amount equal to or greater than the wet-air kinetic temperature rise on the exposed surface as determined by the penetration airspeed.

Collection efficiencies for airfoils can vary from near zero for very small droplets on airfoils that have a large radius of curvature to nearly 100 percent for large droplets in freezing rain on airfoils with little curvature. However, for small, sharp objects like antenna masts, pitot tubes, wiper blades, and propellers, the collection efficiency is very high regardless of droplet size. In other words, blunt objects with a large radius of curvature at lower airspeeds more easily deflect small water droplets. Hence, there is a lower rate of ice accretion per unit area. Conversely, larger water droplets at higher airspeeds more easily impact upon sharp, pointed surfaces because the water cannot be deflected into the surrounding airstream. Hence, there is a higher rate of ice accumulation for the same atmospheric conditions.

Now you know why that little cotter pin and nut on the wiper blade picks up ice so easily. Can you imagine what would happen to a pitot tube without anti-icing?

The rate of ice accumulation often depends on whether you are in a layer-type (stratiform) cloud or cumulus-type cloud with extensive vertical development. For example, under the same temperature conditions, ice will build up twice as fast in cumulus clouds because of their high water content, but the icing flight path in cumulus clouds is usually not as long as that of layer or stratus clouds.

As penetration airspeed increases so does the rate of ice accumulation, up to about 350 to 400 kts of indicated airspeed, at which point ice formation gradually dissipates as a result of skin friction heating. This aerodynamic heating is the temperature rise at the stagnation point resulting from adiabatic compression and friction as the aircraft moves through the atmosphere. The amount of heating varies primarily with indicated airspeed and altitude. Dissipation should result when the total air temperature (outside air temperature + aerodynamic heating) reaches about 2 °C or higher.

The shape and amount of ice accretion have a dramatic effect on aerodynamic performance. The shape of the buildup is the result of the rate of freezing (water concentration × velocity), and small water droplets promote rapid freezing on the icing surface. Such conditions produce a rather smooth and pointed shape that is usually rime in nature, whereas temperatures near freezing, with large water droplets, result in slight delays in freezing when the droplets impact the surface. These conditions create irregular ice formations with flat or concave surfaces, sometimes having protuberances facing the airstream on either side of the centerline (the so-called *double-horn ice formation*).

Ice accretion amount or size is primarily a function of exposure time to the icing conditions.

Kinds of structural icing

Frost is the deposit of a thin layer of ice that forms on exposed aircraft surfaces under certain atmospheric conditions. It frequently occurs when the surface temperature is below freezing during night radiational cooling in a manner similar to the formation of dew and frost on the ground. In flight, when descent is made from subfreezing air into a warm, moist layer, frost also can form.

The effects of frost are perhaps more subtle than the effects of ice on the aerodynamic characteristics of the wing. The accumulation of a hard coat of frost on the upper wing surface provides a texture of considerable roughness. Although the basic shape and aerodynamic contour is unchanged, the increase in surface roughness increases skin friction and reduces the kinetic energy of the boundary layer. The result is increased drag and reduced lift.

This fine crystalline ice formation is often barely visible. However, it can easily distort the normal airflow over wings and control surfaces enough to adversely affect the takeoff characteristics of an aircraft.

Rime ice is formed by the instantaneous freezing of supercooled water droplets upon impact. These supercooled droplets adhere in a spherical shape and trap air within the ice form, thereby giving it an opaque, milky appearance.

Clear ice is frequently encountered in areas of freezing rain in temperature regions slightly below freezing. Freezing rain occurs when liquid precipitation falls from overrunning warm air that is slightly above freezing into cold air that is slightly below freezing. The rain becomes supercooled as it falls through the cold air mass and will freeze when it comes into contact with aircraft surfaces. Thus, an aircraft flying through an area of freezing rain can easily acquire a coat of heavy clear or glaze ice. Freezing rain might be encountered while flying in the colder air mass of both warm and cold fronts.

Glaze ice is sometimes referred to as clear ice but, in fact, is a cross between clear and rime ice in terms of appearance. Glaze ice lacks the new-snow semblance and smooth surface of rime ice and tends to possess a white appearance, in contrast to the near transparency of clear ice. Glaze ice is formed by delays in freezing of liquid moisture, creating rough, irregular ice formations. Some meteorological conditions can produce a mixture of glaze and rime in the same ice accretion.

In-flight ice testing reveals that the most severe glaze icing occurs when the outside air temperature (OAT) is between $-1°$ and $-5°C$. At colder temperatures, between $-8°$ and $-10°C$, a less severe type of mixed (glaze and rime) icing forms. As temperatures decrease to $-11°$ to $-15°C$, rime ice is most likely to form. At about $-20°C$ and below, the probability of ice accretion is reduced significantly.

When the OAT is at or below $-40°C$, the atmosphere normally does not contain moisture in the liquid state. Therefore, any atmospheric moisture will be in the solid or crystalline form and ordinarily presents no accumulation hazard.

In case you are wondering which type of icing most adversely affects aerodynamic performance, no clear-cut answers appear to exist. However, what is most important is the shape and amount of the ice formation, not necessarily the type. The distortion of the airfoil and the disruption of airflow is far more significant in destroying lift and increasing drag, and this distortion occurs with all icing types. In addition, most of the in-flight icing that occurs in nature is of the mixed variety and retains the characteristics of all types.

Airfoil surfaces were designed and manufactured to certain desired specifications. Structural icing distorts the shape of airfoils, control surfaces, and the basic airframe. The results are:

- Increased drag
- Reduced lift
- Reduced performance
- Increased weight
- Increased fuel consumption
- Increase in stall speed (V_s)
- Reduced stall angle of attack

Ice deposits of $1/2$ inch on the leading edge of certain airfoils can reduce their lift by nearly 50 percent, increase drag by an equal percentage, and greatly increase stall speed.

The following definitions apply to rates of accumulation for pilot reporting classifications:

- *Trace*   Icing becomes perceptible, not hazardous unless encountered for an extended period of time.
- *Light*   Rate of accumulation might create a problem if flight is prolonged. Deicing/anti-icing equipment is sufficient to reduce or eliminate buildup when used. Ordinarily, no hazard is presented.
- *Moderate*   Rate of accumulation is such that even brief encounters can become potentially hazardous. The use of deicing/anti-icing equipment or diversion is required.
- *Severe*   A high rate of accumulation where deicing/anti-icing equipment is inadequate to reduce or control the hazard. Immediate diversion is necessary.

When reporting ice, always specify your aircraft type.

Flight planning

Flight planning during winter months will require knowledge in order to protect the aircraft as well as the pilot. Use extra precautions. File a flight plan. In conjunction with an ELT and a little knowledge on winter survival, a flight plan could save your life. Experience has shown that the advice of operators who are located in the area where the operation is contemplated is invaluable, since they are in a position to judge requirements and limitations for operation in their area.

In making business appointments, always give yourself an out by informing your contact that you intend to fly and will arrive at a certain time, unless the weather conditions are unfavorable. You, the pilot, have complete responsibility for the "go, no-go" decision based on the best information available. Do not let compulsion take the place of good judgment.

Aircraft preparation

If your homebase is in a warm climate area, you might not have familiarized yourself with the aircraft manufacturer's recommendations for winterizing your aircraft. Most mechanical equipment, including aircraft and their components, is designed by manufacturers to operate within certain temperature extremes. Manufacturers generally can predict their product's performance in temperature extremes and outline precautions to be taken to prevent premature failures.

Many pilots prepare for really cold weather by having their aircraft checked out by a qualified mechanic. To avoid engine damage, you will want to be sure the engine's timing is correct and the spark plugs are cleaned and properly gapped. Also make certain oil lines and hoses are properly insulated.

Use winterization kits if they are recommended by your aircraft manufacturer. For example, oil cooler covers and special engine baffling might be recommended. Remember, though, that as you fly from colder to warmer climates, you might need to remove the kits.

Many aircraft are equipped with a heat exchanger that encloses the muffler. As the exhaust system becomes hot, so does the heat exchanger, which, in turn, has its air routed to the cabin.

If the exhaust leaks into the exchanger or its shrouding, deadly carbon monoxide can leak into the cabin. You might wish to purchase an inexpensive paper-type carbon monoxide detector from a pilot supply house and affix it to your aircraft panel.

Check the condition of all hoses, tubing, and seals carefully. Worn hoses might not withstand the strain of cold temperatures. Likewise, check clamps and fittings, along with control cable tension. Defective hoses and loose fittings are among the most common causes of maintenance-related accidents.

It's a good idea, too, to change your oil every 50 hours or so, in summer as well as winter. In winter, however, you will want to use either a thinner oil or one of the multiviscosity oils, which can adapt their consistency to a wide temperature range.

Be careful, though, not to overfill the engine with oil. If you do, the breather will dump oil overboard as internal pressures rise. In cold temperatures, crankcase vapors, as they cool in the breather lines, can condense and form ice, freezing the breather system shut.

If you run an engine with frozen breather lines, internal pressures rise until you blow your engine's oil seals. The result is not only messy, but dangerous as well. To help prevent costly internal engine damage, both Avco Lycoming and Teledyne Continental engine manufacturers recommend preheating the aircraft whenever the temperature is 10°F or below.

Whatever preheating system you use (check with your mechanic first), make certain the entire engine is heated and not just the cylinders. Heat directed to the cylinders will help vaporize the fuel and promote combustion, but it will do little for the congealed oil down in the engine sump. As a result, during the first crucial seconds the engine is running, crucial engine parts will be deprived of oil. Bare metal hammers on bare metal, leaving behind flecks of steel to contaminate the engine.

Check to make sure your battery is tested, cleaned, and charged. If the fluid is low, do not permit the battery cells to be topped off with distilled water. Too much water causes the electrolyte to boil over. Remember, the electrolyte eats through aluminum very quickly.

Outside the aircraft, take care to remove all accumulations of snow, frost, or ice from the aircraft surfaces. Don't count on prop blast to carry it away for you. Unless you are blessed with a hangar or can afford a fluid deicing treatment, you will have to remove the snow and ice physically. But be gentle; especially, do not bang on the windshield. It can turn brittle in cold temperatures and crack. A suggested method on sunny days is to put dark trash can liners on the flying surfaces and let the sun do the work. (Do not forget to remove the liners before flight.)

Be extra alert for water in your fuel tanks, due to snow and ice melting around fuel filler caps that may have worn seals or otherwise permit water to contaminate the fuel. If a drain valve is frozen up, do not ignore it. Ask a mechanic to help you free it. A frozen drain valve is a good sign there could be water where it isn't wanted.

Check to see that all control surfaces are free, especially if you have just deiced the airplane in the hangar and then moved it back outside. Melted water might run to the hinges or other control fittings and refreeze, blocking movement.

Carefully examine the speed fairings in the landing gear (if installed) to see if they are obstructed by frozen slush or ice. Many owners remove the speed fairings during winter.

Lastly, make sure you and your passengers are "preflighted" for a winter flight. Dress as though you might be exposed to the harsh winter environment for a long period of time because, however remote the chances, this situation could occur.

A thorough winter preflight should include all of the items covered in the following discussion.

Baffling and winter covers   Baffles are recommended by some manufacturers to be used in augmenter tubes. Winter fronts and oil cooler covers also are added to some engine installations. FAA approval is required for their installation unless the aircraft manufacturer has provided the approval. When baffles are installed on an aircraft, a cylinder head temperature gauge is recommended, particularly if wide temperature differences are to be encountered.

Engine oil   The oil is extremely important in low temperatures. Check your aircraft manual for proper weight oil to be used in low temperature ranges.

Oil breather   The crankcase breather deserves special consideration in cold-weather preparation. A number of engine failures have resulted from a frozen crankcase breather line, which caused pressure to build up, sometimes blowing the oil filler cap off or rupturing a case seal, which caused the loss of the oil supply. The water that causes the breather line to freeze is a natural byproduct of the heating and cooling of engine parts. When the crankcase vapor cools, it condenses in the breather line, subsequently freezing it closed. Special care is recommended during the preflight to ensure that the breather system is free of ice. If a modification of the system is necessary, be certain that it is an approved change so as to eliminate a possible fire hazard.

Hose clamps, hoses, hydraulic fittings, and seals   An important phase of cold-weather preparation is inspection of all hose lines, flexible tubing, and seals for deterioration. After replacing all doubtful components, be certain that all clamps and fittings are properly torqued to the manufacturer's specifications for cold weather.

Cabin heater   Many aircraft are equipped with cabin heater shrouds, which enclose the muffler or portions of the exhaust system. It is imperative that a thorough inspection of the heater system be made to eliminate the possibility of carbon monoxide entering the cockpit or cabin area. Each year accident investigations have revealed that carbon monoxide has been a probable cause in accidents that have occurred in cold-weather operations.

Control cables   Because of contraction and expansion caused by temperature changes, adjust control cables properly to compensate for the temperature changes encountered.

Oil pressure controlled propellers   Propeller control difficulties can be encountered as a result of congealed oil. The installation of a recirculating oil system for the propeller and feathering system has proved helpful in extremely cold climates. Caution should be taken when intentionally feathering propellers for training purposes to ensure that the propeller is unfeathered before the oil in the system becomes congealed.

Care of batteries   Wet cell batteries require some special consideration during cold weather. It is recommended that they be kept fully charged or removed from the aircraft when it is parked outside to prevent loss of power caused by cold temperatures and the possibility of freezing.

Wheel wells and wheel pants   During thawing conditions, mud and slush can be thrown into wheel wells during taxiing and takeoff. If frozen during flight, this mud and slush could create landing-gear problems. Do not recycle the gear after a takeoff in this condition, except as an emergency procedure. The safest method is to avoid these conditions with retractable-gear aircraft. It is recommended that wheel pants installed on fixed-gear aircraft be removed to prevent the possibility of frozen substances locking the wheels or brakes.

Operation of aircraft

The thoroughness of a preflight inspection is important in temperature extremes. It is natural to hurry over the preflight of the aircraft and equipment, particularly when the aircraft is outside in the cold. However, this is the time you should do your best preflight inspection.

Fuel contamination   Fuel contamination is always a possibility in cold climates. Modern fuel pumping facilities are generally equipped with good filtration equipment, and the oil companies attempt to deliver pure fuel to your aircraft. However, even with the best of fuel and precautions, if your aircraft has been warm and then is parked with half-empty tanks in the cold, the possibility of condensation of water in the tanks exists.

Fueling facilities   Another hazard in cold climates is the danger of fueling from makeshift fueling facilities. Fuel drums or *case gas,* even if refinery sealed, can contain rust, and somehow contaminants can find their way into the fuel. Cases are on record of fuel that was not aviation fuel being delivered from unidentified containers. As a precaution:

1. Where possible, fuel from modern fueling facilities. Fill your tanks as soon as possible after landing, and drain fuel sumps to remove any water that might have been introduced.

2. Be sure the fuel being delivered is, in fact, aviation fuel and is the correct grade (octane) for your engine.

3. If a fuel source other than from modern fueling facilities is used, be sure to filter the fuel as it goes into your tanks. *Note*: A funnel with a dirty, worn-out chamois skin is not a filter, nor will a new, clean chamois filter out water after the chamois is saturated with water. Many filters are available that are more effective than the old chamois. Most imitation chamois will not filter water.

4. Special precautions and filtering are necessary with kerosene and other turbine fuels. Manufacturers can supply full details on handling these fuels.

Aircraft fuel filters and sumps   Fuel filters and sumps (including each tank sump) should be equipped with quick drains. Draw off sufficient fuel into a transparent container to see if the fuel is free of contaminants. Experienced operators place the aircraft in level flight position, and the fuel is allowed to settle before sumps and filters are drained. Drain all fuel sumps on the aircraft, including individual tank sumps.

Take extra care during changes in temperature, particularly when it nears the freezing level. Ice could be in the tanks, and could turn to water when the temperature rises and filters down into the carburetor, causing engine failure. During freeze-up in the fall, water can freeze in lines and filters, causing stoppage. If fuel does not drain freely from sumps, this would indicate a line or sump is obstructed by sediment or ice. There are approved anti-ice additives that you can use.

When aircraft fuel tanks do not have quick drains installed, it is advisable to drain a substantial amount (1 quart or more) of fuel from the gascolator, then change the selector valve and allow the fuel to drain from the other tank.

Advisory Circular (AC) 20–43C, entitled "Aircraft Fuel Control," contains excellent information on fuel contamination. Paragraphs 10 and 11 are especially pertinent to many light aircraft and include a recommendation for periodic flushing of the carburetor bowl. You can obtain copies of AC 20–43C by writing to:

U.S. Department of Transportation
Utilization and Storage Section, M-443.2
Washington, DC 20590

Aircraft preheat   Low temperatures can change the viscosity of engine oil; batteries can lose a high percentage of their effectiveness; instruments can stick; and warning lights, when "pushed to test," can stick in the pushed position. As a result, a preheat of engines, as well as the cockpit, before starting is considered advisable in low temperatures.

Use extreme caution in the preheat process to avoid fire. The following precautions are recommended:

1. Preheat the aircraft by storing it in a heated hangar, if possible.
2. Use only heaters that are in good condition, and do not fuel the heater while it is running.
3. During the heating process, do not leave the aircraft unattended. Keep a fire extinguisher handy for the attendant.
4. Do not place heat ducting so it will blow hot air directly on parts of the aircraft such as upholstery, canvas engine covers, flexible fuel, oil and hydraulic lines, or other items that can cause fires.

Be sure to follow the manufacturer's procedures.

Engine starts   In moderately cold weather, engines are sometimes started without preheat. Particular care is recommended during this type of start. Oil is partially congealed, and turning the engines is difficult for the starter or by hand.

There is a tendency to overprime, which results in washed-down cylinder walls and possible scouring of the walls. It also causes poor compression and, consequently, harder starting. Sometimes aircraft fires have been started by overprime, when the engine fires and the exhaust system contains raw fuel. Other fires are caused by backfires through the carburetor. It is good practice to have a fireguard handy during such starts.

Another cold-start problem that plagues an engine that is not preheated is icing over the spark-plug electrodes. This situation occurs when an engine only fires a few revolutions and then quits. There has been sufficient combustion to cause some water in the cylinders but insufficient combustion to heat them up. This little bit of water condenses on the spark plug electrodes, freezes to ice, and shorts them out. The only remedy is heat. If no large heat source is available, remove the plugs from the engine and heat them to the point where no more moisture is present.

Engines can quit during prolonged idling because insufficient heat is produced to keep the plugs from fouling out. Engines that quit under these circumstances are frequently found to have iced-over plugs. After the engine starts, use of carburetor heat may assist in fuel vaporization until the engine obtains sufficient heat.

Radios Do not tune radios prior starting the engine. Turn on radios only after the aircraft electrical power is stabilized. Allow them to warm up for a few minutes, then tune them to the desired frequency.

Removal of ice, snow, and frost A common winter accident is caused by trying to take off with frost on the wing surface. It is recommended that you remove all frost, snow, and ice before you attempt flight. It is best to place the aircraft in a heated hangar. If so, make sure the water does not run into the control surface hinges or crevices and freeze when the aircraft is taken outside. Don't count on the snow blowing off on the takeoff roll.

Often, frost adheres to the wing surface below the snow. You can use alcohol or one of the ice-removal compounds for this operation. Use caution if you have taken an aircraft from a heated hangar and allowed it to sit outside for an extended length of time when it is snowing. The falling snow might melt on contact with the aircraft surfaces and then refreeze. It might look like freshly fallen snow, but it usually will not blow away when the aircraft takes off.

Blowing snow If an aircraft is parked in an area of blowing snow, give special attention to openings in the aircraft where snow can enter, freeze solid, and obstruct operation. These openings should be free of snow and ice before flight. Some of these areas are as follows:

- pitot tubes
- heater intakes
- carburetor intakes
- antitorque and elevator controls
- main wheel and tailwheel wells, where snow can freeze around elevator and rudder controls

Fuel vents Check fuel tank vents before each flight. A vent plugged by ice or snow can cause engine stoppage, collapse of the tank, and possibly very expensive damage.

Taxiing

Taxiing on ice and snow is hazardous at best. Keep speed to a minimum and use extreme caution. Increase distances between aircraft to ensure safe stopping distances and to eliminate any melted snow that could result from jet exhaust. Use minimum power and avoid sharp turns. Stop gradually to avoid locking of tires and subsequent skidding.

Keep in mind that braking action on ice or snow is generally poor. Avoid short turns and quick stops. Do not taxi through small snowdrifts or snowbanks along the edge of the runway. Often there is solid ice under the snow. If you are operating on skis, avoid sharp turns, since they put torque on the landing gear in excess of that for which it was designed. Also, for ski operation, make sure safety cables and shock cords on the front of the skis are inspected carefully. If these cables or shock cords should break on takeoff, the nose of the ski can fall down to a near vertical position, which seriously affects the aerodynamic efficiency of the aircraft and creates a landing hazard.

If it is necessary to taxi downwind with either wheels or skis and the wind is strong, get help or don't go. Remember, when you are operating on skis, you have no brakes and no traction in a crosswind. On a hard-packed or icy surface, the aircraft will slide sideways in a crosswind and directional control is minimal, particularly during taxiing and landing roll, when the control surfaces are ineffective.

Takeoff

Prior to commencing a takeoff in snow, slush, or standing water, consideration must be given to the resultant extended ground roll and the possibility of damage from spraying contaminants. At takeoff speeds, the viscosity and resistance of the contaminants increase dramatically. The resultant wheel drag considerably increases the takeoff roll. When the runway is contaminated by water, slush, or wet snow of more than 1/2 inch, do not take off.

Dry snow (snow that cannot readily be made into a snowball) also penalizes takeoff performance. Ordinarily, 2 inches of dry snow approximates the reduction in performance equivalent to 1/4 inch of slush or water. Similarly, 4 inches of dry snow would equate to 1/2 inch of water or slush, and you should not take off when depth exceeds this amount.

Slush drag refers to water or partially melted snow, which—through its depth, water content, and density—retards the forward acceleration of an aircraft by the resultant drag built up between the contaminants and the aircraft's tires. Under conditions adverse enough, the retarding force actually could prevent acceleration to rotation speed.

The retardation force of slush drag is proportional to fluid depth, its density, and the square of the forward groundspeed velocity. This proportion is true up to the onset of dynamic hydroplaning.

Two inches of slush or water on a runway can produce enough resultant drag to overpower engine thrust and reduce the aircraft acceleration rate to zero. As a result, most jet aircraft would be unable to reach rotation speed (V_r) regardless of runway length.

By now it should be evident that slush, standing water, wet snow, and dry snow slow the acceleration during the takeoff roll. This retardation becomes more noticeable as velocity increases. Often, the ability to successfully abort the takeoff when well down the runway becomes very questionable.

Ice, snow, and frost must be removed before flight is attempted, since takeoff distances and climbout performance can be seriously affected. The roughness and distribution of the ice and snow could vary stall speeds and characteristics to a dangerous degree.

Smooth, clear ice can form on the upper wing surfaces with ambient temperatures above freezing. This condition can develop when subfreezing temperature fuel contacts the underside of the wing's upper surface. Any condensation, such as fog, drizzle, or rain, can freeze when it contacts the chilled wing's upper surface. Such ice accumulation is very difficult to detect during preflight inspection.

Takeoffs in cold weather offer some distinct advantages, but they also offer some special problems. A few points to remember are as follows:

1. Do not overboost supercharged engines. This is easy to do because at very low density altitude, the engine "thinks" it is operating as much as 8000 feet below sea level in certain situations. Exercise care in operating normally aspirated engines. Power output increases at about 1 percent for each 10° of temperature below that of standard air. At −40°F an engine will develop 10 percent more than rated power even though rpm and mp limits are not exceeded.

2. If the temperature rises, do not expect the same performance from your aircraft as when it was operated at the lower-density altitudes of cold weather.

3. Use carburetor heat as required. In some cases, it is necessary to use heat to vaporize the fuel. Gasoline does not vaporize readily at very cold temperatures. Do not use carburetor heat in such a manner that it raises the mixture temperature barely to freezing or just a little below. In such cases, it could induce carburetor icing. An accurate-mixture temperature gauge is a good investment for cold-weather operation. It might be best to use carburetor heat on takeoff in very cold weather in extreme cases.

If your aircraft is equipped with a heated pitot tube, turn it on prior to takeoff. It is wise to anticipate the loss of an airspeed indicator or almost any other instrument during a cold-weather takeoff, especially if the cabin section has not been preheated.

Climbout

Ice collected during climb will reduce the rate of climb and range. If excessive ice formation remains after the use of anti-icing/deicing, attempt to climb or descend from the icing environment where liquid water exists in the 0° to −15°C range.

Always use engine/airfoil anti-icing as specified in the operating manual. The preferred method is to activate these systems prior to the anticipated icing conditions.

Heavy ice accumulation greatly increases the stalling speed. Therefore, increase airspeed during low-altitude flight, approach, and landing under such conditions.

During climbout, keep a close watch on head temperature gauges. Because of restrictions (baffles) to cooling airflow installed for cold-weather operation and the possibility of extreme temperature inversions, it is possible to overheat the engine at normal climb speeds. If the head temperature nears the critical stage, increase the airspeed, open the cowl flaps, or both.

En route

Weather Weather conditions vary considerably in cold climates. In the more remote sections of the world, weather reporting stations are generally few and far between, and reliance must be placed on pilot reports. However, do not be lured into adverse weather by a good pilot report. Winter weather is often very changeable. One pilot might give a good report and five or ten minutes later VFR might not be possible. Remember, mountain flying and bad weather do not mix. Set yourself some limits and stick to them.

Snowshowers and whiteouts Snowshowers are, of course, quite prevalent in colder climates. When penetration of a snowshower is made, the pilot might suddenly find himself or herself without visibility and in IFR conditions. Snowshowers often will start with light snow and build.

Another hazard that has claimed as its victims some very competent pilots is the *whiteout*. This condition is one in which there are no contrasting ground features within the pilot's visibility range. Obviously the smaller the visibility range, the more chance there is of a whiteout; however, whiteout can occur in good visibility conditions. A whiteout conditions calls for an immediate shift to instrument flight. The pilot should be prepared for this situation, both through training and with aircraft equipment.

Carburetor ice The subject of carburetor icing was covered in chapter 4; however, a brief review at this point might be helpful as it relates to winter operations.

The three categories of carburetor ice are:

1. Impact ice formed by impact of moist air at temperatures between 15° and 32°F on airscoops, throttle plates, heat valves, etc. usually forms when visible moisture such as rain, snow, sleet, or clouds are present. Most rapid accumulation can be anticipated at 25°F.

2. Fuel ice forms at and downstream from the point that fuel is introduced when the moisture content of the air freezes as a result of the cooling caused by vaporization. It generally occurs between 40° and 80°F, but might occur at even higher temperatures. It can occur whenever the relative humidity is more than 50 percent.

3. Throttle ice is formed at or near a partly closed throttle valve. The water vapor in the induction air condenses and freezes as a result of the venturi effect, cooling as the air passes the throttle valve. Since the temperature drop is usually around 5°F, the best temperatures for forming throttle ice would be 32° to 37°F, although a combination of fuel and throttle ice could occur at higher ambient temperatures.

In general, carburetor ice will form in temperatures between 32° and 80°F when the relative humidity is 50 percent or more. If visible moisture is present, it will form at temperatures between 15° and 32°F. A carburetor air temperature (C.A.T.) gauge is extremely helpful to keep the temperatures within the carburetor in the proper range. Partial carburetor heat is not recommended if a C.A.T. gauge is not installed.

Partial throttle (cruise or letdown) is the most crucial time for carburetor ice. It is recommended that you apply carburetor heat before reducing power and that you use partial power during letdown to prevent icing and overcooling of the engine.

Carbon monoxide poisoning   Do not count on symptoms of carbon monoxide to warn you. The gas is colorless, odorless, and tasteless, although it is usually found with exhaust gases and fumes. If you smell fumes or feel any of the following symptoms, you should assume that carbon monoxide is present.

Feelings of sluggishness, warmth, and tightness across the forehead followed by headache, throbbing, pressure at the temples and ringing in the ears indicate carbon monoxide poisoning. Severe headache, nausea, dizziness, and dimming of vision may follow. If any of these conditions exist, take the following precautions:

1. Shut off the cabin heater or any other opening to the engine compartment.

2. Open a fresh air source immediately.

3. Don't smoke.

4. Use 100 percent oxygen if available.

5. Land as soon as possible.

6. Be sure the source of the contamination is corrected before you attempt further flight.

Spatial disorientation   Spatial disorientation also can be expected any time the pilot continues VFR flight into adverse weather conditions. Flying low over an open body of water during low visibility and a ragged ceiling is another ideal situation for disorientation.

Letdown

Engine operation   During letdown there might be a problem of keeping the engine warm enough for high-power operation if needed. It might be desirable to use more power than normal, which might require the extension of landing gear or flaps to keep the airspeed within limits. Carburetor heat also might be necessary to help vaporize fuel and enrich the mixture.

Blowing snow and ice fog   Blowing snow can be a hazard on landing, and throughout the flight you should maintain a close check, as to the weather at your destination. If the weather pattern indicates rising winds, then blowing snow can be expected, which might necessitate an alternate course of action.

Ice fog is a condition opposite to blowing snow and can be expected in calm conditions about −30 °F and below. It is found close to populated areas, since a necessary element in its formation is hydrocarbon nuclei such as that found in automobile exhaust gas or the gas from smokestacks.

Both of these conditions can form very rapidly and are only a few feet thick (usually no more than 50 feet). They can be associated with clear enroute weather. Therefore, always make a careful check of the forecast and weather, and make cautious preflight planning for alternate courses of action.

Landing

A landing surface can be very treacherous in cold-weather operations. In addition, caution is advised regarding other hazards, such as snowbanks on the sides of the runways and poorly marked runways. Obtain advance information about the current conditions of the runway surface. If it is not readily available, take the time to circle the field before landing to look for drifts or other obstacles. Be aware that tracks in the snow on a runway do not ensure safe landing conditions. Often snowmobiles will use runway areas and give a pilot the illusion that aircraft have used the airport and the snow is not deep.

Hydroplaning   The presence of winter contaminants on a runway surface disrupts the contact between the tire footprint and the pavement. The contaminants interfere with the development of the frictional or tractional forces required for directional control and effective braking.

Dynamic hydroplaning occurs when the standing fluid is not displaced from under the tire at a rate fast enough to allow the tire to make contact over its entire footprint area. This type of hydroplaning might be either partial (a portion of the tire is still in contact with the pavement) or total (the tire is completely detached from the surface). During this type of hydroplaning, the aircraft is either partially or totally supported by the fluid pressure between the tire and the pavement. Hydroplaning can result in the complete loss of tire friction, steering, and braking.

If a runway surface is rough, grooved, or textured, and the ties have good tread depth, then the fluid depth must exceed both the tread and the runway groove depth for hydroplaning to occur.

During slow speeds, the aircraft tire mass is sufficient to displace the fluid beneath it. It is primarily at higher speeds, where the fluid cannot escape, that the tire is lifted off the surface and thereby supported by a thin layer of fluid and hydroplaning occurs.

Viscous hydroplaning is a technical term used to describe the normal slipperiness or lubricating effect that occurs on a wet surface. This type of hydroplaning can occur at speeds well below that required for total dynamic hydroplaning.

Some recommended techniques for landing when you anticipate hydroplaning include:

1. Land at the slowest possible approach and touchdown speed to decrease the time for hydroplaning.
2. Make a firm touchdown.
3. When anti-skid is inoperative or not available, judiciously apply the brakes. Exercise caution to avoid locking tires, which could result in a blowout as the aircraft crosses over a dry runway section.

Ski wheels   Ski-wheel combinations are popular and very convenient; however, forgetting to use the landing gear appropriate to the runway surface can be dangerous.

Skis   In level flight, skis will cut cruising speed to some extent because of their relatively dirty profile. In addition to some loss of aerodynamic efficiency, skis have other disadvantages. They require more care in operating because bare spots must be avoided to keep from wearing the bottom coating of the skis, although the bottom coating must be renewed on some skis periodically. There is now on the market an antifriction tape that is very useful for this purpose.

Skis equipped with the antifriction coating do not freeze to the surface like those that expose bare metal to the snow. Another method of keeping skis from freezing to the snow is to taxi the aircraft up onto poles placed across and under the skis, which prevents them from touching the snow for most of their length.

Extra care in the use of skis during takeoff and landing is also recommended. Rutted snow and ice can cause loss of ground control, even failure of skis or landing gear parts. Deep powder snow can adversely affect ski operation. Prolonged takeoff runs in deep powder are expected and it might be deep enough that no takeoff is possible under existing conditions. In this case, experienced operators pack a takeoff path with snowshoes or taxi back and forth until an adequately packed runway is available.

Postflight

The following are a few items to consider before leaving the aircraft after the flight:

1. As soon as possible, fill the tanks with the proper grade of clean aviation fuel, even if the aircraft is going into a heated hangar.

2. If the aircraft is to be left outside, put on engine covers and pitot covers.

3. If the weather forecast is for snow or "clear and colder," put on rotor or wing covers and save yourself from a snow- or frost-removal job in the morning.

4. Control locks or tied controls are suggested if the aircraft is left outside and there is a chance of high wind conditions. Tie downs are, of course, also suggested in high winds.

5. If the aircraft is equipped with an oil-dilution system, consider the advisability of dilution of the engine oil. If you decide to dilute, carefully follow the manufacturer's recommendations commensurate with the temperature expected.

6. During engine shutdown, a good practice is to turn off the fuel and run the carburetor dry. This operation lessens the fire hazard during preheat the next morning.

Surviving a crash

In the event of a crash landing, it is best to leave the aircraft as soon as possible. Take time to analyze the situation and help others. Take care of any injuries first. Stay away from the aircraft until all gasoline fumes are gone. Sit down and think. Keep in mind that survival is 80 percent mental, 10 percent equipment, and 10 percent skills. Since mental factors are the number one problem, establish a goal to conquer regardless of the consequences. Do not proceed without taking time to think out each problem.

Whether to stay with the aircraft or start out on foot could be a major decision. Did you file a flight plan? If you did, it might be best to let them find you. Is your emergency locator transmitter operating? Do you have a survival kit? Don't fight a storm. Stay put and find shelter. Most storms are of short duration. What do you have in the aircraft that can be used to aid in survival? The following list includes some of these items:

- The compass will keep you going in one direction.
- Gasoline will help make a fire.
- Oil can be used for smoke signals.
- Seat upholstery can be used to wrap around feet or hands.
- Wiring can be used for tie strings.
- The battery can be used to ignite fuel.

Use whatever is available to protect the body from the loss of heat. Don't waste body heat by eating snow. Make a fire; heat water before drinking. You can conserve energy to last three weeks if you have water and stay dry. Body heat can escape 240 times faster from wet clothing than from dry clothing. It is best to eat small amounts of sugary foods to replace the energy lost through body heat.

A good survival kit is well worth its weight. The following would be a useful kit; however, you can assemble an inexpensive survival kit of your own.

1. First you need a metal container with a lid. This container can be used to heat water and make tea, used as a digging tool, or polished as a signal mirror.

2. Life-support tools:
   - Hacksaw, single handle with wood blade and metal blade
   - Plier, vise grip
   - Plier, slip joint
   - Screwdriver set (multiple)

3. First aid kit, personal:
   - Sealable plastic container
   - 2 compress bandages
   - 1 triangle bandage
   - Small roll 2-inch tape
   - 6 3-×-3 gauze pads
   - 25 aspirin
   - 10 bandaids
   - Razor blades or scissors
   - Hotel-size soap
   - Tampons, purse size
   - Facial tissues, purse size, or toilet paper
   - 6 safety pins
   - 1 small tube of Unguentine® or Foile®

4. Shelters (minimum of 2):
   Large plastic sheets, 9 × 12 feet, heavy gauge (one for each person) colored red or yellow preferred for signal panels.

5. Life-support kit:
   - Waterproofed matches
   - Candle or fire starter
   - Signal mirror
   - Compass, small
   - Knife, Boy Scout style
   - Insect repellent
   - Mosquito net
   - Box of matches (wrapped in plastic)
   - Leaf bag (pull over head, cut hole for face)
   - Garbage bag (step in, pull up, and tuck in pants or tie around waist). You now have body protection from heat loss.
   - Whistle
   - 50 feet of 1/8-inch nylon rope or shroud line
   - Smoke flares or red day/night flares

6. Food and energy package, 1-Man, 5-day rations:
   - 2 or 3 cans of Sego®, Nutriment®, or Metrecal® for liquid and energy
   - 30 sugar cubes, wrapped
   - 10 pilot bread or 25 crackers
   - 10 packets of salt
   - 3 tea bags
   - 12 rock candy
   - 5 sticks of gum
   - 10 bouillon cubes
   - 20 protein wafers (if available)
   - Poly bags for water storage

Put each item in a small plastic bag and seal. Put everything in a small metal can (cook pot), seal with poly bag and tape.

A person can live without air for approximately 3 minutes; without body shelter, for about 6 hours in severe weather; and, without water, for about 3 to 6 days. Without the wind blowing, the body (normally covered) can withstand a greater degree of cold. But let the wind blow, even a slight breeze, and the body heat loss can become critical. Of course, body heat is a product of energy.

Table 5-1 will give you an idea as to what to expect in equivalent temperatures. It also points a need for protective clothing or shelter.

To use the table, find the estimated or actual windspeed in the left-hand column and the actual temperature in degrees F in the top row. The equivalent temperature is found where these two intersect. For example, with a windspeed of 10 mph and a temperature of $-10\,°F$, the equivalent temperature is $-33\,°F$. This temperature lies within the zone of increasing danger of frostbite, and protective measures should be taken.

Table 5-1. Wind-Chill Chart

Estimated wind speed mph	Actual Thermometer Reading °F										
	50	40	30	20	10	0	−10	−20	−30	−40	−50
	Equivalent temperature °F										
Calm	50	40	30	20	10	0	−10	−20	−30	−40	−50
5	48	37	27	16	6	−5	−15	−26	−36	−47	−57
10	40	28	16	4	−9	−21	−33	−46	−58	−70	−83
15	36	22	9	−5	−18	−36	−45	−58	−72	−85	−99
20	32	18	4	−10	−25	−39	−53	−67	−82	−96	−110
25	30	16	0	−15	−29	−44	−59	−74	−88	−104	−118
30	28	13	−2	−18	−33	−48	−63	−79	−94	−109	−125
35	27	11	−4	−20	−35	−49	−67	−83	−98	−113	−129
40	26	10	−6	−21	−37	−53	−69	−85	−100	−116	−132

Wind speeds greater than 40 mph have little additional effect

Little danger for properly clothed person

Increasing danger

Great danger

Danger from freezing of exposed flesh

Source: FAA

Note that the wind-chill chart is of value in predicting frostbite only to exposed flesh. Outdoorsmen can easily be caught out in 30 °F temperature. Winds of 30 mph will produce an equivalent wind-chill temperature of −2 °F.

Key terms

Frost
Rime ice
Clear ice
Glaze ice
Slush drag
Dynamic hydroplaning
Viscous hydroplaning

Review questions

1. When will icing occur?
   What factors affect the rate of ice accumulation?
   Describe the various types of structural icing.

List the effects of structural icing on the shape of airfoils, control surfaces, and the basic airframe.

Describe the pilot-reporting classifications for ice accumulation.

2. Describe in general terms some of the more important precautions that should be considered in preparing an aircraft for winter operations.

What are the major precautions in examining the following items: baffling and winter covers; hose clamps, hoses, hydraulic fittings and seals; cabin heater; wheel wells and wheel pants; and aircraft fuel filters and sumps?

What precautions should be taken in preheating an aircraft?

In removing ice, snow, and frost from surfaces?

3. What are some precautions that should be taken when taking off in cold weather?

Describe the types and conditions under which carburetor ice can form.

What are the symptoms of carbon monoxide poisoning?

What precautions should be taken if these symptoms occur?

4. Compare *dynamic hydroplaning* and *viscous hydroplaning*.

Identify some of the items that should be considered before leaving an airport following a flight.

List the major items that should be included in a survival kit in the event of a crash landing.

What is the wind-chill factor?

Takeoffs and landings

Outline

Learning objectives

When you have completed this chapter, you should be able to:

△ Recognize the importance of slow-flight procedures training.

△ Understand the problem of turning back to the airport at low altitudes following an engine failure on takeoff.

△ List the steps to be taken following an engine failure during takeoff and after takeoff.

△ Describe the recommended preflight engine checks to avoid engine failure.

△ Discuss the hazard of wake turbulence to light-aircraft operators.

△ Describe the importance of proper traffic advisory practices when flying in the vicinity of an airport.

△ Describe some of the factors that must be taken into consideration in planning safe landings.

△ Give several techniques that can be used to avoid gear-up landings.

△ Describe some of the problems associated with undershooting a runway and selecting the correct airspeed.

△ Define the cross-control stall and how it can be avoided.

△ Describe the steps that can be taken to avoid hard landings and porpoising.

△ Explain how directional-control accidents can be reduced.

△ Discuss the factors that affect the length of your landing roll.

△ Describe the recommended steps to be taken in executing a go-around.

△ Discuss some of the hazards of landing at night.

Introduction

According to NTSB statistics, over one-half of reportable airplane accidents occur during takeoffs and landings. In these two phases of flight, airspeed is low and pilot attention is often diverted to other tasks.

Pilots who are skillful and confident in operating an airplane at slow speeds can easily avert the dangers that can confront the hapless pilot unable to handle an airplane at minimum controllable airspeeds. With a little training and practice, pilots can recognize that their airplane is approaching, or has attained, a critically low airspeed and learn how to control the airplane at speeds just above stall.

However, learning to fly safely at low airspeeds involves more than merely showing how slowly the airplane can be flown. You also should study such areas as airplane attitude at minimum controllable airspeed—power required vs. airspeed produced; trim needed—control effectiveness; turns and rate of turn compared to degree of bank; stall as a result of a level turn; effects of flap extension and retraction; descents and descending turns; climbs and climbing turns; and go-around procedures.

There are a lot of things to consider in the realm of flight at minimum controllable airspeed. First, and most important, all slow-flight maneuvers should be practiced at an altitude sufficient for safe recovery in the event of an inadvertent stall. Second, pilots who are not thoroughly trained or experienced in flight at minimum controllable airspeed should attempt these maneuvers only when accompanied by a flight instructor.

Minimum controllable airspeed is best described as a speed just above stall or a point at which a further reduction in airspeed, or an increase in angle of attack or load factor, will cause an immediate physical indication of a stall. The minimum controllable airspeed for the aircraft you are flying is not a set figure. It will vary with loading configuration, power setting, and pilot technique.

Slow-flight procedure

In cruise flight at cruising airspeed, use the rudder, aileron, and elevator, noting the pressure applied and the response rate. Then, while maintaining heading and altitude, reduce power, slowing the airplane to minimum controllable airspeed.

As speed is reduced, note changes in pitch. A change in pitch attitude is needed to maintain altitude. There will be a point at which pitch change alone does not increase lift sufficiently to maintain altitude. Power must be added.

Next, recognize that the airplane is close to operating limits: sight, sound, and feeling. The pitch attitude of the nose, the angle of the wingtips in reference to the horizon, the sound of the engine compared to a reduction in wind noise, the lowered resistance to control pressures, and the lack of elevator and rudder trim all indicate that the airplane is at a low speed. Everything still affects the airplane the same way, with reference to control movements, except that greater control movement is needed to produce the same rates of response that were obtained at cruise speed.

Roll into a medium-banked turn to show that the airplane is maneuverable even at low airspeed. The medium bank will result in a high rate of turn at this low airspeed. It will seem as though the airplane is almost pivoting around a point on the ground.

The turn made at medium bank also demonstrates that a level turn does increase stall speed and, unless power is added, a stall will occur soon after the turn is established. When you feel the first indication of a stall, recover by simultaneously reducing the angle of attack, adding power and rolling out of the turn.

Return to straight-and-level flight and again set up minimum controllable airspeed to demonstrate why proper coordination of rudder and aileron in turn entry and recovery is important. If you use aileron only to establish a banked attitude, the application of left aileron causes the nose to swing, or *yaw*, to the right. You can also use the wingtip as a reference to show yaw. As left aileron is used, the right wingtip appears to move aft. Finally, use both aileron and rudder control to show how entries and recoveries are properly executed.

Next on the list is demonstration of the effects of flaps on minimum controllable airspeed and airplane attitude. Extending full flaps will cause the airplane to balloon above the desired altitude. Drag also results from flap extension. As the airplane decelerates, lift is reduced. After flap extension, and when all forces are again stabilized, the airplane will have a new, lower, minimum controllable airspeed and a different pitch attitude for level flight. The power setting might be the same as before the flaps were added; if a power change is needed to maintain level flight, it will be a small one.

When the airplane is established in straight-and-level flight with the flaps down, demonstrate turns, again noting response rates to control pressures and the high rate of turn produced by medium-banked turns. Perform descents by reducing power while maintaining airspeed.

While descending, practice turns to the right and left. Now, apply power to climb. At this time, if the airspeed has been allowed to get excessively low, it might be impossible to climb even with full power. By reducing the amount of flap extension, you also reduce drag and should then be able to climb.

If the flaps are manually actuated, rapid retraction can result in a stall. If the flaps are electrically or hydraulically actuated, retraction might be slow enough that the airplane will accelerate so that flaps-up stall speed is attained before the flaps are fully retracted. In the case of manual flap operation, slower, smoother retraction will also permit acceleration as drag is reduced, and a stall will be avoided.

To complete the demonstration, attempt (at a safe altitude) a simulated go around with flaps fully extended. As in attempting a climb, conditions of power, load, and configuration might make acceleration and climb impossible. If the pilot's operating handbook for your airplane recommends a specific procedure, I suggest you follow it. Otherwise, consult your certified flight instructor.

Practicing flight at minimum controllable airspeed takes a few minutes to go through, so be alert for engine overheating, as indicated by cylinder head or oil temperatures. If the airplane is equipped with cowl flaps, use them to keep temperatures within limits. If no cowl flaps are installed, you might need to increase speed for cooling.

By practicing flight at minimum controllable airspeed, you will become competent and confident in your ability to control the airplane. By applying the knowledge gained through this practice, you can escape the hazards that are potential threats during takeoff and landing.

Engine failure

When the engine fails on a light single-engine aircraft during takeoff, time is of the essence. The average pilot takes at least 4 seconds to react when faced with loss of power. Because the typical lightplane climbs in a rather nose-high attitude, it is sitting nose-up with no power, and the airspeed indicator begins to wind down rapidly.

By the end of those 4 seconds, the message should have gotten through to the pilot: "Lower the nose and safeguard the airspeed." At that stage, all the good advice of your flight instructor and those textbooks is thrown away, and you roll into a bank to get back to the airport. Not wishing to risk a spin, you limit yourself to a standard-rate turn. How long does it take to do a 180 at standard rate? 60 whole seconds!

In addition, pilots often forget that turns require room and the faster you fly the bigger the turn will be. Even at the modest, 70-kt gliding speed of a light single-engine aircraft, the radius of a standard-rate turn is an astonishing 2240 feet. By the time direction has been reversed, you are roughly 4480 feet to one side of the runway. Figure 6-1 shows that the turn must be continued for another 45 degrees before the aircraft is pointing in the general direction of airfield, so total turning entails changing direction for a total of 225 degrees.

Suppose your engine stalled at 300 feet AGL. First, there is a 4-second reaction time. Then you use up 60 seconds to turn through 180 degrees at standard rate and 15 seconds more for the extra 45 degrees necessary to point you at the airfield. Total time since power failure so far is 79 seconds. An average lightplane in a turn will descend at, say, 1000 fpm: at that rate, 79 seconds translates into a height loss of 1316 feet. Having started the emergency procedure at 300 feet, it would be impossible to return to the runway before running out of altitude.

Supporters of turning back no doubt will counter this argument with the suggestion that a standard-rate turn is not the way to handle the emergency. Why not increase the angle of bank?

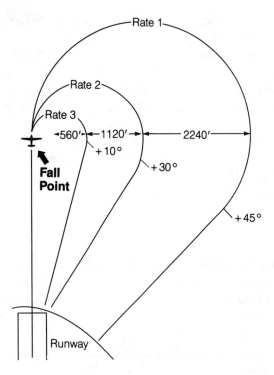

Fig. 6-1. Turning rates following takeoff.

It is common knowledge that, because of loading, stalling speeds increase with angle of bank. Table 6-1 shows the relationship between stall speed and bank angle for a typical four-place single-engine aircraft. When an engine fails at a safe height for turning back (to be discussed shortly), 45 degrees of bank should be regarded as the absolute maximum.

*Table 6-1. Relation of stall speed
to bank angle for a typical
4-place single-engine aircraft*

Bank angle	Stall speed	Increase (%)
0°	49 knots	0%
35°	53 knots	8%
45°	59 knots	20%
60°	71 knots	43%
75°	97 knots	97%

Another factor often overlooked by supporters of tight-turning back to the field is the need to increase gliding speed as bank is added beyond, say, 20 degrees, and the increase in descent rate that is bound to result. Taking the light-plane with its 70-kt gliding speed as an example, if you roll on 45 degrees of bank, common prudence demands that you increase the airspeed to 80 kts—any steeper and up go the G-forces, inflating both stalling speed and descent rate.

At 80 kts, a 45 degree bank would approximate to a four-times standard-rate turn, meaning 15 seconds will be necessary to change direction 180 degrees. Take another look at FIG. 6-1. Although for a 70-kt turn it shows a radius of 560 feet and adding 10 kts will not make a lot of difference, to point back at the airfield it is necessary to fly through another 10 degrees. In terms of time, you have 4 seconds in which to react, 15 for the turn through 180 degrees and another 1 second for the extra 10 degrees needed to head for the airfield, for a total of 20 seconds.

Even if the rate of descent remains unchanged (although it is bound to increase while banked at 45 degrees), $1/3$ minute while descending at 1000 fpm means you will have lost 333 feet at the end of the turn, which you started from 300 feet AGL.

Table 6-2 shows how much time is required to head back to the field at different rates of turn. In addition, you must add the 4-second reaction time to the figures shown in the last column because the table is confined to turning time. As with FIG. 6-1, the table assumes a gliding speed of 70 kts and, although speed will have to be increased for a two- or four-times standard-rate turn, the larger radius will be balanced by the higher speed.

Table 6-2. Time to turn back to the runway following takeoff for a typical 4-place single-engine aircraft

Turn rate	Time to turn 180°	Additional turn req'd	Total time
standard (3°/second)	60 seconds	45°	75 seconds
twice standard (6°/second)	30 seconds	30°	35 seconds
four times standard (12°/second)	15 seconds	10°	15.8 seconds

So far we have considered only the numbers. On that count alone, turning back at low level is a nonsolution. However, there are other reasons why that turn should not be attempted unless circumstances offer a sporting chance. First, there is the obvious hazard of landing against oncoming traffic. Even if the airfield is quiet and you have the place to yourself, however, there still is a downwind landing to contend with. At worst, final approach might be downwind and crosswind, a situation that could result in more damage than a well-executed arrival in a plowed field. The crosswind further complicates the problem because it extends or reduces your turn radius according to whether you bank left or right on the way back. At low level, with all the pressures and anxieties of an engine failure, do you feel confident enough to make the right decision?

If you are confronted with nothing but buildings or trees in all directions, and provided you have gained at least 600 feet prior to engine failure, there is a reasonable chance of regaining the airfield provided you start a 9-degree-per-second, gliding turn without delay and increase speed by about 10 kts above that for a straight glide. At the end of the turn, however, you will face a difficult landing.

Obvious factors affecting the outcome of turning back are the glide performance of the aircraft and, most importantly, the pilot's skill. In summary, it can be concluded that turning back to the airport when flying below 600 feet AGL can be very hazardous.

One of the reasons some pilots are reluctant to land ahead if the engine quits after takeoff is the feeling of being denied the right to exercise their judgment. To some extent, this reasoning is correct. Obviously landing straight ahead might be potentially dangerous, for example if there is a stand of trees or a housing development, as shown in FIG. 6-2.

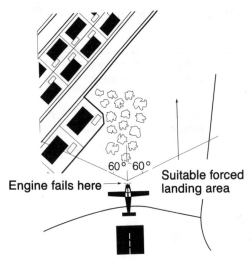

Fig. 6-2. Searching for a landing site up to 60° on either side of the aircraft heading.

The best approach is to scan a relatively wide area approximately 60 degrees to the right and left of the take-off path. There is no reason the aircraft cannot be maneuvered safely within those far-ranging limits.

Even assuming that no obstacle-free landing area can be found within this 120-degree scanning area (60 degrees both left and right of the climbout heading), most light singles have relatively slow gliding speeds, and when a wind is blowing, groundspeed at point of contact can be modest.

You should practice the following engine-out procedures at least once every six months, preferably in the company of a flight instructor.

Engine failure during takeoff

Assuming the engine fails during your takeoff roll, take the following steps:

1. Close the throttle.
2. Brake firmly.
3. Maintain runway heading.
4. While the aircraft slows down, turn off the fuel, switch off the mags, and pull the mixture into idle-cutoff to minimize fire risk.
5. When there is a risk of passing the end of the runway, or even of running off the airfield entirely, swing onto the grass. Take firm avoidance action when obstacles are present.

Engine failure after takeoff

If the engine quits after takeoff and below 400 feet, the following steps are recommended:

1. Immediately depress the nose and trim into the glide at optimum speed.
2. Look through an arc of about 60 degrees left and right of the aircraft heading and select the best available landing area (see FIG. 6-2).
3. Turn off the fuel and mags. Pull the mixture to idle-cutoff to minimize fire risk.
4. If your aircraft has a tailwheel, avoid the risk of turning over during the landing by retracting the gear (if applicable). It is better to leave the nosegear extended on trigear aircraft to absorb the first shock of arrival.
5. Make gentle turns to avoid obstacles.
6. When you are sure of reaching the chosen landing area, lower the flaps—in stages if necessary—but aim to have full flaps before touchdown. Do not allow the airspeed to increase.
7. On short final, turn off the master switch and unlatch the cabin doors (to guard against the risk of being trapped in the cabin through the doors jamming).
8. Resist the temptation to turn back to the field!

When engine failure takes the form of a noiselessly windmilling propeller, without obvious signs of mechanical damage, the cause could be fuel starvation. In such cases you should change to another fuel tank (if there is one) after selecting your best landing field. Continue through the list if the engine will not restart.

Few experienced pilots would disagree that an engine failure after takeoff, particularly in a single-engine aircraft, is one of aviation's most challenging situations. Fortunately, engine failure is rare these days, but it nevertheless remains a fact of aviation life.

Preflight engine checks

The engine that, for one reason or another, comes apart (connecting rod through the crankcase, rocker arm broken, etc.), might be outside the pilot's control. So often, however, an engine failure could have been prevented through sensible preflight action. Following are some common-sense precautions prior to takeoff.

1. It is vital to check for water in the fuel tanks. There is little point in letting the fuel strainer spray onto the ground—that will tell you nothing. Use a small jar and keep running the strainer until fuel, not water, comes out. Having used the fuel strainers, make absolutely certain they are shut correctly. Otherwise your tanks will run dry in no time at all.

2. Look into the tanks, make a visual check of fuel level, and compare it with fuel indications when you enter the cabin.

3. Check the oil and replace the filler cap correctly.

4. On reaching the holding point, change tanks prior to the runup to check the fuel system. On no account change tanks after the power checks and just before taxiing onto the runway.

5. Check the magnetos, hot air (or alternate air), and, when fitted, the propeller pitch change.

6. It is vital to check the fuel pressure without the electric pump working because only then can you be sure the mechanical pump is functioning. This is the time to check all engine temperatures and pressures, as well as vacuum and electric charge, but do it with power on, not at idle rpm.

7. During the early part of the takeoff run, be alert for any unusual roughness, vibration, or unfamiliar noise. Even when it all sounds good, take a quick look at the engine instruments as soon as direction is ensured and satisfy yourself that everything is in the green. If there is the slightest hint of abnormality, close the throttle, and abandon the takeoff.

Wake turbulence

Another potential hazard faced by pilots, particularly during the takeoff and landing phases of flight, is wake turbulence. This problem should be a particular concern to pilots operating out of or in the vicinity of airports serving large transport aircraft.

Every airplane in flight generates a wake. It used to be that when pilots encountered this wake in flight, the disturbance was attributed to "prop wash." It is known today, however, that this disturbance is caused by a pair of vortices—or whirlwinds—that trail from the wingtips.

Lift is generated by the creation of a pressure differential over the wing surfaces. This pressure differential also triggers the rollup of the airflow aft of the wing, resulting in swirling air masses downstream of the wingtips. After the roll-up is completed, the wake consists of two counterrotation cylindrical vortices.

The vortices from large aircraft can pose very real problems to any size aircraft that inadvertently encounters them. For instance, the wake of large aircraft can impose rolling movements that exceed the roll-control capability of some aircraft. The probability of induced roll increases when the encountering aircraft's heading is generally aligned with the vortex trail or flight path of the generating aircraft.

It is a rare instance when an encounter with wake turbulence would cause in-flight structural damage of catastrophic proportions. However, wake turbulence easily can damage aircraft components and equipment.

Pilots must learn to envision the location of wake turbulence and adjust their flight paths accordingly. That is not as difficult as it might sound. Trailing vortices have certain behavioral characteristics that can help us deal with this unseen hazard.

For example, the strength of the vortex is governed by the weight, speed, and shape of the wing of the aircraft generating it. The greatest vortex strength occurs when an aircraft is heavy, "clean," and slow. Peak vortex velocities have been recorded as high as 133 kts.

Vortices are generated from the moment aircraft leave the ground. Pilots should take off at a location prior to the point when a heavy aircraft left the ground. On approach to landing, stay at or above the large aircraft's approach path and touch down at the point beyond where the heavier aircraft landed (see FIG. 6-3).

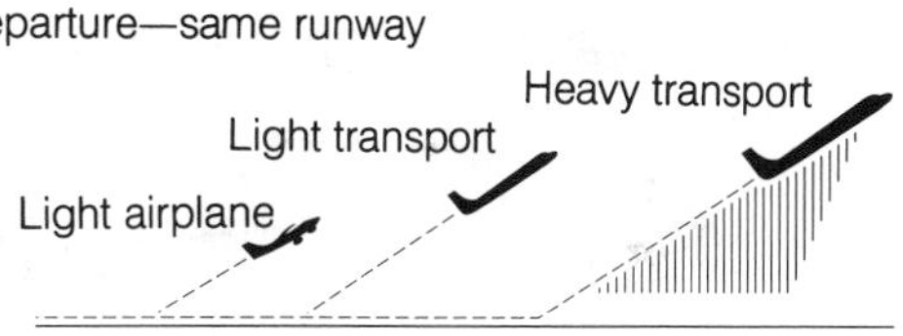

Departure—same runway

Fig. 6-3. Departing behind a heavy jet.

Heavy transport

Light transport

Light airplane

The vortex flow field of large aircraft covers an area about two wing spans wide and one wing span deep. Vortices remain about a wing span apart, even when they're drifting with the wind. If persistent vortex turbulence is encountered, a slight change of altitude and lateral position, preferably downwind, will provide a flight path clear of the turbulence (see FIG. 6-4). Request upwind runway if practical. If not, stay above the heavy jet's final approach path. Note his touchdown point and land beyond a point abeam his touchdown spot.

Vortices from large aircraft sink at a rate of 400 to 500 feet per minute. They tend to level off at a distance of about 900 feet below the flight path of the generating aircraft.

Vortex strength diminishes with time and distance behind the generating aircraft, and atmospheric turbulence hastens breakup. Fly at or above the large aircraft's path, altering course as necessary to avoid the area behind or below the generating aircraft (see FIG. 6-5).

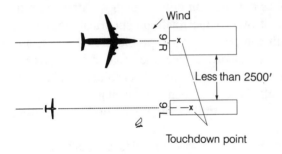

Fig. 6-4. Landing behind a heavy jet when parallel runway is closer than 2500 feet.

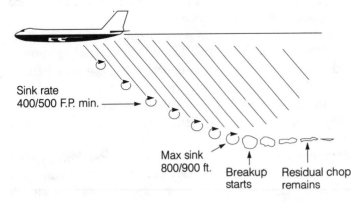

Fig. 6-5. Vortex sink characteristics.

When the vortices of large aircraft sink within 200 feet or so of the ground, they tend to move laterally over the ground at a speed of about 5 kts. Pilots should be alert to large aircraft upwind from their approach and takeoff flight paths (see FIG. 6-6).

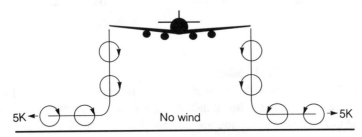

Fig. 6-6. Vortex movement in ground effect—no wind.

Under certain conditions, airport traffic controllers apply procedures for separating aircraft from heavy jet aircraft. For VFR departures behind heavy jet aircraft, controllers are required to use at least a two-minute separation interval, unless a pilot has requested permission to deviate from the interval and indicates acceptance of responsibility for avoiding wake turbulence.

The controller also might provide VFR aircraft the position, altitude, and direction of flight of large aircraft, followed by the warning, "Caution—Wake Turbulence."

Whether or not specific warnings have been issued, however, pilots are expected to adjust their operations and flight paths as necessary to preclude serious wake encounters.

Wake turbulence is technically an unseen hazard, but by studying its characteristics and exercising reasonable caution, pilots can see and avoid it.

Traffic advisory practices

There is no substitute for alertness while operating in the vicinity of an airport, particularly since other airplanes might not have communications capability or their pilots might not communicate their presence or intentions. To achieve the greatest degree of safety, it is essential that all radio-equipped aircraft transmit and receive on a common frequency identified for the purpose of carrying out airport advisory practices.

An airport might have a full- or part-time tower or flight service station (FSS) located on the airport or a full- or part-time unicom station, or no aeronautical station at all. There are three ways for a pilot to communicate his or her intentions to obtain airport-traffic information when operating at an airport that does not have an operating tower: by communicating with an FSS, by communicating with a unicom operator, or by making a self-announce "blind" broadcast.

The key to communicating at an uncontrolled airport is selection of the correct common frequency. *Common Traffic Advisory Frequency* (CTAF) is synonymous with this program.

The CTAF for uncontrolled airports is disseminated in various publications, such as the Airport/Facility Directory and aeronautical charts. You also can obtain the appropriate CTAF frequency by contacting any FSS.

Use of the appropriate CTAF, combined with visual alertness and application of the following recommended operating practices, will enhance the safety of all flight into and out of all uncontrolled airspace.

All inbound traffic should monitor and communicate as appropriate on the designated CTAF from 10 miles to landing. *Airport Advisory Service* (AAS) is a service provided by an FSS physically located on an airport that does not have a control tower or where the tower is temporarily closed or operated on a part-time basis.

In communicating with a CTAF FSS, establish two-way communications before transmitting outbound/inbound intentions or information. Departing aircraft should state the aircraft type, full identification number, type of flight planned (VFR or IFR), and the planned destination or direction of flight. Report before taxiing and before taking the active runway for takeoff. If communications with a unicom are necessary after the initial report to the FSS, return to the FSS frequency for traffic updates.

Unicoms are nongovernment air/ground radio communication stations that can provide airport information at public-use airports where there is no tower or

FSS. On pilot request, unicom stations can provide pilots with weather information, wind direction, the recommended runway, or other necessary information.

When you are communicating with a unicom station, the following practices will help reduce frequency congestion, facilitate a better understanding of pilot intentions and location in the traffic pattern, and enhance safety of flight:

1. Select the correct unicom frequency.

2. State the identification of the unicom station you are calling in each transmission. Make sure you receive a response from the station being called, since unicom stations and aircraft at other nearby airports might be using the same unicom frequency.

3. Speak slowly and distinctly.

4. Call when you are approximately 10 miles from the airport and state your aircraft identification, type of aircraft, altitude, and location relative to the airport. Request wind information and runway in use.

5. Report on downwind, base (optional), and/or final approach, as appropriate.

6. Report clearing the runway.

Self-announce is a procedure whereby pilots broadcast their position, intended flight activity, or ground operation in the blind on the designated CTAF. This procedure is used primarily at airports that do not have an FSS or unicom station on the airport.

You also should use the self-announce procedure if you are unable to communicate with the designated CTAF FSS or unicom. Note, however, that aircraft operating to or from another nearby airport might be making self-announce broadcasts on the same unicom frequency. To help identify one airport from another, give the airport name at the beginning and end of each self-announce transmission.

If an airport has a tower that is temporarily closed or operated on a part-time basis and there is no FSS on the airport or the FSS is closed, use the CTAF (usually the tower local control frequency) to self-announce your position or intentions.

If there is a unicom station in operation on the airport, obtain the wind direction and runway in use from the unicom station. Then return to and monitor the CTAF and make self-announce broadcasts as appropriate.

Remember that, no matter how proper your communications have been with the appropriate facility and how well you have communicated your position and intention, you still must be on the lookout for other aircraft. Do not expect the FSS to spot all traffic for you, and certainly do not rely on the unicom operator to do so. The "see-and-avoid" responsibility is up to every pilot.

Planning safe landings

You should begin thinking about your landing even before you depart, especially if the flight is to another airport. Obtain and study as much information about the destination airport as is available. There are many excellent sources of airport information, ranging from the Airport/Facilities Directory and aeronautical charts to commercial airport directories. If these are not available, telephone the airport for the information you need.

At the very least, know the airport's location, its elevation, runway length and surface, traffic pattern altitude and direction, and runway alignment, windsock location. Also find out whether there are airport aids, such as visual approach slope indicators and runway lights. The more information you have, the more time you'll have during landing to handle tower instructions, the wind, and the overall movement of your landing.

It is a good idea to check, also, for any NOTAMs that concern your destination airport. If, for example, a runway has a temporarily displaced threshold because of construction, you'll want to know that before you're ready to flare.

As you approach the airport and are approximately 10 miles out, run through your landing checklist. It's preferable to use a printed checklist so you don't forget an item. Some pilots mentally say, "GUMP," for gas, undercarriage, mixture, and props. That covers the major bases, but, depending on the complexity of the aircraft you're flying, there might be other important checklist items, as well.

Even though pilot techniques vary, there are a few general considerations that must be taken into account for a successful landing. Wind is the first. The direction it is blowing, its speed, and whether it's gusty or steady have a great effect on your landing. We all know the potential hazards of downwind landings, but some pilots still attempt them, either intentionally or because they didn't know which way the wind was blowing.

Wind effects in the traffic pattern can have a definite bearing on a safe landing when you are using a runway with a strong crosswind component. A strong westerly wind blowing across a north/south runway presents a new set of problems for every leg of the traffic pattern. Know the maximum crosswind speed for both you and your airplane.

Pilots frequently get into trouble trying to circle an airport or making a low pass over it to check out the field before landing. Circling while looking at something on the ground and abrupt maneuvers at low altitudes when the airspeed is slow can quickly invite a stall/spin situation.

The turn to final is when many landing problems start. A tailwind on base will tend to make the pilot overshoot the turn to final. When that happens, there is a strong tendency to sharpen the turn and maybe even kick in a little bottom rudder, too. The result? A steep bank and a stall too close to the ground for recovery.

The final approach is, of course, crucial to a successful landing. You should know the final approach speed for the airplane you are flying and adjust it to given conditions. Once you are established on the proper approach angle, stick with it. Flying a roller-coaster approach is just asking for trouble at touchdown.

Above all, remember to fly the airplane. That may sound like a ridiculously simple thing to say, but accident facts bear out the contention that some pilots merely steer the airplane to the ground, failing to use rudder, ailerons, throttle, and fore/aft control movement. You must be in full physical and mental control of the landing and not merely a "passenger."

One of the more common landing accidents in tricycle-gear airplanes occurs when there's an improper weight distribution on the wheels at touchdown. This situation is usually the result of sloppy flying and excessive airspeed during the approach. The combination of a sloppy pilot technique and excess speed results not only in higher maintenance cost (tires, brakes) but, as in the case of the tricycle-gear aircraft, in weight concentrated on the nosewheel, where you absolutely do not want it. Under these conditions, nosewheel failure often is inevitable and expensive to repair. If the nosewheel should happen to hold up, you've still got a potential problem: wheelbarrowing. With all that weight forward, steering is difficult, if not impossible.

Landing accidents are not often serious—when, that is, the airplane stays on the ground. When a pilot attempts to salvage a bad landing, instead of a bad approach, by going around, the situation can turn serious quickly. Generally, go-arounds are performed for one of two reasons: the approach doesn't feel right to the pilot, or too much runway will be used to slow up the airplane for landing.

Gear-up landings

Gear-up landings continue to occur with alarming regularity. Each year, a few hundred or so airplanes are substantially damaged—sometimes beyond repair—when their pilots inadvertently fail to lower the landing gear prior to touchdown.

The vast majority of gear-up landings are attributed to pilot error, not to systems failure. Pilots simply forget to lower the gear or fail to confirm the gear position visually. By the time the error is discovered, it's generally too late.

Probably the best way to remember to lower the gear is to follow a prelanding checklist. In some airplanes, an abbreviated checklist is placarded on the instrument panel. Use it or an acceptable alternative.

Some pilots commit a landing drill to memory. For instance, you might try remembering the acronym GUMP. Whatever kind of checklist you use, it's a good tip to remember to call out aloud each of the checklist items and to think about what you're doing.

A number of situations can work to distract a pilot from his or her normal routine during a landing: an inflight emergency; an approach in bad weather; heavy traffic at an unfamiliar field. All can become so unsettling to the pilot that he or she even fails to hear the gear-up horn blaring.

Some airplanes have automatic gear-down devices that are activated by a combination of low power setting and slow airspeed. Although such devices might "save" some pilots who forgot to lower the gear, they also might be something of a mixed blessing.

Pilots who fly aircraft with automatic gear-down devices might be lulled into thinking that because the gear will lower itself, they needn't be as vigilant as they should. The fact that pilots of these airplanes often fly other types without automatic gear extension devices should be cause for even greater care.

According to federal accident statistics, a high percentage of gear-up landings occurs after a go-around. During the go-around, the pilot retracts both the gear and the flaps. On final approach, however, the flaps are again extended, but the gear is left up. The outcome is quite predictable.

Once an airplane has landed gear up on a runway and the propeller blades have contacted the surface, a go-around should never be attempted to salvage the landing. Once an airplane has contacted the surface, chances are good that serious damage has been done and that a go-around would likely turn an embarrassing situation into a potentially disastrous one. Letting the airplane belly slide to a stop on the runway is by far the wiser and safer thing to do.

Gear-up accidents can be caused in a variety of ways. For example, some pilots remember to pull the lever to lower the gear, but then fail to visually check the gear positions or to check the indicator lights to make certain the wheels are down and locked.

Gear levers in many airplanes have neutral, as well as up and down positions, so make certain you've positioned the lever properly. Also, double-check those indicator lights. If a light does not come on, do not just assume it's bad. Pop it out and try a good bulb in its place.

Once you have landed, try not to touch anything but the control yoke and throttle until you're clear of the active runway and have plenty of time to think about what levers you are pulling. If you hurry to raise the flaps, close cowl flaps, turn on the air conditioner, or whatever, you might inadvertently hit the gear switch and collapse the airplane on the asphalt.

Most airplanes have switches to preclude gear retractions when on the ground, but these switches often do not function when there's not a lot of weight on the wheels, such as during the early stages of a landing roll. Too, these switches, like everything else on an airplane, can malfunction.

Another type of landing-gear accident involves prematurely retracting the landing gear on takeoff. Some pilots have actually taken off with the landing gear level in the up position during the takeoff roll. At the very least, this could make for a dramatic takeoff as the gear folds up the moment the aircraft leaves the runway. Far worse is the situation in which the airplane settles back to the runway for some reason with its wheels neatly tucked away.

Some airplanes seem more susceptible to certain types of gear problems than others. It would be well worth a pilot's time to discuss individual aircraft idiosyncrasies with a local mechanic. Another good source of potential maintenance problems can be found in compilations of the FAA's Defect or Malfunction Reports, copies of which are available from flight standards district offices.

On a final note, know how to use the backup landing gear system before you have to use it. Although most airplanes have an arrangement to lower the gear manually if the primary system fails, not all operating procedures are the same.

Executing proper landings

This next section will cover some of the more common problem areas causing landing accidents.

The undershoot

At one time or another, every pilot has miscalculated an approach and started to *undershoot* the runway. Poor pattern techniques, such as flying too wide a pattern on downwind or making a late turn to base leg, are frequent causes of undershooting. Some pilots succumb to "runway fixation" and unconsciously try to "carry" the airplane up to the landing spot by easing the nose up without adding power—this doesn't work very well.

You can help set up a proper and constant distance from the runway for all airports by placing the runway centerline at a specific point on the leading edge of the wing (for a low-wing airplane) or a point along the strut (for a high-wing airplane). You can even put a mark or piece of tape at the proper wing strut position (see FIG. 6-7).

Using the runway centerline as your guide takes care of wide or narrow runways. (Of course, this reference line or point only works when the wings are level.)

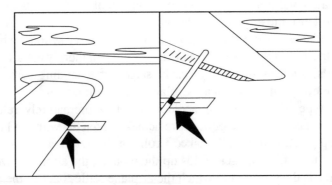

Fig. 6-7. Lining up the runway on the downwind leg.

When traffic isn't a factor, turn base when the point of intended touchdown is 45 degrees behind the wing. At a familiar airport, you might be able to use the "crutch" of familiar landmarks to determine proper turning points. At unfamiliar airports, however, you won't have such "hometown" references.

When there is other traffic in the pattern, you can avoid the common problem of the "ever-lengthening downwind" by starting your turn to base just after the airplane you're following turns final and passes behind your wing (assuming that it's not using a much slower approach speed than yours).

Correct airspeed

Pilots of large aircraft always determine what their approach speeds will be in advance. They calculate the aircraft's landing weight, then look at charts for the right *reference speed*, or *V-ref*. The keystone V-ref, although different on almost every approach, is based on the airplane's stall speed and other factors at its estimated landing weight.

Added to V-ref by the pilot is additional airspeed required to maintain an adequate safety margin while maneuvering in the pattern, as well as additional airspeed to compensate for wind gusts, turbulence, and windshear. Approach segment airspeeds, based on V-ref, ensure that the aircraft has just the right amount of extra airspeed margin above V-ref.

Smaller aircraft do not come with V-ref tables. Some manufacturers, however, furnish recommended approach speeds corresponding to different aircraft weights. The following recommendations apply with respect to correct airspeed:

1. On downwind, fly no faster than the "top of the flap operating range" and no slower than 1.4 times the calibrated stall speed for your airplane at its actual landing weight, or 1.4 Vso.

2. Maintain an airspeed no lower than 1.4 Vso until after turning final.

3. Then, on final, let your airspeed decay to 1.3 Vso as you near the runway.

4. If you encounter any turbulence, wind gusts, or windshear, compensate with additional airspeed on each segment of the approach.

VFR approach

Make your normal pattern entry and extend your landing gear on downwind, if applicable. Abeam the intended landing point, reduce your power to the predetermined value that works best for your airplane. While holding altitude with pitch, slow the airplane down in preparation for turning base. Then set partial flaps, if you have not already done so. If you have reduced power properly, you can now trim the aircraft and set up a descent.

Begin your turn to base when the point of touchdown is 45 degrees behind the wing. Turn base, then final, keeping all banks to 30 degrees or less. Should you need to increase your rate-of-descent, do so either by reducing power or by further extending flaps to increase drag. If you do extend flaps, remember that you have just modified your approach configuration and that you might need to add power to stay on the selected glide path at your targeted speed.

A fundamental key to flying a stabilized approach is the interrelationship of pitch and power. At any targeted airspeed in any configuration, adding more power will make the glide path shallower; reducing power will make it steeper. This interrelationship means that any changes to one element in the approach equation must be compensated for by adjustments in the other. So, after you have selected a glide path, the means of staying on it and maintaining your targeted airspeed can only be achieved by adjusting pitch and power together.

Experienced pilots know the power settings and airspeeds for different landing weights, drag configurations, and rates of descent for their airplanes. Then, these pilots need only make minor adjustments to pitch and power to maintain the selected glide path and airspeed.

The important (if not basic) points are to never let your airspeed decay below the targeted airspeed for each segment of the approach and to never let the airplane sink below its selected glide path.

One final point: full flaps should be used for all normal landings unless the manufacturer suggests otherwise. And, once flaps have been extended, they should not be retracted. That's why it is always good practice not to go to the final flap setting until your landing is assured.

IFR approach

The same basic concepts given for the VFR approach apply to the IFR approach. First, transition the airplane to the approach configuration—that is, slow the airplane and retrim it. Do this well before you intercept the glide slope, unless traffic flow requires otherwise.

Some pilots extend their landing gear to help them slow down, then add flaps after the airspeed drops into the flap operating range. If the gear has not already been used for speed control, extend the gear as you intercept the glide slope or reach the final approach fix. Additional power might be necessary with the gear and flaps extended. Be sure to retrim for each configuration change.

You should now be able to hold the selected airspeed and set up a stabilized rate of descent. With the runway in sight and a landing assured, extend final landing flaps. Retrim again and maintain positive control of the aircraft, since adding flaps without promptly retrimming could cause you to "balloon" back into the clouds.

Glide path selection

Selecting an aim point on the runway is a great aid in making good, safe landings. The *aim point* is an imaginary bulls-eye on the runway. It can be between two particular runway lights, or wherever. It is the reference point at the end of your selected glide path, not the actual touchdown point. If your aim point appears to be moving toward you when you are established on final, you know that your airplane will overshoot that point. A constant position of the aim point in your windshield means things are right on target. If the aim point appears to be moving away from you, it is a sure sign of an undershoot.

Once you have selected your aim point, you must also select the right glide path. Without a Visual Approach Slope Indicator (VASI) or Instrument Landing System (ILS), selecting the right glide path becomes a personal decision. Select a glide path that works best for a particular situation, but make sure it allows for clearance of all obstacles and for a safe rate of descent.

A VASI is a good aid to help establish a safe glide path. Remember, though, that although all VASIs will keep you clear of obstacles, approach angles vary. Also some "complex" VASIs provide multiple approach angles to assist everything up to jumbo jets, while many smaller airports might have only nonstandard VASI systems. One such nonstandard system is nothing more than three plywood (or plastic) panels to be aligned by adjusting your glide path on approach.

The *Airman's Information Manual* provides a detailed description of how standard and nonstandard VASIs work. Additionally, the *Airport Facility Directory* provides VASI glide angle information for standard VASIs for each runway where they are installed. In Canada, comparable references are the *Aeronautical Information Publication-Canada (AIP-Canada)* and the *Canada Flight Supplement*.

Wind and turbulence

On final, your glide path can be affected by wind, windshear, microbursts, and other turbulence, including wake turbulence. As discussed previously, *windshear* is a major variation in wind speed and direction between horizontal layers of air. *Microbursts* are sharp, very strong downdrafts, associated with thunderstorms. Impossible to outmaneuver and usually invisible to the eye, they are good reasons to avoid a landing at any airport with a thunderstorm nearby. *Turbulence* also results from airflow over nearby mountains and winds disrupted by nearby woods, hangars, or other airport structures.

Always be ready for turbulence and its effect on your approach. When you find it, especially on short final, be prepared to add power and go around if necessary. The sooner you add power, the less likely you are to wind up between a rock and a hard place. Whenever you operate at an airport served by large aircraft, be alert for wake turbulence. Study the wake turbulence avoidance procedures from time to time. They, too, are published in the *Airman's Information Manual*, the *AIP-Canada*, and in other publications.

Cross-control stall

Stalls are a frequent cause of landing accidents, and the deadliest of all is the *cross-control stall*. A cross-control stall is usually set up on base, and the potential for it becomes greater in the presence of a tailwind on that leg. A tailwind creates greater groundspeed, which gives you less time to react. Add a distraction such as conflicting traffic or a problem in the cockpit and you are set up for a late turn onto final and the potential for a cross-control stall.

Making that turn to final, you don't want to make a steep banked turn because you know that the stall speed increases with bank angle. Instead, you try to increase the rate of turn with rudder alone, all the while keeping your bank shallow with opposite aileron. Of course, now you will need more "up" elevator because the combination of inside rudder and "down" aileron drag makes the nose drop. As you pull back, you slow down and, bang, there's a stall and a snap roll toward the lower, inside, wing.

This situation can be avoided by good planning, including a properly flown pattern, proper airspeeds, and a timely go-around when things don't feel right.

Some other points include the following:

1. Complete as much of your "before landing checklist as possible before entering the pattern.
2. Look outside the cockpit for helpful indications of wind—flags, smoke, and ponds, for example.
3. Listen to the radio for UNICOM and ATIS advisories on landing conditions.
4. When you have the option, handle a direct crosswind situation by flying a pattern that gives you a headwind, not a tailwind, on base.

Rough landings

This section includes three types of landing-phase accidents that can cause considerable damage, even though they are not as critical as undershoots or cross-control stalls. They are hard landings, bounced landings, and loss of directional control on roll-out.

Hard landings Drop-in or "hard" landings cause a great deal of monetary damage to airplanes each year. These accidents result from several causes. Firstly, many pilots set themselves up for a hard landing by not looking out ahead of the airplane and losing perspective relative to the ground. Loss of perspective also can be the result of improper scanning during flare and touchdown.

Remember to look outside the cockpit—way outside. Do not forget to use your peripheral vision as well. It is something you learned way back in presolo: to focus your attention ahead of the airplane.

Hard landings are also the result of distractions. A typical distraction is a disturbance with passengers in the cabin. Don't be distracted! The landing is the last part of the flight, the part when you're the most tired, yet it's the point where the most concentration is required. To alleviate distractions, airlines have adopted the *sterile cockpit concept*. Below a certain altitude, all conversation is limited only to matters concerning aircraft operations. It is a rule you might want to adopt.

Ballooning is another cause of hard landings and often results from excess airspeed combined with poor flare technique. (Yanking back on the controls before touchdown can put you above the runway with airspeed decaying rapidly.) If this happens, ease the nose over gently and add power if necessary. Remember, too, a full-power go-around might be your best bet after ballooning.

Another cause of hard landings, as discussed earlier, is trying to stretch a final approach by raising the nose without adding power. Also beware of running out of elevator control during flare. A typical example happens when you are too slow with too much weight up front. You might not have the flare power you need. A high descent rate makes these conditions even more serious.

In summary, if you think you are headed for a hard landing:

1. Add power to arrest the sink rate.
2. Keep your wings level.
3. If you decide to make a go-around, make the decision sooner, rather than later.

The bounced landing The bounced landing, or *pilot-induced oscillation* (*porpoising*), was supposed to be cured by the introduction of tricycle landing gear. Not so. In a bounced landing, the airplane comes in nosewheel first (or for a taildragger, main gear first), setting off a series of motions that imitate the jumps and dives of a porpoise—hence the name. The problem is improper aircraft attitude at touchdown, sometimes caused by not paying attention, by not knowing where the ground is, by mistrimming, or by trying to force the aircraft onto the runway. No matter what the cause, the situation must be corrected immediately.

Ground effect, a factor from the surface to a height of about half the plane's wing span, decreases elevator control effectiveness and increases the effort required to raise the nose and hold the airplane off. Not enough elevator (or stabilator) trim can result in a nose-low contact with the runway and a porpoise.

The secret to a good landing is proper aircraft attitude at touchdown. For tricycle-gear planes, it's the attitude that ensures that the main wheels will touch before the nosewheel. You will need to develop a feel for this attitude in your particular aircraft and stay proficient at it. You also will need to know what it "feels like" at all combinations of weight and cg.

Porpoising also can be caused by improper airspeed control. Usually, if an approach is too fast, the airplane floats and the pilot tries to force it on the runway when the airplane still wants to fly. A gust of wind, a bump in the runway, even a slight tug on the wheel will send the aircraft aloft again.

First, do no push the nose over. Ease it over and reland, this time holding the proper pitch attitude until the aircraft touches down. Add back pressure continually as the aircraft slows during the flare. Too many airplanes have been pranged because of the pilot's desire to put the airplane on the ground. A go-around might be the answer in some cases of porpoising.

To avoid porpoising:

1. Always trim the airplane for a stabilized approach.
2. Avoid excess airspeed and "floating."
3. Don't be distracted.
4. Maintain proper pitch attitude.
5. Stay proficient.

Loss of directional control   A *ground loop* is an uncontrolled turn, often violent, usually on landing and rollout. It is important to avoid loss of directional control. Recognize and correct problems early. Stop any incipient turn to swerve almost before it starts. Get right on it.

Also, use your controls to their best advantage. Keep the weight of tricycle-gear aircraft on the mains with elevator back pressure. This method also desensitizes the nosewheel.

In taildraggers, full back stick puts more weight on the tailwheel for better directional control. Lack of sufficient back pressure can multiply the effects of small rudder movements (or reactions to crosswinds)—overcorrections that can induce trouble.

If you get in trouble, close the throttle, apply back pressure, and regain control.

Crosswinds can be a real problem. Remember, in a crosswind landing, the longitudinal axis of the airplane must remain parallel to the runway centerline, as must the flight path of the airplane. If you don't do both, strong side loads might be exerted on the landing gear, and a ground loop could occur, resulting in even higher side loads.

Proper crosswind technique is a must. In the case of a left crosswind, the left wing must be lowered into the wind and this control input countered with right rudder to maintain the proper track down to the runway. Again, the longitudinal axis of the airplane must be aligned with the flight path, which, hopefully, is parallel to the runway centerline.

You should know the crosswind limitations of your airplane and yourself. In some cases, it is best to stay on the ground, or, if airborne, to locate another runway more aligned with the wind.

One of the worst ego bruises occurs when the pilot tries to clear the runway before he or she has slowed down enough. This is even more of a problem in some crosswind conditions. Simply following the yellow exit line might lead to an unplanned ground loop. A much better technique is to stay on the runway centerline until you have slowed down to taxi speed.

There is only one principal cause for loss of directional control: pilot error. Recent studies also point to preoccupation, stress, fatigue, or just inattentiveness.

To summarize, directional-control accidents can be greatly reduced if, as pilots, we follow these simple rules:

1. Maintain proficiency
2. Stay ahead of the airplane
3. Avoid wheelbarrowing by holding back pressure on the controls during rollout
4. Keep your flight path and longitudinal axis parallel to the runway centerline
5. Double-check wind conditions on short final
6. Stay within the demonstrated crosswind capabilities for both you and the airplane
7. Slow down the airplane before taxiing clear
8. Keep your thoughts on the landing; that is, don't be distracted

Landing long

It is important to review the landing performance charts for the aircraft you fly. Aircraft performance charts are presented in one of two different formats: graphical and tabular. Some performance charts provide different approach speeds for different landing weights, while others provide only the maximum-weight approach speed.

How many factors affect the length of your landing roll? Of course, landing speed and landing weight, as well as wind and *density altitude*; the combination of pressure altitude and temperature is density altitude. Did you remember runway slope and runway surface? They affect braking. Runway length itself is also a factor, since it affects where you locate your aim point.

These eight factors must be thoroughly understood and controlled to avoid the hazards of landing long.

Airspeed Control   Airspeed control is the most important factor in achieving landing precision. The secret of precise airspeed control begins in the traffic pattern with the stabilized approach.

Begin mastering airspeed control by checking "the numbers" in your pilot's operating handbook or owner's manual. You should know and use the appropriate airspeeds for each segment of your approach. If you cannot locate them, get help from a knowledgeable flight instructor. Again, manufacturer's numbers should be used when available.

On short final with wings level, your airspeed should be at the recommended approach speed. If that speed is not stated, use 1.3 Vso. Although the official definition of *Vso* is qualified in many ways, for purposes of this discussion, Vso is the calibrated power-off stall speed of the airplane in the landing configuration and usually with a forward cg.

There are a few times when the use of 1.3 Vso on short final is not acceptable. First, the recommended approach speed for twin-engine airplanes is at or above Vyse, the best single engine rate-of-climb speed, which might be more than 1.3 Vso.

Second, the presence of strong, gusting winds is a problem that will be discussed later. Also, if you are unfortunate enough to be trying to land with an unwanted load of ice, the stall speed will be much higher than normal. If you carry too much airspeed at the moment of touchdown, your roll-out distance ratio will increase by the square of the ratio of your actual touchdown speed over your normal touchdown speed. For example, if an airplane that should be landed at 50 kts touches down at 55 kts (10 percent faster, or a factor of 1.1), the ground roll-out distance will be increased by the square of this factor, or 1.21 *if all other factors are constant*. The distance used from touchdown to a full stop will then be 21 percent greater than for the minimum touchdown speed. This could be ample justification for a go-around. An approach flown at 70 kts, or 20 kts faster than your normal approach speed, will require 96 percent more roll-out distance, or nearly double the runway for rollout alone.

However, at anytime, if you happen to be carrying extra airspeed in the flare, the airplane will *float*—that is, glide from over your aim point—past the intended touchdown point, until that excess airspeed has dissipated. Sometimes at a busy airport you are asked to keep the speed up then land short, and turn off quickly. This procedure can be tough and requires concentration and control. There might be situations where your best and safest option is to tell the air controllers "unable to comply."

Landing Weight Landing light also can mean landing long. Remember, the 1.3 Vso formula is based on the actual weight of the aircraft, not the maximum landing weight. If you use your customary max weight 1.3 Vso number all the time, you will float as the airplane dissipates the excess energy. Assuming that you will want to land at or close to the stall, runway distance will be eaten up during the process. There has been a lot of confusion about this fact. Many pilots assume that the "lower end of the white arc" on the airspeed indicator is Vso for all landing weights. It is not! It is really the stall speed for maximum landing weight at the most unfavorable cg within the allowable loading range. Depending on the aircraft's year of manufacture, this "lower end of the white arc" could be marked in either calibrated or indicated airspeed.

Larger aircraft above 12,500 lbs. have detailed and very specific information to determine Vref for all landing weights, as well as other approach speeds at various flap settings. This information is needed for the simple reason that all aircraft stall at slower speeds when they are lighter. In the case of an airliner, that difference in weight can be measured in tons. In a light aircraft, the difference of a few hundred pounds in landing weight can make a similar difference.

A fine point, but a very important one: airplanes manufactured before the mid-1970s had their airspeed-indicator color-coded speed-range arcs marked in calibrated airspeeds, and shown in miles per hour. (Some were marked in both mph and knots.) To determine 1.3 Vso at maximum landing weight for airplanes built prior to the mid- to late 1970s, multiply the calibrated Vso airspeed (given in the owner's manual or marked at the bottom of the white arc) by 1.3.

Most airplanes built after the mid-1970s had their airspeed indicators marked in indicated airspeed. Check the manufacturer's information about this for your specific airplane. For most aircraft built since the mid- to late 1970s, you must use the calibrated airspeed values as published in your handbook because calibrated airspeed (CAS) is indicated airspeed corrected for position and instrument error (or what the "perfect" airspeed indicator system would show). Always use calibrated airspeed to calculate the proper approach speed at any landing weight, and then convert it to indicated airspeed for practical use. You should do so because, for some airplanes, the indicated airspeed near the stall has a significant error.

Wind   Wind is another major factor in landing long. To determine the effect of wind on landing rollout, consult your performance charts. But you might be surprised to learn that a light headwind is not to be counted in rule-of-thumb computations for a decreased landing roll unless it exceeds 10 percent of your touchdown speed. Any tailwind does have a significant impact on your landing rollout and has the same effect as excess airspeed on touchdown in no-wind conditions. A tailwind compounds your landing roll-out distance by the square of the ratio of the tailwind component plus your "actual" touchdown speed over your normal touchdown speed.

For example, if your normal landing speed is 50 kts CAS, and you have a 10-kt tailwind, and you also touch down 10 kts too fast—that is, at 60 kts CAS— you will almost double your landing roll-out distance, if all other factors are equal.

$$\left(\frac{60+10}{50}\right)^2 = 1.96$$

In the case of a headwind component greater than 10 percent of the normal touchdown speed (in CAS), the rule of thumb is 0.9 minus (the headwind component over the normal touchdown speed) times the no-wind landing roll-out distance, which then equals the new, estimated landing roll-out. For example:

"No-wind" landing rollout   =   1000 ft
Touchdown speed (CAS)   =   50 kts
Headwind component   =   10 kts

$$0.9 - \frac{10}{50} = 0.9 - 0.2 = 0.7$$

Estimated landing rollout $= 0.7 \times 1000 = 700$ ft

If you land with a tailwind, as the following example shows, a 10-kt tailwind will increase your touchdown speed from 50 kts (your normal touchdown speed) to 60 kts, or 20 percent, a factor of 1.2. Squaring this gives 1.44, and multiplying 1.44 times your no-wind ground roll-out distance gives an expected ground roll of 1440 feet. Thus, if a 10-kt headwind in the previous example had shifted to a 10-kt tailwind, the expected landing roll-out distance of 700 feet (again, from the previous example) would be more than doubled.

"No-wind" landing rollout   =   1000 ft
Touchdown speed (CAS)   =   50 kts
Headwind component   =   10 kts

Therefore, groundspeed at touchdown $=60$ kts

$$\frac{60}{50} = 1.2 \times \text{Normal touchdown speed}$$

$$(1.2)^2 = 1.44$$

$1.44 \times 1000 = 1440$ ft extra runway roll-out distance required

Remember that these are just rules of thumb to advise you of the advantages of landing with a headwind, and conversely, the hazards of landing with a tailwind. They are not intended to substitute for manufacturer's information. It is best to check your pilot's operating handbook or owner's manual for specifics.

Wind gusts   The gust factor, the difference between the steady-state wind and the maximum gust, should be factored into your final approach airspeed in some form. It should also be added to your various approach segment airspeeds for downwind, base, and final.

One recommended technique many pilots use is to divide the gust factor by two and add this amount to the normal approach speed. Some pilots add all of the steady wind and half the gust and no steady wind.

To increase safety, your final approach airspeed needs to be precisely calculated, then precisely flown. Do not forget, however, that your approach airspeed and whatever gust factor you select to add to your final approach airspeed should be flown only after all maneuvering has been completed and the aircraft has been lined up on the final approach.

Runway slope FAA utility airport design standards allow maximum grades of up to 2 percent, or about 1.2 degrees of slope. For these airports, runway slope is a relatively minor factor. However, runway slope can be a real factor at an airport not built to government standards. If you do attempt a landing on an inclined runway, the rule of thumb is to always land uphill, wind and obstacles permitting.

Density altitude Density altitude is the combination of pressure altitude and temperature. These two variables can be read directly from the altimeter (at the 29.92 " Hg. setting) and the outside air temperature (OAT) gauge. Once you know pressure altitude and temperature, pilot operating handbooks provide tables or graphs that allow you to determine the effects of density altitude in one step. Older airplane publications use a two-step method requiring the use of pressure altitude and OAT first to determine density altitude, then use density altitude to determine the effects on aircraft and engine performance.

Although density altitude does not have a great effect on landing rollout as it has on takeoffs, remember that high-density altitude means higher true airspeeds and, therefore, longer runway requirements. High, hot, and humid means that there might be a potential need to lean the fuel-air mixture on landing to ensure good engine performance in case of a go-around. Figure on adding about 5 percent to the landing rollout for each additional 1,000 feet of density altitude.

Runway surface Runway surface makes a big difference on landing long because it plays a big role in braking. A dry concrete runway offers one of the best braking surfaces, while a runway covered with wet, clear ice has one of the worst. Most other conditions fall somewhere between the two.

Do not begin to brake as soon as you touch down. Right after touchdown, the airplane is still producing lift, and a premature application of brakes does nothing more than leave skid marks on the runway. Apply brakes after all three wheels are on the runway and the airplane has slowed to at least 25 percent below touchdown speed. In fact, for most airplanes aerodynamic drag is the single biggest factor in slowing the aircraft in the first quarter of its speed decay. Brakes become increasingly effective as airspeed and lift decrease.

There are two ways to increase braking effectiveness on landing rollout. First, some handbooks and owner's manuals suggest that retracting the flaps will decrease lift and put more weight on the gear. It is really best, however, to wait on flap retraction until you are clear of the runway and less busy, especially in retractable-gear aircraft where a misidentified control could lead to a gear-up landing.

Instead, the safest way to increase braking effectiveness is to hold the wheel or stick full back as you firmly and smoothly apply brakes. Back pressure is needed because the airplane tends to "lean" forward with heavy braking. This method is especially important in taildraggers but is important for nosewheel types as well. Grass is a much less effective braking surface. Wet or frost-covered grass is even worse.

Of course, be sure to avoid surprises by checking brake pedal pressure before entering the traffic pattern. If brakes are soft or mushy, or they "floor-board," land on a longer runway and on one as nearly aligned into the wind as possible.

Best braking results are always achieved with the wheels in an *incipient skid condition*. That means a little more brake pressure would lock up the wheels entirely. In an incipient skid, the wheels are turning, but with great reluctance. Whatever you do, don't lock the wheels. Braking effectiveness drops dramatically in a skid—and tires could be damaged.

Airline flightcrews routinely inspect the condition of their tires prior to each flight—good practice for every general aviation pilot. Do not just check for depth of tread and proper inflation. Look for cuts, bald spots, dry rot, and so forth.

Runway length   Length is also a factor in landing long. Did you know that an otherwise helpful nonstandard VASI can turn a 2,100-foot runway into an 1,800-foot runway? That is because the airport operator who installed the nonstandard VASI will locate the aim point for you, and it might be several hundred feet down the runway to start. Be alert for this situation because a displaced aim point associated with a nonstandard VASI will not be identified in airman publications.

Executing the go-around

A properly executed go-around is one of the best accident-avoidance procedures available to pilots, even though it's one of the least used. If not properly executed, however, it can result in an accident, and one much more serious than landing long. Official reports concerning go-around accidents frequently cite pilot indecision as a cause. What usually happens is pilot fixation—trying to make a bad landing good, resulting in a late decision to go around. It is natural, since the purpose of an approach is a landing. But delay costs valuable runway stopping distance, as well as loss of valuable altitude as the approach continues.

If you have any question about making a safe touchdown and rollout, take the airplane around—and do it early. Treat the go-around as a normal procedure, not an abnormal or emergency action. Always be prepared to go around. Experienced pilots always determine in advance a go-around point on the runway. If they haven't touched down by that point, it's go-around time.

Remember, however, that high-density altitude or rising terrain might put your go-around point at some point before you even reach the runway. So plan ahead. As for go-around technique, your pilot's operating handbook or owner's manual should be your primary source for reviewing purposes. The following steps are recommended:

1. Power is the single most essential ingredient. You must take every precaution to ensure that power is available when you need it. For example, at a high-density altitude airport, be sure your mixture is leaned ahead of time. Other prelanding checklist items to ensure that go-around power will be available include use of carb heat, as necessary, and full rpm on the prop.

2. Planning ahead is another step. Know what you'll do in case of trouble and where and when you should do it.

3. Stick to your decision. Once you decide to go around, stick to it! Too many airplanes have been lost because a pilot vacillated, changed his mind, and tried to land after all.

4. Concentrate on flying the airplane and avoid distractions, including Unicom and passengers for the time being. Make sure maximum available power and stays are applied. Place the carb heat selector in the OFF position. Watch engine limits such as manifold pressure in turbocharged aircraft or EPRs and the like in turbines.

5. Trim to maintain proper pitch control.

6. Establish a positive rate of climb and cross-check inside with outside references.

7. Then and *only* then, slowly retract flaps, further adjusting the pitch attitude. Only after establishing a positive climb, retract the gear if so equipped. As speed increases, accelerate past your best-angle to your best rate-of-climb speed. Adjust cowl flaps as necessary.

8. As you climb out, adjust your track over the ground to stay slightly to the right side of the runway so you can watch for departing traffic. Now, only after the aircraft is under control, communicate with tower or with Unicom.

On the way around for another attempt, be especially sure to use your checklist. A go-around is the best time for a break in normal habit patterns. There is stress. Normal tasks are out of order. More than one pilot has landed gear-up after a go-around.

Practice your go-around procedures so that when you really do have to go around, you'll be on top of the airplane, rather than the other way around. Anytime you make an approach, be prepared to go around. If you do decide to go around, stick to your decision and maintain control. In all cases, when it doubt, go around. This is your go-around checklist: power, pitch, fly the airplane, clean it up, then communicate. Then on your second attempt, strictly adhere to the landing checklist items.

Landing at night

Night landings have a special element of risk. Part of the reason is that pilots often don't maintain their night-flying proficiency. Night flying can be as tough as flying on instruments. Get some dual night flying with an instructor periodically and prepare for the unexpected. Shoot some landings without panel lights and, where permitted, without landing lights.

At night, traffic patterns must be flown with extra care. Allow plenty of time to do your prelanding checklist before entering the pattern. In the pattern maintain the recommended speeds. Give yourself plenty of time to prepare for the approach and landing.

A long, low final is to be avoided at all costs and especially at night. The presence of unseen obstacles around the airport is a prime reason to always check flight-information publications for airport details before you launch. Know where those obstacles are before, not after. On approach, make sure your glide path is high enough to stay well clear of all obstacles—not just the ones you can see.

This is also the time to be sure your directional gyro is aligned with the magnetic compass. It will help you locate the runway you'll want to use.

Set your altimeter. Remember, a 1-inch decrease in barometric pressure means your altimeter reading is about 1000 feet higher than your actual altitude.

On final, take advantage of VASI guidance where available. Never allow a "low" indication to appear at night. Get back up to your glide path immediately or take it around and try again. With ATC permission, you also can make use of an ILS to guide you to your landing runway at night.

If runway lights become fuzzy on final, beware. You might be seeing the effects of ground fog, which can lead to "suddenly" reduced visibility as you near the runway for touchdown. Fog can form in minutes, obscuring all or part of any runway. An alternate airport might be your best bet.

Atmospherics can change colors, light intensities, even depth perception. Even when atmospherics are not a problem, optical illusions can be. You might mistake a lighted area for a runway or one airport for another, resulting in landing at the wrong facility. Landings on roads and parking lots are not unheard of when lighting patterns create confusion.

To cut costs, some airport lighting is now radio controlled. Be sure you know how to use them; know the specific instructions for the runway lighting installed where you're landing. Flight information publications have the data, including frequencies and procedures to activate these lighting systems, as well as how to raise or lower the light intensity. Many systems turn themselves off after 15 minutes. Do not be caught on short final when the lights go out. If you are caught, go around, turn the lights back on, and try again.

Never attempt a landing at an unlighted airport, no matter how well you think you know it. If in doubt about lighting at your destination, do not be embarrassed; call Flight Service.

At a tower-controlled airport, you also might have the option of asking for the raising or lowering of runway light intensity, if needed. You also can ask them to extinguish the sequential strobe approach lights if they become distracting, which they often do when you are close to the runway. An easy way to enhance your ability to see outside obstacles is to dim interior cockpit lighting. Know the color coding: "aviation red" lighting or white strobes mean obstacles to air navigation.

Carry a flashlight at all times. In fact, several might be appropriate. Also important at night is a spare pair of glasses. Your eyes work harder at night and it's going to be tough if you lose a contact lens or break your only pair of glasses in flight.

At an airport that's not very busy, it's often best to fly over once or twice at 50 to 100 feet to check for obstructions and animals at night. Runways hold the day's heat and animals love to congregate there as the cool night progresses.

Conclusion

Landing-phase accidents account for roughly half of all flying accidents each year. It's ironic that they're always the same kinds of accidents. When it comes right down to it, most accidents, including landing-phase accidents, are the result of failure in the human element. More specifically, it is often a failure in the decision-making process.

Most accidents end up as attributed to "pilot error." But that refers to a whole gamut of problems, such as being too stressed, not being mentally alert, or pushing oneself beyond one's limits. Evidence indicates that some of the worst pilot-error accidents happen at night. Perhaps it is tiredness after a full day's work or simply "get-home-itis." In any case, it can led a pilot to rationalize his or her go/no-go decision and lead to a takeoff or landing accident. All of these potential problems require that a pilot review the basics, sharpen flying skills, and maintain proficiency.

Key terms

Minimum controllable airspeed
Wake turbulence
Vortices
Common Traffic Advisory Frequency (CTAF)
Airport Advisory Service (AAS)
Self-announce
Undershoot
Reference speed (Vref)
Aim point
Airman's Information Manual
Airport Facility Directory

Aeronautical Information Publication-Canada (AIP-Canada)
Canada Flight Supplement
Windshear
Microbursts
Turbulence
Cross-control stall
Sterile cockpit concept
Pilot-induced oscillation (porpoising)
Ground loop
Aircraft performance charts
Airspeed control
Approach speed
Calibrated power-off stall speed (Vso)
Indicated airspeed
Calibrated airspeed
Incipient skid condition
Atmospherics

Review questions

1. Why is the skill of operating an airplane at slow speeds so important?
   Describe slow-flight procedures starting with the reduction of power at
      cruising power.
   Discuss some of the maneuvers you should perform in testing your skill.

2. Why is turning back to the airport following an engine failure at low
      altitudes a poor solution?
   What is the best approach?
   List the engine-out procedures during takeoff that should be practiced at
      least once every six months.
   What preflight engine checks should be made?

3. Define *vortices*.
   Why are they of particular concern to light aircraft operators?
   Describe the precautions a pilot should take when taking off or landing
      behind a heavy jet.

4. What are the three ways a pilot can communicate his or her intentions to
      obtain airport-traffic information?
   What is the Common Traffic Advisory Frequency?
   Airport Advisory Service?
   List the accepted practices in communicating with a Unicom station.
   Describe the "self-announce" procedure.

5. What can pilots do in planning their landing before departing?
   Identify several informational sources about the destination airport.
   Discuss the importance of wind.
   Why is the final approach so crucial?
   What is the primary cause of gear-up landings?
   How can a pilot remember to lower the gear?
   What are some of the problems in activating gear levers?

6. What are some of the causes of undershooting a runway?
   Describe a technique that can be used to overcome an undershoot.
   Give some guidelines regarding approach segment airspeeds under VFR and
      IFR conditions.
   What is the *aim point* on the runway?

7. Why is the cross-control stall so dangerous?
   How can this situation be avoided?
   What is the primary cause of hard landings and porpoising?
   Give some corrective actions.
   What steps can be taken to reduce directional control accidents?

8. Why is airspeed control the most important factor in achieving landing
      precision?
   List the eight factors that can affect your landing roll.
   Describe the specific effect that each can have on landing long.
   What is the primary cause of go-around accidents?
   Give the recommended steps in a go-around procedure.

9. What are some of the problems encountered in landing at night?
   Describe some precautions that should be taken.

Midair collisions

Outline

Learning objectives

When you have finished this chapter, you should be able to:

△ Identify the factors affecting the safe separation of air traffic.

△ Compare and contrast the difference between controlled and uncontrolled airspace.

△ Distinguish between the following areas: Continental Control Area, Control Areas, Positive Control Area, and Transition Areas.

△ Distinguish between a Terminal Control Area and Airport Radar Service Area.

△ Explain the difference between a basic transponder, a Mode C transponder, and a Mode S transponder.

△ Discuss some of the limitations of the human eye as our primary means of scanning.

△ Describe the block system of scanning.

△ Summarize the major items in the collision avoidance checklist.

Introduction

The public concern about general aviation aircraft in the air traffic control system stems mostly from the perceived risk to commercial airliners posed by the presence of general aviation aircraft. Historically such risks have, in fact, been quite small. During the past decade, general aviation aircraft were a primary contributing factor in less than 2 percent of all accidents involving jet carriers. For passengers traveling on commuter airlines, general aviation aircraft posed a somewhat greater threat. The risk is greatest among the smallest commuter airlines, which tend to operate more frequently into airports used most heavily by general aviation aircraft.

Although the risk of a midair collision is small, such accidents evoke considerable publicity when a jet air carrier is involved. Between 1975 and 1986 there were 329 midair collisions in the United States, an average of just over 27 per year. Of these accidents, 290 (88 percent) involved two general aviation aircraft. Somewhat surprisingly, over 40 percent of midair collisions did not result in fatalities. Two of the fatal accidents during this period involved jet airliners.

In 1978, a Pacific Southwest Airlines Boeing 727 collided with a four-seat Cessna 172 in the immediate vicinity of San Diego's Lindbergh Field. Both aircraft has been receiving radar traffic advisories from controllers. Prior to the accident, however, the PSA jet had reported the Cessna to be in sight and, consequently, under standard air traffic control practices, had accepted responsibility for separation from the Cessna. The collision occurred at a time when the PSA flightcrew had lost visual contact with the Cessna but had not yet informed controllers to resume their radar-based traffic separation responsibility.

In 1986, an Aeromexico DC-9 airliner collided with a four-seat Piper Archer. The two aircraft collided inside the Los Angeles Terminal Control Area (TCA), airspace that is reserved for aircraft that have been identified on radar and cleared to proceed by air traffic controllers. The Piper had not received clearance to enter the TCA.

Such accidents, coupled with the dramatic postderegulation growth in air carrier traffic, have heightened concerns about midair collisions, and those concerns have focused on reports of near midair collisions collected by the FAA and NASA. General aviation aircraft figure prominently in near midair collisions reported by pilots to the FAA. During the period 1985 through 1987, 2654 near midair collisions were reported to the FAA, of which 2205 (83 percent) involved a general aviation aircraft. During the same period, 1064 near midair collisions involving an air carrier were reported, of which 758 (71 percent) involved a general aviation aircraft. Moreover, reports of near midair collisions between air carriers and general aviation aircraft more than doubled between 1985 and 1987.

Factors affecting safe separation of traffic

Three characteristics of general aviation operations pose challenges to the air traffic control task of maintaining safe separation among aircraft:

1. Most general aviation aircraft are significantly slower than air carrier aircraft, resulting in speed differentials and accompanying problems of traffic mix when the two types of aircraft are in close proximity in the same airspace.

2. Some operations of general aviation aircraft are not under positive control of the air traffic control system. Those aircraft operating under VFR are not in communication with air traffic controllers and, thus, cannot respond to controllers' instructions to change altitude or direction. These "nonparticipants" in the air traffic control system share airspace with "participants" who are under positive air traffic control. This characteristic might be thought of as an issue of control.

3. Not all general aviation aircraft are equipped to provide as much information about their location to the air traffic controller as are air carrier aircraft. Aircraft without so-called Mode C transponders do not provide information to the controller about the altitude at which they are operating. Without Mode C, a controller cannot tell the difference between a general aviation aircraft that poses a collision threat to another aircraft and one that is several thousand feet above or below and thus poses no threat. Operation of aircraft without transponders gives rise to an information issue. A desire to put more information on the radar screen must be tempered, however, by concerns about the limits to the amount of information the air traffic control computers can handle at one time and about the amount of information an individual controller will find useful at one time.

Perhaps the greatest difficulty caused by aircraft with different performance characteristics is when they join together into a single stream while on final approach to land at an airport. Such a final approach stream exists in good weather and bad in the landing pattern for every airport from low-density uncontrolled fields to high-density airports with a control tower and radar approach control.

Sufficient spacing must be maintained between aircraft during final approach to allow each airplane to clear the runway after landing before the next plane can be permitted to touch down. The speed differential between a jet airliner and a small single-engine general aviation aircraft can be as much as 100 mph. A slow aircraft mixed in the approach stream of faster aircraft requires a large, empty space behind it. The greater the speed disparity in a traffic mix, the fewer aircraft can be landed in a given period of time and the more difficult it is for controllers to ensure adequate spacing. Consequently, speed mix can contribute to traffic congestion, as well as increase controller workloads. Some of the slower turbo-prop aircraft operated by regional airlines also create traffic mix problems, although most of the newer regional airline turboprops fly fast enough to mix into the approach stream without difficulty.

The air traffic control system

The air traffic control system is designed to separate aircraft that are participating in the system, and participation is mandatory in low-visibility conditions—under IFR. However, when the weather is clear enough to allow flight under VFR, those under positive air traffic control can share the airspace with many aircraft who are not participants in the air traffic control system. With only a very few exceptions, most commercial flights are under IFR even in good weather, so most VFR flights are made by general aviation aircraft.

In addition to its primary mission of separating participating aircraft from each other, air traffic control also tries to protect participating aircraft from the threat of collision with nonparticipating VFR aircraft. (Air traffic control cannot protect nonparticipating aircraft from one another because it is not in radio contact with these aircraft and, therefore, cannot give instructions about how to avoid an impending collision.

Air traffic control can protect participating aircraft from nonparticipating aircraft in two ways. First, the FAA can use "hardware" or technical means to gain information about nonparticipating aircraft through enhanced radar detection and automatic reporting of altitude information. Second, the FAA can use regulatory means to reserve certain airspace solely for aircraft under positive control.

Uncontrolled airspace

Airspace is controlled by one of two factors:

1. Weather minimums that force the pilot to meet VFR requirements
2. An area that, because of traffic loads, needs the special guidance of Air Traffic Control (ATC).

The Airman's Information Manual defines *uncontrolled airspace* as that which has not been designated as a Continental Control Area, Control Area, Control Zone, Terminal Control Area, or Transition Area. It is simply everywhere else. A pilot is free to fly there as long as he or she meets VFR flight weather minimums and ATC procedures, if they apply. (See FIG. 7-1.)

The areas of uncontrolled airspace are steadily shrinking as more legislation is passed in the name of safety. The maximum altitude you may fly and remain in uncontrolled airspace is 14,500 feet MSL. However, that airspace remains in only a very few precious places. The vast majority of uncontrolled airspace lies below transition areas and has a maximum altitude of 1200 feet AGL. This uncontrolled airspace, for the most part, lies between airports that have no FAA controlling facilities. In these uncontrolled areas, you may fly VFR anytime you desire, to anywhere you desire, as long as you have at least 1-mile visibility and remain clear of the clouds.

If you find uncontrolled airspace in an area that is above the 1200-feet AGL level but below 10,000 feet MSL, you then have to have at least 1 mile of visibility and fly no closer than 500 feet below, 1000 feet above, and at least 2000 feet horizontally from any clouds.

In uncontrolled airspace that is both more than 1200 feet above the surface, and at or above 10,000 feet MSL, you must have at least 5 miles visibility and remain 1000 feet above and below the clouds, as well as 1 mile horizontally. A review of the VFR Cloud Clearance and Visibility Chart (see FIG. 7-2) should help you understand the visibility and cloud clearance requirements.

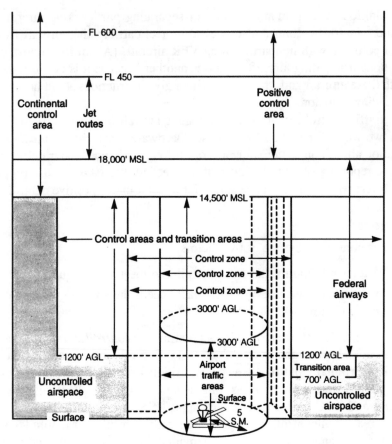

Fig. 7-1. The airspace system.

Controlled airspace

Controlled airspace consists of those areas designated as Continental Control Area, Control Area, Control Zones, Terminal Control Areas, and Transition Areas. In these areas of control, some or all of the aircraft are under the control of ATC. These areas are usually supported by ground-to-air communications, navigation aids, and air traffic services. In other words, you will probably have to have a VOR to navigate with and an ATC of some sort.

Traveling through most controlled airspace does not mean that you are required to talk with anyone unless the ceiling and visibility are below VFR conditions. You can fly right through the Continental Control Area, a Transition Area, or on any Control Area, such as VOR (Victor) airway and not be under the influence of ATC unless the weather is below VFR minimums. The following section includes a brief review of the controlled areas.

Continental Control Area   The Continental Control Area covers the entire 48 contiguous states, Alaska, and the District of Columbia from 14,500 feet MSL on

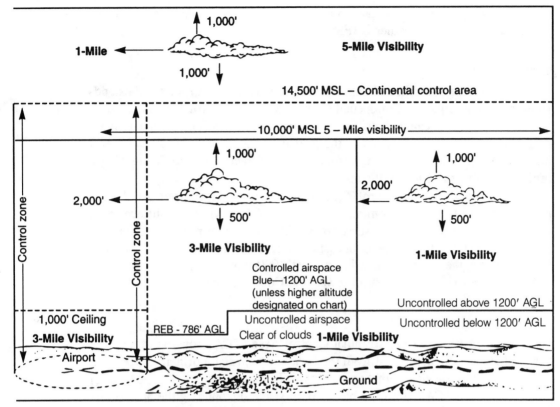

Fig. 7-2. VFR visibility and cloud minimums.

up. Any airspace 1500 feet (or less) above the surface of the earth is not covered. This means if you were standing on a mountain that was 14,500 feet high, the first 1500 feet of air above you would not be in the Continental Control Area.

Control Areas Control Areas consist of the airspace designated as Colored Federal Airways, VOR Federal Airways, Additional Control Areas, and Control Area Extensions, but do not include the Continental Control Areas.

Positive Control Area The Positive Control Area consists of certain airspace within the United States that begins at 18,000 feet MSL and goes up to flight level 600 (60,000 feet). To operate in the PCA, you have to be instrument-rated, on an IFR flight plan, and in an aircraft equipped for IFR flight.

Transition areas

Transition Areas are designated on your Sectional maps by the blue and magenta colors around airports that do not have control towers but still have instrument-approach procedures. The controlled airspace begins at 700 feet above the surface in the case of the magenta (red) color and at 1200 feet in the case of the blue. Just remember, the only time you have to concern yourself about this airspace being controlled is when the weather is IFR.

Control Zones

Control Zones are controlled airspace that surrounds certain airports and extends from the surface up to the Continental Control Area. A Control Zone is based on a primary airport but can include others within its boundary. This boundary has a radius of 5 miles from the center of the primary airport with extensions for IFR arrival and departure corridors. Control Zones are depicted on your Sectional by a broken blue line surrounding the airport.

An airport can have a Control Zone and not have a control tower. All the airport has to have is two-way communication with ATC down to the surface and a federally certificated weather observer taking hourly weather reports and relaying them to the ATC facility in charge of that Control Zone. To operate VFR within a Control Zone, the weather must be at least 1000-foot ceiling and visibility 3 miles. If the airport has no control tower, the Control Zone "disappears" if the weather is VFR.

Terminal Control Area   A Terminal Control Area (TCA) consists of airspace when all aircraft are controlled from the surface upward at a primary airport. In other words, it is mandatory that pilots obtain clearance from Air Traffic Control before entering a TCA. TCAs are blocks of airspace surrounding the busiest airports throughout the United States—e.g., Atlanta, Chicago, New York, Los Angeles, and San Francisco—and are divided into two groups. Aircraft equipment requirements to operate into a *Group II TCA* are a two-way radio, VOR or TACAN receiver, and a 4096 code transponder. In addition to the Group II requirements, *Group I TCAs* require transponders to have Mode C automatic altitude reporting capability and pilots to hold at least a private pilot certificate to land or take off at the primary airport within the TCA.

Airport Radar Service Area   An Airport Radar Service Area (ARSA) consists of controlled airspace surrounding certain airports in which all aircraft are subject to operating rules and minimum pilot and aircraft equipment requirements. They might be thought of as mini TCAs. The dimensions of an ARSA are also rather like a TCA in that it, too, looks like an inverted wedding cake when viewed from the side. An ARSA has three basic areas: an inner circle, an outer circle, and an outer area. The work they do is designed to help aircraft flow with additional safety by utilizing radar. (See FIG. 7-3.)

The services a pilot receives within the ARSA include radar sequencing of all aircraft arriving at the primary airport, standard sequencing of IFR aircraft, and traffic advisories for both IFR and VFR aircraft.

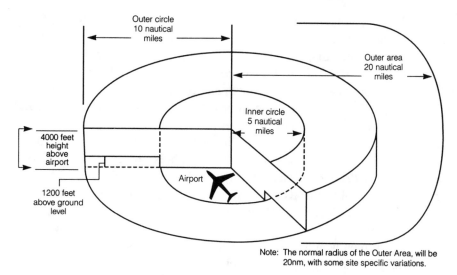

Note: The normal radius of the Outer Area, will be 20nm, with some site specific variations.

Fig. 7-3. Airport Radar Service Area (ARSA).

Within the outer area, the same radar services are offered as within the inner area when you establish two-way radio communication. In the outer area, the FAA strongly encourages your participation with ATC, although it is not mandatory. Beyond the outer area, ATC will offer you standard IFR separation and basic radar service. One of the primary reasons for establishing ARSAs back in the early 1980s was to reduce near misses and midair collisions.

The transponder

The most immediate concern when considering aircraft that fly in proximity to air carrier operations is whether the nonparticipating aircraft appear on ATC radar in a manner that allows the controller to determine quickly if a collision threat exists.

The ability of radar to track aircraft targets can be enhanced with the use or airborne transponders. To acquire information from transponder-equipped aircraft, a ground radar set transmits a secondary "interrogation" pulse that, when received by an airborne transponder, causes the transponder to transmit its own "reply" to the ground radar set. The two-way transmission results in a far more distinct and reliable radar target than a primary target that comes simply from the reflection of radar energy off an aircraft's metal skin.

A basic transponder can transmit, as a reply, a code assigned by air traffic control and set into the airborne transponder by the pilot. This code is used by the ground radar computer to display the identity of the target to the air traffic controller.

A basic transponder only fixes the geographical position of an aircraft on controller's radar but provides no information to the controller about the aircraft's altitude. Altitude can be reported verbally by pilot to controller when radio contact is established, but the controller will not be in radio contact with nonparticipating aircraft in the airspace. However, if an aircraft is equipped with an encoding altimeter—a *Mode C transponder*—its altitude will automatically be read from the onboard altimeter, encoded, and transmitted to the ground radar as part of the reply pulse. The altitude information is then displayed on the radar screen, completing the controller's picture.

A visitor to an approach control facility at a major airport, on a day when the weather is good, would find several types of symbols on the controllers' radarscopes (known as *Primary Visual Displays*, or PVDs). Traffic that was actively being controlled would show as a symbol with a "data block" adjacent to it. The data displayed in the block includes the identity and type of the aircraft, its altitude, and its airspeed.

The radar screen would also show other symbols (plus signs, squares, asterisks, and triangles) moving across the scope, as well as what are best described as vague smudges that appear to move. Controlled traffic would be observed to fly close to the unmarked symbols and smudges on occasion, or even appear to merge with them on the radar. The unmarked symbols and smudges are the nonparticipating VFR aircraft that are equipped in a variety of ways. However, controllers know that when they observe this VFR traffic, they might not be seeing all of the nonparticipating aircraft. Because of blind spots and other characteristics of radars, some aircraft (especially those that do not have transponders) might appear only sporadically on the screen or might not appear at all. In addition, some of the smudges on the screen might not be aircraft. Depending on the surrounding terrain, it is not unusual for radar to track large trucks moving on nearby highways.

If the aircraft are flying in clear weather, the pilots of both controlled and uncontrolled aircraft have the legal responsibility for traffic separation by visual means. However, if their workload permits, the air traffic controllers try to issue advisories to controlled aircraft about nonparticipating traffic observed on the radar that might pose a threat of collision. The more information that the controllers have about the VFR traffic, the more informative advisories they can give. A radar symbol with an altitude attached can be "called out" as traffic with a certain position and altitude. This radar symbol is generated by a VFR aircraft equipped with a transponder and an encoding altimeter (a Mode C transponder). Receipt of this traffic advisory by a participating aircraft pilot would generate immediate attention, and a visual search could be commenced in the correct quadrant of the sky. If the altitude of the VFR aircraft was substantially different from that of the controlled aircraft, this call normally would not be made.

A square or asterisk radar symbol can be safely ignored by a busy controller. These radar symbols are also generated by aircraft equipped with a transponder and encoding altimeter but not operating at an altitude for which the controller is responsible. They have been "filtered" by the ATC computer, and the symbology tells the controller that the traffic is either above or below the airspace that he is controlling and, consequently, that the indicated VFR traffic is not in potential conflict with any of that controller's aircraft.

A plus or circle radar symbol is generated by an aircraft equipped with a transponder but no encoding altimeter. Using this information, the controller can issue traffic advisories to controlled aircraft that include the relative position of the VFR aircraft, but not its altitude. As an example, a VFR aircraft might be inside the Los Angeles Terminal Control Area and in proximity to commercial airliners, for example, if it is cruising at some locations between 3000 and 7000 feet—areas reserved for such VFR traffic. The VFR aircraft could just as well be outside the control area by being either above or below its vertical limits. In other words, the aircraft could, and if it were following correct procedures would, be in places reserved for this type of operation and thus posing no threat to controlled aircraft. For these reasons, the radar symbol will not be interpreted as seriously by the controller. He might issue the advisory as "altitude unknown," or if he is very busy he might not issue any advisories concerning the numerous radar symbols representing aircraft that are usually—but unfortunately not always—well above or below the areas of conflict.

Finally, the vague smudges on the radarscope are generated by aircraft without any transponder equipment. They are the "primary" radar reflections from the aircraft's metal skin. Observed on the radar screen, they also might have been generated by rain showers or even by trucks on the highway. They provide little information that is useful for traffic advisories or separation.

When a more distinct radar target is provided by an airborne transponder and altitude information is provided by an encoding altimeter, accurate traffic advisories can be given by controllers. Furthermore, controller workload can potentially decrease when fewer needless advisories are issued about VFR traffic that is readily seen by controllers not to be in a conflict situation with the controlled traffic once the VFR target's altitude is known.

ATC computers that are currently in use are limited in the number of targets they can track simultaneously. Clearly, if the entire fleet of general aviation aircraft brought their transponders and encoding altimeters to any one high-density airport and turned on their equipment, the air traffic control computer would be overwhelmed. In fact, in the unlikely event of this occurrence, not only the radar system but also the airspace and airport would be overwhelmed. However, the normal observed peaking of general aviation traffic in any one area is far less severe and well within the capability of existing computers. Control facilities in the densest area, such as Los Angeles, report that a high percentage of nonparticipating VFR traffic observed on the scopes is already equipped with transponders. The computer at Los Angeles is currently estimated to be tracking approximately 65 percent of its maximum capacity at peak times.

It is possible, though, that with high levels of growth in aviation operations, computer limits might be reached before new high-capacity computers are installed in all facilities. In this event, again unlikely, there are "patches" that can be installed to make a busy computer stop tracking targets that are outside the control facility's area of responsibility. Thus, even if all general aviation aircraft were equipped with Mode C transponders, it seems very unlikely that computers would be overtaxed. If they were, however, there are other "fixes" to these problems.

A potential limitation on ATC's ability to use the new information is scope clutter on the radar screens. The radar symbols with altitude information take more space on the scope, and the larger symbols might even obscure other crucial information. However, controllers have the ability to move these blocks to avoid such problems, and electronic filters can be used to permit only those data blocks that were important for the controller to see to be displayed on the screen.

The transponders and encoding altimeters report their information passively, allowing controllers to use the reported information without being in radio contact with nonparticipating aircraft. For this information to be of use, of course, it must be accurate. Historically, controllers have relied on the altitudes reported by encoding altimeters only after verifying the reported altitudes via radio contact with the pilot. Reliability of the encoding altimeters has been satisfactorily proven, especially when the equipment is checked periodically, as must be done for non-VFR flights. The FAA has recently changed its internal policies to allow controllers to make use of unverified altitude reports from encoding altimeters.

Of course, altitude reports from nonparticipating VFR aircraft are always unverified. In order for controllers to enjoy a workload reduction from not giving needless advisories about traffic that is passively reporting an altitude far above or below, they must make use of the unverified altitude reports.

The historic regulatory philosophy regarding Mode C transponders has been to require them on IFR aircraft and on VFR aircraft flying in areas of high-density commercial traffic. The equipment is currently required for all aircraft flying above 12,500 feet and for all aircraft flying in the Terminal Control Areas that surround 23 high-density airports. However, because of the "inverted wedding cake" shape of most TCAs and special corridors in some TCAs, aircraft without Mode C transponders still can appear on the screens of air traffic controllers. In the overwhelming majority of cases, these aircraft are where they are supposed to be and pose no threat to commercial airliners. In some cases, including the Cerritos accident and numerous near midair collisions, the aircraft are not where they are supposed to be and do pose a threat. The difficulty is that without Mode C transponders, the controller has no reliable way of distinguishing between those aircraft that do and those that do not pose a threat.

Mode C transponders

Federal Aviation Regulation 91.215(b)(2), ATC transponder and altitude reporting equipment and use, requires that certain aircraft be Mode C transponder-equipped in order to operate within the 30-mile veil of several terminal control areas. This requirement recently has been suspended until December 30, 1993. The suspension affects approximately 300 general aviation airports.

Pilots can operate without a Mode C transponder at certain airports at or below a specified altitude and subject to the following conditions:

1. The aircraft must be operated within a 2-nautical-mile radius of the airport.
2. The aircraft must be operated only along a direct route between that airport and the outer boundary of the Mode C veil.

Air Traffic Control may expand the 2-nautical-mile radius out to a radius of 5 nautical miles for an aircraft if the situation requires it. ATC also can vary the exit route of a non-Mode C equipped aircraft departing one of the airports to the edge of a veil.

Operating at or below the designated altitude and on the most direct route to the edge of the veil does not relieve pilots of compliance with FAR 91.119 (minimum safe altitudes). Routes to and from each airport are intentionally unspecified to allow pilots to avoid obstructions, noise-sensitive areas, etc., and to remain in compliance with FAR 91.119.

The Mode C transponder requirement will have to be met after December 30, 1993, unless the FAA extends that date. One of the factors in that decision will be the radar coverage within the TCA Mode C veil airspace as new radar equipment is installed. FAA determined that safety would not be compromised by the suspension within or near the airports listed because ATC radar cannot adequately cover the affected airspace near those airports. As the FAA installs new, upgraded ATC radar equipment, FAA will review each airport's radar coverage and determine on a case-by-case basis whether to continue the suspension. Another factor in determining which airports to include in the suspension list was the need to eliminate airports served by scheduled air carrier operations using aircraft that will be required to install TCAS (*traffic alert and collision avoidance system*) equipment.

TCAS

All airliners with more than 30 seats must be equipped with TCAS II in order to fly in the United States after December 31, 1993. The basics of TCAS II are a computer, some form of display in the cockpit, and a transponder. (TCAS I, a simpler system, is being designed for general aviation use and includes only traffic advisories.) The newest generation of transponder operates in *Mode Select*, or *Mode S*, which allows the transponder to be addressed individually and enables data to be passed between ground radars and airplanes and between airplanes, so two airliners can exchange coordination information in order to execute avoidance maneuvers. (Airplanes with older transponders still can be detected and displayed in the cockpit, but they can't participate in resolving a conflict with a coordinated maneuver.)

Once each second, a Mode S transponder emits a "squitter" signal that contains a unique code, or address. A computer on a TCAS-equipped aircraft detects this squitter and issues its own interrogation to the address it just received. With the help of antennas that determine the direction of a signal, the computer determines the relative bearing to the aircraft and, by measuring time intervals, its range. The computer gets the aircraft's altitude by decoding the altitude data portion of the reply.

The TCAS II computer tracks and lists every transponder it detects within a bubble of airspace measuring a minimum of 15 nautical miles (about 17 statute miles) in front and about half that distance to the rear. It also knows its own flight path and altitude. The computer's collision avoidance logic—the heart of the system—can produce a display in the cockpit showing each aircraft it is tracking and can estimate the nearest point at which it will pass.

The computer also generates two kinds of advisories: traffic alerts and resolution advisories. Traffic alerts, which merely give bearing and distance information to the pilot, occur when an intruder is about 35 to 45 seconds away. At 20 to 30 seconds' separation, the computer will generate a resolution advisory telling the pilot how to maneuver to avoid collision.

Before that advisory is used, the two airplanes' TCAS computers must communicate. Each transmits its intent to either climb, dive, or, if already diving or climbing, to hold at a certain vertical speed range. First, however, each computer checks to see if it has received an intent, in case nearly simultaneous "I intend to climb" (or the digital equivalent) signals ring out from both airplanes. There's even a final arbiter: the airplane with the higher transponder code is programmed to back off and change its intention.

Pilots using TCAS II can get their information through various displays. One, like a miniature radarscope, shows the traffic around the airplane as if viewed from high overhead. Another shows what to do to avoid the collision by indicating a maneuver and a vertical speed—a climb at the rate of 1500 feet per minute, for example.

With TCAS II, conflicts are resolved only with vertical maneuvers because turning involves banking the aircraft, which affects the orientation of the TCAS antennas and requires additional software. When TCAS III comes, if it ever does, lateral maneuvers will be added. Neither the FAA nor the airline industry claims that TCAS is perfect, but then it is not the primary means for separating air traffic. That remains with the controllers and the ATC system.

Avoiding midair collisions

Studies of the midair collision problems form certain definite warning patterns. It might be surprising to some that nearly all midair collisions occur during daylight hours and in VFR conditions. Perhaps not so surprising is that the majority happen within 5 miles of an airport, in the areas of greatest traffic concentration.

Also surprising, perhaps, is the fact that the closing speed (rate at which two aircraft come together) is relatively slow, usually much slower than the airspeed of either aircraft involved. This is because the majority of midair collisions are the result of a faster aircraft overtaking and hitting a slower plane.

In most cases, at least one of the pilots involved could have seen the other in time to avoid contact if he or she had just been using his or her eyes properly. So it is really that complex, vulnerable, little organ—the human eye—that is the leading cause of midair collisions.

Limitations of the eye

By definition and function, the human eye is one of the most important and complex systems in the world. Basically, its job is to accept images from the outside world and transmit them to the brain for recognition and storage. In other words, the organ of vision is our prime means of identifying and relating to what's going on around us.

It has been estimated that 80 percent of our total information intake is through the eyes. In the air we depend on our eyes to provide most of the basic input necessary for performing during a flight—attitude, speed, direction, and proximity to things (like the ground) and opposing air traffic that might constitute a danger of midair collision. As air traffic density and aircraft closing speeds increase, the problems of midair collision grow proportionately, and so does the importance of the "eyeball system." A basic understanding of the eyes' limitation in target detection is probably the best insurance a pilot can have against running into another airplane.

The eye, and consequently vision, is vulnerable to just about everything: dust, fatigue, emotion, germs, fallen eyelashes, age, optical illusions, and alcohol. In flight, our vision is altered by atmospheric conditions, windshield distortion, too much or too little oxygen, acceleration, glare, heat, lighting, aircraft design, and so forth.

Most of all, the eye is vulnerable to the vagaries of the mind. We can "see" and identify only what the mind lets us see. For example, a daydreaming pilot staring out into space sees no approaching traffic and is probably the No. 1 candidate for midair collision.

One function of the eye that is a source of constant problems to the pilot is the time required for accommodation. Our eyes automatically accommodate for (or refocus on) near and far objects. However, the change from something up close, like a dark panel two feet away, to a well-lighted landmark or aircraft target a mile or so away, takes 1 to 2 seconds, or longer, for eye accommodation. That can be a long time when you consider that you need 10 seconds to avoid in-flight collisions.

Another focusing problem usually occurs at very high altitudes, but it can happen even at lower levels on vague, colorless days above a haze or cloud layer when no distinct horizon is visible. If there is little or nothing to focus on at infinity, we do not focus at all. We experience something known as *empty-field myopia*; we stare but see nothing, even opposing traffic, if it should enter our visual field.

The effects of what is called *binocular vision* have been studied seriously by the National Transportation Safety Board (NTSB) during investigations of midair collisions, with the conclusion that it is also a causal factor. To actually accept what we see, we need to receive cues from both eyes. If an object is visible to one eye, but hidden from the other by a windshield post or other obstruction, the total image is blurred and not always acceptable to the mind.

Another inherent eye problem is that of narrow field of vision. Although our eyes accept light rays from an arc of nearly 200 degrees, they are limited to a relatively narrow area (approximately 10 to 15 degrees) in which they can actually focus and classify an object. Although we can perceive movement in the periphery, we cannot identify what is happening out there, and we tend not to believe what we see out of the corner of our eyes. This, aided by the brain, often leads to *tunnel vision*.

This limitation is compounded by the fact that, at a distance, an aircraft on a collision course with you will appear to be motionless. It will remain in a seemingly stationary position, without appearing either to move or to grow in size for a relatively long time, and then suddenly bloom into a huge mass filling one of your windows. This is known as *blossom effect*. Since we need motion or contrast to attract our eyes' attention, this effect becomes a frightening factor when you realize that a large bug smear or dirty spot on the windshield can hide a converging plane until it's too close to be avoided.

In addition to the built-in problems, the eye is also severely limited by environment. Optical properties of the atmosphere alter the appearance of traffic, particularly on hazy days. *Limited visibility* actually means limited vision. You might be legally VFR when you have 3 miles, but at that distance on a hazy day, opposing traffic is not easy to detect. At a range closer than 3 miles, even though detectable the other aircraft might not be avoidable.

Lighting also affects our vision stimuli. Glare, usually worse on a sunny day over a cloud deck or during flight directly into the sun, makes objects hard to see and scanning uncomfortable. Also, an object that is well lighted will have a high degree of contrast and will be easy to detect, while one with low contrast at the same distance might be impossible to see. For instance, when the sun is behind you, an opposing aircraft will stand out clearly, but when you're looking into the sun and your traffic is "backlighted," it is a different story.

Another contrast problem area is trying to find an airplane over a cluttered background. If it is between you and terrain that is varicolored or heavily dotted with buildings, it will blend into the background until it is quite close.

Of course, there is also the mind, which can distract us to the point of not seeing anything at all or lull us into cockpit myopia—staring at one instrument without "seeing" it. How often have you filed IFR on a CAVU day, settled back at your assigned altitude with autopilot on, then never looked outside, feeling secure that radar was tracking your progress? Radar has its limitations. It is fine to depend on instruments, but not to the exclusion of the see-and-avoid system.

Visual perception is affected by many factors. Pilots, like everyone, tend to overestimate their visual abilities and misunderstand visual limitations. Since the primary cause of midair collisions is failure to adhere properly to the see-and-avoid concept, the best way to avoid them is to learn how to do an efficient external scan.

Scanning

Learn how to scan properly, first by knowing where to concentrate your search. It would be preferable, naturally, to look everywhere constantly but, that not being practical, concentrate on the areas most critical to you at any given time. In the traffic pattern especially, clear yourself before every turn and always watch for traffic making an improper entry into the pattern. On descent and climbout, make gentle S-turns to see if anyone is in your way. (Make clearing turns, too, before attempting maneuvers, such as pylons and S-turns, about a road.)

During that very crucial final approach stage, do not forget to look behind and below, at least once, and avoid tunnel vision. Pilots often rivet their eyes to the point of touchdown.

In normal flight, you generally can avoid the threat of a midair collision by scanning an area 60 degrees to the left and to the right of your center visual area. This does not mean you should forget the rest of the area you can see from side windows every few scans. Horizontally, the statisticians say, you will be safe if you scan 10 degrees up and down from your flight vector. This scanning will allow you to spot any aircraft that is at an altitude that might prove hazardous to your own flight path, whether it is level with you, below and climbing, or above and descending. The slower your plane, the greater your vulnerability, hence the greater scan area required.

But do not forget that your eyes are subject to optical illusions and can play some nasty tricks on you. At one mile, for example, an aircraft flying below your altitude will appear to be above you. As it nears, it will seem to descend and go through your level, yet, all the while it will be straight and level below you.

Although you might not have much time to avoid another aircraft in your vicinity, use your head when making defensive moves. Even if you must maneuver to avoid a real midair collision, consider all the facts. If you miss the other aircraft but stall at a low altitude, the results might be the same for you.

Scan patterns

The *block system of scanning* has proven to be best for most pilots. This type of scan is based on the theory that traffic detection can be made only through a series of eye fixations at different points in space. Each of these fixes becomes the focal point of your field of vision (a block 10 to 15 degrees wide). By fixating every 10 to 15 degrees wide, you should be able to detect any contrasting or moving object in each block. This gives you 9 to 12 "blocks" in your scan area, each requiring a minimum of one to two seconds for accommodation and detection.

One method of block scan is the "side-to-side" motion. Start at the far left of your visual area and make a methodical sweep to the right, pausing in each block to focus. At the end of the scan, return to the panel.

The second form is the "front-to-side" version. Start with a fixation in the center block of your visual field (approximately the center of the front windshield in front of the pilot). Move your eyes to the left, focusing in each block, swing quickly back to the center block, and repeat the performance to the right.

External scanning is just part of the pilot's total visual job. To achieve maximum efficiency in flight, one has to establish a good internal (panel) scan, as well, and learn to give each its proper share of time. The amount of time one spends viewing outside the cockpit in relation to what is spent inside depends, to some extent, on the workload inside the cockpit and the density of traffic outside. Generally, the external scan will take about three to four times as long as a look around the instrument panel.

An efficient instrument scan is good practice, even if you limit your flying to VFR conditions, and being able to quickly scan the panel gives you a better chance of doing an effective job outside, as well. The following *panel scan system* is taught by FAA and AOPA Air Safety Foundation to instrument students.

Start with the attitude indicator. It will show changes in attitude in the two most crucial areas of flight: heading and altitude. Move to the directional gyro for heading, to altimeter, airspeed indicator, rate of climb, and turn and bank. It is a good idea to skim over the attitude indicator each time you move on to a new instrument, since it is your chief control instrument. Include your VOR and engine instruments every third scan or so, or as the flight situation dictates.

Developing an efficient time-sharing plan takes a lot of work and practice, but it is just as important as developing good landing techniques. The best way is to start on the ground, in your own airplane or the one you usually fly, and then use your scans in actual practice every chance you get.

Collision avoidance checklist

Collision avoidance involves much more than proper visual techniques. You can be the most conscientious scanner in the world and still have a midair collision if you neglect other important factors in the overall see-and-avoid picture. It might be helpful to use a collision avoidance checklist as vigorously as you do the pre-takeoff and landing lists. Such a checklist might include the following nine items:

1. *Check yourself.* Start with a check of yourself. Your eyesight and your safety depends on your mental and physical condition.

2. *Plan ahead.* Plan your flight ahead of time. Have charts folded in proper sequence and within handy reach. Keep your cockpit free of clutter. Be familiar with headings, frequencies, distances, etc., ahead of time so that you spend minimum time with your head down in your charts. Some pilots even jot these things down on a flight log before takeoff. Check your maps and the special general and area notices in AIM in advance for restricted areas, oil burner routes, intensive student jet training areas, and other high-density spots.

3. *Clean windows.* During the walk-around, make sure your windshield is clean. If possible, keep all windows clear of obstructions, like solid sun visors and curtains.

4. *Adhere to SOPs.* Stick to Standard Operating Procedures and observe the regulations of flight, such as correct altitudes and proper pattern practices. You can get into big trouble, for instance, by "sneaking" out of your proper altitude as cumulous clouds begin to tower higher and higher below you, or by skimming along the tops of clouds without observing proper separation. Some typical situations involving midair mishaps around airports include: entering a right-hand pattern at an airport with left-hand traffic or entering downwind so far ahead of the traffic pattern that you might interfere with traffic taking off and heading out in your direction. In most midair collisions, at least one of the pilots involved was not where he was supposed to be.

5. *Avoid crowds.* Avoid crowded airspace en route, such as directly over a VOR. You can navigate on VFR days just as accurately by passing slightly to the left or right of the omni stations. Pass over airports at a safe altitude, being particularly careful within a 25-mile radius of military airports and busy civil fields. Military airports usually have a very high concentration of fast-moving jet traffic in the vicinity and a pattern that extends to 2500 feet above the surface. Jets in climbout might be going as fast as 500 mph.

6. *Compensate for design.* Compensate for your aircraft's design limitations. All planes have blind spots; know where they are in your aircraft. For example, a high-wing aircraft that has a wing down in a turn blocks the area you are turning into. A low wing blocks the area beneath you. One of the most critical midair potential situations is a faster low-wing plane overtaking and descending on a high-wing on final approach.

7. *Equip for safety*. Your airplane can, in fact, help avoid collisions. Certain equipment that was once priced way above the lightplane owner's reach now is available at reasonable cost to all aviation segments. High-intensity strobe lights increase your contrast by as much as 10 times day or night. In areas of high density, use your strobes or your rotating beacon constantly, even during daylight hours. The cost is pennies per hour—a small price to pay for conspicuousness.

   Transponders, available in quick installation kits, significantly increase your safety by allowing radar controllers to keep traffic away from you and vice versa. Now mandatory for flight into certain high-density airport areas, transponders also up your chances of receiving radar traffic advisories, even on VFR flights.

8. *Talk and listen*. Use your radios, as well as your eyes. When approaching an airport, whether or not you're going to land, call in 15 miles out and tell them your position, altitude, and intentions. Find out what the local traffic situation is. At an airport with radar service, call the approach control frequency and let them know where you are and what you are going to do. At uncontrolled fields, call airport traffic advisory service on 123.6 MHz, or other FSS frequency, or on the appropriate Unicom or tower frequency.

   Since detecting a tiny aircraft at a distance is not the easiest thing to do, make use of any hints you get over the radio. A pilot reporting his position to a tower is also reporting to you. And your job is much easier when an air traffic controller tells you your traffic is "three miles at one o'clock." Once you have that particular traffic, do not forget the rest of the sky. If your traffic seems to be moving, you are not on a collision course, so continue your scan and watch it from time to time. If it does not appear to have motion, however, watch it very carefully, and get out of its way, if necessary.

9. *Scan*. The most important part of your checklist, of course, is to keep looking where you're going and to watch for traffic. Make use of your scan constantly.

   Basically, if you adhere to good airmanship, keep yourself and your plane in good condition, and develop an effective scan time-sharing system, you'll have no trouble avoiding midair collisions. As you learn to use your eyes properly, you also will benefit in other ways. Remember, despite their limitations, your eyes provide you with color, beauty, shape, motion, and excitement. As you train them to spot minute targets in the sky, you also will learn to see many other important "little" things you might now be missing, both on the ground and in the air. If you couple your eyes with your brain, you will be around to enjoy these benefits of vision for a long time.

Key terms

Air Traffic Control System
Uncontrolled airspace
Controlled airspace
Continental Control Area
Control areas
Positive Control Areas
Transition areas
Control zones
Terminal Control Area (TCA)
Airport Radar Service Area (ARSA)
Mode C transponder
Primary Visual Displays
TCAS (traffic alert and collision system)
Mode Select (Mode S) transponder
Empty-field myopia
Blossom effect

Review questions

1. Describe some of the challenges faced by air traffic controllers in separating general aviation and air carrier traffic.

   Basically, air traffic control can protect participating aircraft, or those under control and nonparticipating aircraft in two ways. Explain.

2. Define: *Uncontrolled airspace; Controlled airspace; Continental Control Area; Control Areas; Positive Control Area; Transition Areas;* and *Control Zones*.

   Distinguish between a Terminal Control Area (TCA) and Airport Radar Service Area (ARSA).

3. What is the difference between a basic transponder and a Mode C transponder?

   Discuss the Federal Aviation Regulation pertaining to Mode C transponders. What is TCAS?

   Describe how the Mode S transponder works.

4. Describe some limitations of the human eye as a means of identifying and relating what is going on around us.

   What is *empty-field myopia*?

   How is the eye limited by environment?

5. What is the block system of scanning?

Describe the panel scan system.

Identify and briefly describe the nine items included in a collision avoidance checklist.

8
CHAPTER

Miscellaneous in-flight hazards

Outline

Learning objectives

When you finish this chapter, you should be able to:

△ Understand the importance of dead reckoning as a supplement to radio navigation.

△ Explain how dead reckoning can be used in establishing a "running position fix."

△ Discuss some of the problems associated with fuel selector valves.

△ Describe how impending failure of gyroscopic instruments might appear.

△ Identify some of the hazards associated with night flying and discuss the importance of preflight and enroute planning.

△ Describe the two basic types of military training routes and the importance in obtaining current information regarding their usage.

△ Discuss some of the factors that can lead to wire strikes by general aviation aircraft.

△ Discuss the importance of having appropriate safety seats aboard an aircraft when carrying children.

Most all of the serious in-flight accidents fall into one of the categories covered in this chapter, but there are a few hazardous items remaining. These do not account for a substantial number of annual problems, but that does not obviate their hazardous nature.

Dead reckoning navigation

Dead reckoning (DR) originated with maritime navigation and refers to "reckoning or reasoning one's position relative to something stationary or dead in the water." It is a method of predicting enroute progress based on the direction of flight and the estimated groundspeed since the last known position.

It is generally agreed that the compass is a pilot's primary navigation tool. When it comes to specifying the second most valuable such device in the cockpit, however, there is often some difference of opinion. Most younger pilots generally favor the VOR receiver. Those with more experience prefer the clock. If something goes wrong with the electronic guidance system, a pilot must resort to basics.

The reliable compass and clock become his primary weapons in a battle of wits against the elements. The compass indicates where he's going and the clock tells him how far. Without either of these allies, a pilot can get lost very fast, especially when he or she is above clouds or over terrain where checkpoints are confusingly few and far apart.

Compass-and-clock, or dead-reckoning navigation, however, is slowly becoming a lost art as increasingly more reliance is placed on electronic guidance. Although no one can deny that VOR navigation has simplified cockpit workloads, pilots must avoid becoming too complacent.

Some, for example, do not keep track of their forward progress while navigating along a radial. They simply wait for the TO-FROM flag to drop, which might provide the first positive fix since passing the previous station. But shouldn't a pilot always know his position relative to the nearest airport? Dead reckoning is a relatively simple procedure that can and should be combined with radio navigation so that a pilot is aware of his or her approximate position at all times. In addition, it can be more relaxing holding a constant heading than reacting to the semaphore—like movements of a VOR needle.

Prior to a VFR flight, simply use a yardstick and a VFR planning chart to plot a direct course between your departure and destination airports (assuming that intervening terrain and other restrictions do not pose a threat to safety or legality). You can then use the forecasted winds aloft together with TABLES 8-1 and 8-2 to determine the true heading and groundspeed. Assume, for example, that the measured true course is 040 degrees and the winds aloft are expected to be from 010 degrees at 40 kts. In other words, the wind will be blowing from 30 degrees to the left of the nose, Using TABLE 8-1, we can determine that this is equivalent to a 35-kt headwind component and a 20-kt, left crosswind component.

If, for example, the planned true airspeed is 220 kts, you can expect the enroute groundspeed to be 185 kts ($220-35=185$).

Next, referring to TABLE 8-2, we can see that a 20-kt, left crosswind component combines with 220 kts of airspeed to require a 5 degree (left) wind correction angle. The true heading for the proposed flight, therefore, is 040 degrees less 5 degrees, or 035 degrees.

Crabbing, or turning into the wind, results in some loss of groundspeed, but this can be ignored when the crab angle is less than 10 degrees. When the crab angle exceeds 10°, use TABLE 8-3 to determine loss of groundspeed solely as a result of crabbing.

Table 8-1. Headwind/tailwind and crosswind components*

Angle between Wind Direction and True Course

Wind Speed	0°	10°	20°	30°	40°	50°	60°	70°	80°	90°
10	10 / 0	10 / 2	9 / 3	9 / 5	8 / 6	6 / 8	5 / 9	3 / 9	2 / 10	0 / 10
20	20 / 0	20 / 3	19 / 7	17 / 10	15 / 13	13 / 15	10 / 17	7 / 19	3 / 20	0 / 20
30	30 / 0	30 / 5	28 / 10	26 / 15	23 / 19	19 / 23	15 / 26	10 / 28	5 / 30	0 / 30
40	40 / 0	39 / 7	38 / 14	35 / 20	31 / 26	26 / 31	20 / 35	14 / 38	7 / 39	0 / 40
50	50 / 0	49 / 9	47 / 17	43 / 25	38 / 32	32 / 38	25 / 43	17 / 47	9 / 49	0 / 50
60	60 / 0	59 / 10	56 / 21	52 / 30	46 / 39	39 / 46	30 / 52	21 / 56	10 / 59	0 / 60
70	70 / 0	69 / 12	66 / 24	61 / 35	54 / 45	45 / 54	35 / 61	24 / 66	12 / 69	0 / 70

*Table 8-1 provides headwind/tailwind and crosswind components for various wind velocities. The upper-left figure in each square represents a headwind or tailwind component, depending on whether the wind is coming from ahead or behind; the lower-right figure represents a left or right crosswind component, depending also on wind direction.

Source: FAA

If you will encounter more than one wind condition en route, they can be arithmetically averaged with reasonable accuracy if wind directions do not vary by more than 90 degrees and wind speeds are within 15 kts of each other. For example, assume that the winds aloft for each of three flight segments along the direct route are forecast to be 80°/15kt, 100°/30kt, and 150°/30kt. The average

Table 8-2. Crab Angles

True Airspeed

Crosswind Component		80	100	120	140	160	180	200	220	240
	5	4°	3°	2°	2°	2°	2°	1°	1°	1°
	10	7°	6°	5°	4°	4°	3°	3°	3°	2°
	15	11°	9°	7°	6°	5°	5°	4°	4°	4°
	20	14°	12°	10°	8°	7°	6°	6°	5°	5°
	25	18°	14°	12°	10°	9°	8°	7°	7°	6°
	30	22°	17°	14°	12°	11°	10°	9°	8°	7°
	35	26°	20°	17°	14°	13°	11°	10°	9°	8°
	40	30°	24°	19°	17°	15°	13°	12°	10°	10°
	45	34°	27°	22°	19°	16°	14°	13°	12°	11°
	50	39°	30°	25°	21°	18°	16°	14°	13°	12°

*Table 8-2 provides the crab angle necessary to compensate for a given crosswind component when flying at a given true airspeed and is valid for knots or mph.

Source: FAA

Table 8-3. Groundspeed loss when crab angle exceeds 10 degrees*

Wind Correction Angle (Crab)

True airspeed	10°	15°	20°	25°	30°
80	−1	−3	− 5	− 7	−11
100	−2	−3	− 6	− 9	−13
120	−2	−4	− 7	−11	−16
140	−2	−5	− 8	−13	−19
160	−2	−5	−10	−15	−21
180	−3	−6	−11	−17	−24
200	−3	−7	−12	−19	−27
220	−3	−7	−13	−21	−29
240	−4	−8	−14	−22	−32

*Table 8-3 provides groundspeed loss due to crabbing into the wind when flying at a given true airspeed and is valid for knots or mph.

Source: FAA

wind direction is:

$$(080° + 100° + 150°) \div 3 = 110°.$$

Similarly, the average wind speed is 25 kts. This technique should not be used, however, when maximum accuracy is required, such as on a long, overwater flight.

En route, you can keep track of your progress visually or by using elapsed time and estimated groundspeed to plot a DR position. Dead reckoning works and it is reasonably accurate.

If an aircraft maintains its predicted groundspeed and track, then a positive fix obtained at any time during the flight will agree with the aircraft position as determined by DR methods. More likely, however, an actual fix (using radio or pilotage/or both) will disagree with the DR position. Usually, this situation occurs because one or more variables have been appraised incorrectly. In other words, there is an element of uncertainty surrounding every fix determined purely by dead reckoning.

A rule of thumb states that 90 percent of the time the maximum dead reckoning error (per hour of flight) is 20 miles plus 1 percent of the estimated distance flown during that hour.

Figure 8-1, for example, shows where the pilot of a 150-kt aircraft has computed his position to be at the end of one hour. The radius of the *circle of uncertainty* is equal, therefore, to 20 nautical miles (nm) + 1 percent of 20 nm, which equals 21.5 nm. In other words, there is a 90 percent probability that the pilot is actually within 21.5 nm of where he thinks he is.

Fig. 8-1. Circle of uncertainty.

It also can be shown that 50 percent of the time the aircraft is located within a circle with only one-third the radius of the larger circle. In this case, the pilot has a fifty-fifty chance of being within 7.2 nm of the DR position.

One way to reduce the size of the circle of uncertainty is to make sure the compass deviation card is reasonably accurate. The FAA does not require a periodic compass swing, but pilots would be wise to perform this check at least annually. Deviation errors can change significantly over a period of time.

Also, make it a habit to glance at the compass whenever you are lining up on a runway of known magnetic direction. Remember, however, that the runway number usually represents the magnetic direction rounded off to the nearest 10 degrees. Some runway numbers disagree by more than 10 degrees with the actual magnetic directions. For example, a runway might be designated 11L and have a magnetic direction of 122 degrees.

None of this should be interpreted as an argument against VOR navigation in favor of DR. However, it is good to know that there is an alternate, reliable way to get from one place to another when VOR is unavailable and pilotage is difficult. All that is required is some common-sense reasoning. The idea is to be aware of the wind and its effects and to maintain a running score of flight progress, either by using a flight log or by making marks on the chart and labeling each position (estimated or actual) with the time of passage.

Not only can DR be used to compute progress along a radial, it also can be used in conjunction with VOR to arrive at a "running fix." Consider the pilot flying from A to B in FIG. 8-2. He is not necessarily lost, but it has been a while since the last positive fix. He is also having trouble correlating contour lines on the chart with those on the ground.

At 1 PM, the aircraft crosses a railroad track, an excellent line of position (LOP). But one LOP does not establish a fix. Eighteen minutes later, the pilot is within range of a VOR station and determines that he is on the 230 degree radial.

A fix can be obtained by advancing the 1 PM LOP (the railroad tracks) toward the second LOP (the radial). This is accomplished by first estimating the distance flown since crossing the first LOP.

Assume, for example, that the estimated groundspeed of the aircraft in FIG. 8-2 is 150 kts. In 18 minutes, therefore, the distance flown is about 45 nm. The

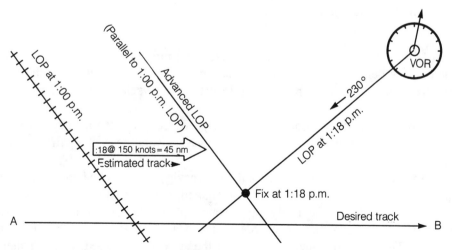

Fig. 8-2. Advancing a line of position to establish a fix.

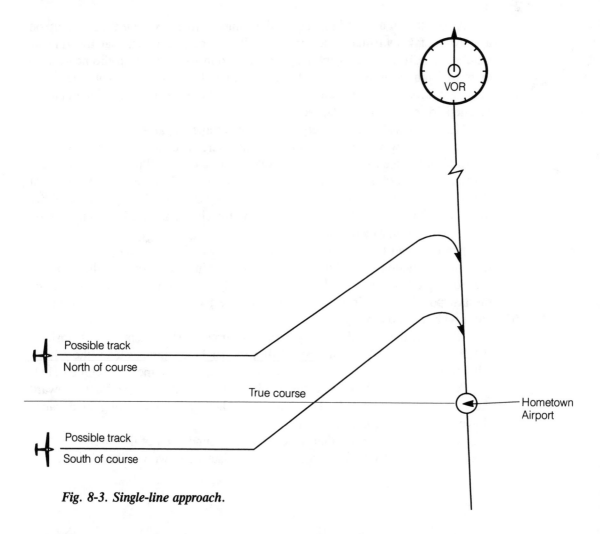

Fig. 8-3. Single-line approach.

first LOP is then advanced (parallel to itself) 45 nm in the direction of the estimated track being flown. The point where the advanced LOP intersects the VOR
radial (the second LOP) is the fix for 1:18 PM and shows the aircraft to be north of
course.

A running fix can be obtained using any two LOPs as long as they cross at a
reasonably obligue angle. They can be highways, rivers, or even a pair of radials
crossed at different times.

Another combination of DR and VOR navigation is called the *single-line
approach*. This technique can be life saving and is illustrated in FIG. 8-3.

A pilot is endeavoring to fly a true course of 090 degrees toward Hometown
Airport, which is on the 170-degree radial of a VORTAC (far to the north of
course). The pilot estimated arriving over the airport at 2:55 PM. Unfortunately,
he has been unable to obtain a reliable and recent fix and isn't sure that he's on

course. So, what should he do if, upon intercepting the 170-degree radial, he cannot find the airport? Should he fly north or south along the radial to find the destination? Since he is running low on fuel, he can't afford to turn in the wrong direction.

Dead reckoning (or common-sense) navigation offers a logical solution. About 45 minutes prior to ETA, the pilot should make a sufficiently large turn and purposefully intercept the radial north (or south) of the airport. When he does, the pilot knows with reasonable confidence which way to turn. By turning off course intentionally, he eliminates the likelihood of turning, searching, and wasting fuel in the wrong direction.

This procedure is also known as the "landfall intercept" and doesn't require that the destination be on a VOR radial. The airport could be situated on a river, shoreline, highway, railroad, or anything else that is easily identifiable and is approximately perpendicular to the true course. Nor does the single-line approach have to be reserved for locating a destination. It can be used with equal effectiveness to find a needed enroute checkpoint.

Fuel selector valves

An aircraft fuel selector valve should be one of the easiest devices to use, but recent accident statistics indicate otherwise. With alarming regularity, pilots manage to run a fuel tank dry or somehow manage to shut off the fuel supply and kill an engine. The principal reasons fuel selectors are used, of course, are to control fuel flow from the aircraft tanks and to permit the fuel supply to be shut off by the pilot in the event of an emergency.

The fuel selector valve in the typical light general aviation aircraft has three positions: OFF, LEFT, and RIGHT. But there are so many variations in fuel selector valve designs that pilots with little flight time in a particular type aircraft might well be confused when operating the selector valve.

Some aircraft have been shown to have a higher incidence of fuel selector-related accidents. They include the Beech 35 Bonanza, Beech 95 Travel Air, Piper PA-22 Tri-Pacer, and Piper PA-24 Comanche.

Other aircraft types, on the other hand, have had a much lower incidence of such accidents, notably the Cessna 150, 172, and 182. On the Cessna 150, the fuel system is either ON or it is OFF. The fact that Cessna Skyhawks and Skylanes have had "very low" incidence ratings might be partially attributed to the fact that these aircraft have a BOTH TANKS position, which is probably where the valve stays most of the time.

So why do some fuel selectors have to be so complicated? That's a question that has been posed by many aviation safety groups and one that aircraft manufacturers have, to date anyway, seemed reluctant to address. Clearly, there is little industry standardization of fuel selector valves, with each manufacturer developing its own designs.

For example, on Beech aircraft, the shorter end of the fuel selector handle points toward the selected tank. On Cessna, Piper, Mooney, Rockwell, and Bellanca aircraft, however, the long end of the handle is used as the pointer.

Some aircraft have been found to have fuel selectors mounted in awkward, out-of-the-way positions, which is apt to divert the pilot's attention from flying the aircraft. For example, one old Mooney model has the valve located on the floor between the pilot's knees. Other aircraft models—the Rallye and Piper Seminole, among them—require you to go through the OFF position when changing tanks.

FAA certification standards for the fuel selector valves in most light singles rather vaguely require that the valve be located somewhere behind the firewall. A manufacturer can install as many fuel tanks and selector positions as it deems necessary, except that "there must be a means to guard against inadvertent operation of each shutoff valve and allow appropriate flightcrew members to reopen each valve rapidly after it has been closed."

Additionally, the regulations state that a fuel selector must be located "so that the pilot can see to reach it without moving any seat or primary control when his seat is in any position in which it can be placed."

Switching tanks at low altitudes or while in the traffic pattern preparing to land is an invitation to disaster. Shutting off the fuel supply during any critical flight phase can mean trouble.

Pilots are encouraged to understand fully the fuel system operation of all aircraft they fly, before leaving the ground. Remember that the fuel selector valves of various types and models of aircraft are likely to be somewhat different.

It is a good idea to inspect the fuel selector visually, to become acquainted with its operation, and to ensure that it works properly. In this way, if the system has any particular quirks, you will learn about them before they become a problem.

Pneumatic system malfunction

The NTSB has reported air pump/system failure as a factor in an average of two accidents per year over the past years. About one-half of the reported cases involved other overriding factors such as losing control with a backup electrical gyro available, non-instrument-rated pilots flying in instrument weather conditions, and departing with pneumatic systems known to be inoperative.

The most disturbing factor is that the remaining half, an average of about one accident per year, occurred to instrument-rated pilots who recognized the pneumatic system failure, flew on partial panel in instrument weather conditions for 30 to 45 minutes, and then lost control during high task loads, such as during an instrument approach. Another common denominator was that all aircraft involved were high-performance, retractable-gear, single-engine aircraft.

The lessons are clear. The first is that loss of a pneumatic system in actual instrument conditions, without a backup system, is an emergency that can become life-threatening unless the airplane can be flown by partial panel into visual weather conditions. This might not be possible because of either weather conditions or lack of pilot practice with partial-panel flying.

An airplane with a single pneumatic system, with no backup system or backup instruments, should not be flown in any IFR conditions that do not provide for quick access to VFR conditions. IFR flight "on top" of cloud layers with good ceiling underneath should create minimal problems with pneumatic system failure, but flying in actual IFR with low ceilings and visibilities underneath sets the stage for serious difficulties.

The second lesson is that any airplane used regularly in IFR weather should be equipped with either a backup power source, such as dual pneumatic systems, or backup electrically powered gyroscopic instruments. Although it is legal to fly single-engine aircraft without dual power sources for gyroscopic instruments, and the exposure rate to accidents resulting from pneumatic system failure while in actual instrument weather is low, prudence suggests that a backup power source is good insurance against being forced to fly partial panel in adverse weather without sufficient practice.

Gyroscopic instrument power

Normal instrument flight relies in part on three gyroscopic instruments: an attitude indicator (artificial horizon), a heading indicator (directional gyro, or "dg") and a turn and slip indicator ("needle and ball," "turn and bank," or "turn coordinator").

These gyroscopic instruments might be powered by pneumatic (vacuum or pressure) or by airplane electrical systems. Which power source is used for which instruments might vary in the same make and model of airplane, depending on the use intended at the time of manufacture or modifications made after manufacture.

The most common arrangement for single-engine airplanes without back up instrumentation or systems is a single vacuum system, which powers the directional and attitude gyroscopic instruments. The other gyro instrument, the "turn and bank" or "turn coordinator" is usually electrically driven.

The gauge on the instrument panel may be marked as either a "suction gauge," a "vacuum gauge," or a "pressure gauge" and indicates in inches of mercury. The correct operating range (around 4.5″ to 5.5″ hg.) is given in the handbook of each airplane. Some airplanes also have warning lights when the vacuum or pressure is out of tolerance.

Pneumatic systems, like other mechanical systems, can malfunction suddenly or slowly. A slow decrease in gauge indication might indicate a dirty filter, dirty screens, a sticking regulator, a worn-out air pump, or a leak in the system. Zero pressure could indicate a sheared pump drive, a pump failure, a collapsed line, or a malfunctioning gauge. Any operation out of the normal range requires immediate attention by a mechanic.

A complete pneumatic loss is noticeable immediately on the gauge or within minutes by incorrect gyro readings. A slow deterioration might lead to sluggish or incorrect readings, which might trap a pilot who is not constantly cross-checking all instruments—including the vacuum or pressure gauge.

An additional factor involves an initial lack of recognition of the cause of the conflicting instrument indication, which develops when one instrument, usually the attitude indicator, malfunctions. Although possibly proficient in flying partial panel, many pilots are not trained or skilled in deciding to revert to a partial-panel scan unless an instructor or safety pilot has forced the scan by covering the attitude indicator. It is important for pilots to scan all instruments whenever conflicting information develops and not attempt to make control inputs on the basis of the attitude indicator alone. Once the all-important first step of recognition of the need for partial-panel scan is accepted, it is also helpful to remove the malfunctioning instrument from the scan, usually by covering it with a disk or pieces of paper.

The possibility of pneumatic system or gyroscopic instrument failure is the reason every instrument instructor drills students on partial-panel flying without reference to gyroscopic heading and attitude instruments. It is very rare that the failure itself results in a fatal accident, but it can set the stage for one if the pilot is not proficient in partial-panel flying and the failure occurs during instrument flight conditions.

Gyroscopic instrument operating tips

A few operating tips concerning your gyroscopic instruments might be useful at this point. For example, the heading indicator should be accurately set to some magnetic reference, such as a properly calibrated magnetic compass, just before takeoff, but after the gyro has come up to full speed. (With venturi-driven gyros, this procedure must be done in straight-and-level flight.)

Use a runway heading for reference only if it is exactly known. Runway numbers might vary as much as five degrees from precise runway magnetic headings.

Non-slaved heading indicators must be periodically compensated for drift. Three degrees in 15 minutes is normal. Significantly greater drift rates might signal impending gyro failure.

Panel-mounted gyro instruments, especially attitude indicators, should be caged before aerobatics are commenced.

Impending failure of gyroscopic instruments might announce itself in several ways:

1. A heading indicator that shows excessive drift—that of more than three degrees per 15 minutes—might do so because of worn bearings, causing friction and, hence, precession, or because of lack of power (air or electric), which keeps the gyro at the proper speed.

2. Sluggish response by turn indicators or turn coordinators.

3. Noise. Gyros instruments might become noticeably noisy as a result of internal bearing wear or damage. Such noise can best be perceived immediately after engine shutdown when the cockpit is quiet. Take a moment and listen.

4. Attitude indicators might be slow to erect or show deviation from level flight when the aircraft is, in fact, straight and level, if bearings are worn, or the power to spin the rotor is insufficient.

The first step when any of these symptoms is evident is to check power sources: vacuum gauge, if air driven; electric power indicators (meters or warning lights); and connections (air or electric) to the instrument case.

If your connections are venturi-powered, remember that ice in the venturi will disable your instruments and can form under conditions similar to those conducive to carburetor icing.

Help your gyroscopic instruments breathe. Airborne contaminants will damage the precision bearings in your gyroscopic instruments. Avoid smoking in the aircraft. Ensure that air filters for air-driven units are cleaned or replaced as necessary, particularly if you operate in a dusty environment.

Shock damage is the surest way to turn a gyro instrument into scrap. Avoid shock damage to delicate bearings.

Every pilot should know the instrument power sources for each airplane flown, and particularly know the consequences of loss of any source of power, air or electrical, or loss of any instrument, and be prepared to cope with the loss.

Airplanes can be flown safely with loss of one or more gyroscopic instruments. Every instrument-rated pilot demonstrated the ability to do so prior to receiving the rating. The problem is that many never practice the skill and only a few have ever practiced in turbulence, since it seems an unlikely need in routine operations.

Professional pilots who are required to take semiannual simulator training, practice a lifetime of emergencies each training session although they rarely encounter emergencies in daily operations. Most general aviation pilots remain "current" by flying in the system and may rarely face or practice emergency situations. For most pilots, continued flight in IFR conditions with failed gyro heading and attitude instruments is a high workload situation that could lead to a fatality.

If you are not instrument rated and inadvertently encounter instrument weather, the 180-degree turn is usually the best course of action. If your gyro instruments fail, it is still possible to make a 180-degree turn by using the turn and bank (or turn coordinator), magnetic compass, and clock. Likewise a descent through clouds to VFR conditions can be made using the turn indicating instrument. These procedures can be tailored to each airplane type and model and should be demonstrated by and practiced with an instructor. It might be too late to learn them when faced with actual need. Avoid conditions that risk encountering instrument weather.

If you are instrument rated and gyro instruments fail or mislead, do not be afraid to ask for help. ATC personnel know where to find better weather and are able to give "no gyro" heading directions. The whole system—radar, weather reports, communication, and personnel—is instantly available to assist you.

Also, cover the dead or lying instruments. Most partial-panel practice is done with covered instruments, but in real cases the artificial horizon will be sagging and giving erroneous information that your instincts want to accept as correct. Autopilots using these instruments as sensors must be turned off immediately.

Finally, if your airplane has no backup capability, be cautious in the type of IFR you fly. Solid IFR from takeoff to touchdown can be very difficult on partial panel.

Night flying

The decision to fly VFR at night is up to the pilot. If you do not feel comfortable flying at night the best advice is do not. On the other hand, night flying can be enjoyable if certain safety precautions are taken.

Generally, night flight is more pleasant than daytime flight. Radio traffic usually is sparse; there's less traffic; and the air is usually smoother and cooler.

However, there also are a number of potential hazards involved in night flying. Judgment of the landing approach and flare is harder. Clouds and bad weather might be difficult or impossible to see. Electrical failures can cause anxious alertness. Successful forced or precautionary night landings can be almost impossible to achieve.

A thorough preflight preparation is crucial before night flight. Check all cockpit and navigation lights and pay special attention to the electrical system, including the battery. Carry extra fuses.

A flashlight—you should carry two—will be necessary during the preflight inspection. You will need the flashlight to show your way, but also to check the color of the fuel and the fuel sample you drain to check for water and other possible contaminants.

Next, organize the cockpit. Searching for something during a day flight can be a nuisance; at night, groping about in the dark can have much more serious consequences.

There are several flight-planning considerations for night flying. One is to plan a more generous fuel reserve than you normally do. Darkness robs you of the option of making a safe precautionary landing, makes pilotage much more difficult, and puts a heavier load on the electrical system, which can suddenly leave you without navaids. Also, fuel is available at fewer airports at night.

Select high cruising altitudes. Range is greater at higher altitudes; gliding distance is greater; and pilotage and radio navigation might be easier.

The route you select might well be different than the one you would fly in the daytime. Consider selecting a route that keeps you within landing reach of an airport as much of the time as possible. Mark the route on your chart with a bold pen, not red ink, so you can easily see it at night. Remember to check carefully for terrain clearance.

Inside the cockpit, you will want to keep the panel lights as dim as possible, so as not to interfere with your "night vision." It takes about 30 minutes for your eyes to adjust to the darkness.

Lack of oxygen also decreases night vision and causes an increase in time required for dark adaptation. While flying at 12,000 feet without supplemental oxygen, a person's night vision is only about one-half of that normally experienced at sea level.

Smoking also has a detrimental effect on night vision. Three cigarettes smoked at night can reduce visual sensitivity as much as being at an increased altitude of 8000 feet.

During your flight, report your progress to a flight service station. Not only is such a report a good safety idea, but having someone to talk to, if only a "voice," can be reassuring to many pilots. Remember, too, to keep up with the weather over Flight Watch of an FSS.

Well before landing, familiarize yourself with data for the destination airport. Assuming you have remained on course, locating the airport shouldn't be difficult if it has a rotating beacon, which alternates a white and green light. Be sure to get an altimeter setting prior to landing.

During the landing, fly a carefully standardized approach pattern, using your altimeter to verify your rate of descent. Fly the approach as you would during daylight hours, but consider keeping the final approach leg a little steeper in order to give you an extra margin of safety in case there are trees, wires, or other obstructions short of the runway.

Some pilots prefer to land with the landing lights on; others leave them off. The portion of the runway illuminated by the landing lights seems higher than the black hole surrounding it, which can lead to a hard, and costly, landing.

Focusing your attention on the area immediately in front of the airplane is poor practice on any landing, and yet this is exactly what the landing lights encourage. Perhaps a better approach would be to use the runway lights instead, assuming they are available. By looking at the distant end of the runway and using the rising light lines on either side as peripheral cues for the flare and touchdown, you might find that you can flare more nearly the correct height and that your landing attitude is better.

If your airplane is in excellent operating condition and you are confident about your own flying and navigation abilities, night flying can be very rewarding and relatively safe. Remember, though, just as in virtually all flying situations, the "go or no-go" decision is up to the pilot.

Military training routes

Pilots should be ever mindful of military training routes (MTRs) that cross or come close to the intended route of flight. In recent years, the FAA has recorded close to 100 military-civilian "near-misses" a year. There also have been a number of fatal midair collisions. It is possible, too, that some civilian aircraft downed for unexplained reasons could have survived a near-miss only to be sent out of control or broken up as a result of tornadic wingtip vortices generated by 600-mph military aircraft.

In terms of ensuring pilot preparedness, training and special mission flights over these routes are essential to the nation's defense. To maintain sharp pilot proficiency, pilots of various military aircraft must practice, in the real environment, missions such as aircraft intercept, air-to-air combat, and photo reconnaissance. Routes frequently are flown close to the ground to simulate penetration of enemy radar. Often, then, military aircraft barrel along at near supersonic speed through low-altitude, often unrestricted airspace shared by general aviation pilots. This can be a distressing fact of aviation life, especially considering that many civilian pilots are not even aware MTRs exist. Many other pilots who know of the MTR routes do not give them proper respect during preflight.

Generally, MTRs are established below 10,000 feet MSL for operations at speeds in excess of 250 kts. There are two basic types: VRs or VFR routes and IRs or IFR-only routes. As one might expect, VR routes are flown only in accordance with visual flight rules, and IR routes are flown in accordance with instrument flight rules, regardless of weather conditions. Routes are identified as follows:

1. IR and VR at or below 1500 feet AGL (no segment above 1500) are identified by four-digit numbers, such as IR 1006 or VR 1007.

2. IR and VR above 1500 feet AGL (segments of these routes might be below 1500) are identified by three-digit numbers, such as IR 008 or VR 009.

Route width varies for each MTR and can extend several miles on either side of the charted centerline.

Pilots should contact FSS stations within 100 nm of a particular MTR to obtain current information on route usage in their vicinity. The briefer will call up the route information by computer and quickly tell whether the MTR is *hot,* or in use, and what the affected altitudes and times are.

Briefers will not inform a pilot about MTRs unless they are asked. Although the routes do not take long to fly, they are often in use more than once during weekdays and Saturdays (rarely on Sundays).

By reviewing the in-use time with the briefer, a pilot will be able to select a route, altitude, and flight time that will steer him or her clear of military traffic.

Once you are airborne and flying in the vicinity of an MTR, it's still a good idea to maintain a heads-up vigil against any military traffic. Should you spot one aircraft, be on the lookout for others. Often, missions are flown with, perhaps, as many as four aircraft. Depending again on the maneuvers called for the mission, the flight paths can vary from straight-and-level to aerobatic-type maneuvers. You can be somewhat assured that military pilots should be looking out for you, too. Or at least that's the flight plan. Fighter pilots flying MTRs are specifically briefed to spend about 95 percent of their time watching out for checkpoints and other visual reference.

To the military, the American skies will remain free only as long as the nation is willing to bear the burden of defending them. And for the general aviation pilot to request MTR information in his weather briefing is not asking too much. With reasonable caution, the sky can safely be shared by both military and civilian pilots.

Wire strikes

Recent NTSB statistics indicate that wire strikes are the cause of roughly 1 in every 20 general aviation accidents. Worse, about 1 out of 5 wire-strike accidents result in fatalities. Most wire-strike accidents occur in the general vicinity of an airport familiar to the pilot. The wires are seldom hidden or unmarked, accident reports note, and are generally known to the local pilot population.

The question arises as to why pilots familiar with the location of wires manage to fly into them with what seems to be alarming regularity. Obviously, it is because the pilot, for whatever reason, is somewhere he or she should not be, or doing something he or she should not be doing. For example, most wire-strike accidents in the vicinity of an airport are caused by pilots undershooting the approach. Approaches at night also account for several wire-strike accidents each year.

The pilot who loads an airplane over its gross takeoff weight and tries to climb out of a high-density altitude airport is a very good candidate for flying into wires off the end of the runway. Takeoffs from soft and wet sod airstrips over power lines also can be extremely hazardous. Failure to execute a go-around in time can result in a wire strike. If a pilot becomes confused or momentarily flustered during a balked landing and go-around, he or she might permit the airplane to drift into power lines. Likewise, if a pilot attempts to go around with full flaps and the carburetor heat on, or dumps flaps suddenly, chances begin improving that he or she will come into contact with something—maybe wires—near the end of the runway.

Although not accounting for the greatest number of wire-strike accidents, intentional low flying is the greatest killer of pilots and passengers who mix it up with wires. Nearly 4 out of 10 wire-strike accidents involving low-altitude flying result in fatalities. Most of these involved pilots out sightseeing over lakes and rivers, flying low over their houses or objects of interest on the ground, or "buzzing" objects on the ground. Flying low over a lake or river "for the thrill of it" is just asking for disaster. Yet, that's exactly what many pilots apparently do. An unfortunate number fly low enough to snag lines or wires just 50 to 75 feet above the surface.

Interestingly, studies by Aviation Safety newsletters have shown that low flights over water often are conducted by persons possessing student or private licenses, or none at all. Seasoned pilots, it seems, are less tempted to fly low over water and hit wires. On the other hand, pilots involved in wire strikes associated with buzzing are more likely to be experienced pilots. In fact, a majority of pilots hitting wires in a buzz job have commercial licenses or better and an average of more than 3800 hours of experience. These interesting findings would indicate that the pilot who flies low over a river doesn't perceive the danger, while the flight into wires during a buzz job involved a pilot who knows of the danger, but believes himself capable of avoiding it.

Unwarranted low flying is also the probable cause of those wire-strike accidents that occur while in cruise over land. In most of these situations, the ill-fated aircraft were flown at altitudes of less than 200 feet above the ground!

A relatively large number of wire strikes also occur following engine failure. During a forced landing, pilots occasionally fly into unseen power lines, usually of the telephone or low-voltage electric wire variety. These accidents are generally less frequently fatal than most other accidents.

How can wire-strike accidents be avoided? It's often difficult, if only because it's virtually impossible to see power lines until it's too late. A pilot would have to be within 150 feet of the typically sized power line across a river to see it, and then he would have less than two seconds to avoid it.

Therefore, pilots can best avoid wire strikes by being alert to those conditions mentioned earlier that account for most wire-strike crashes. That means flying over rivers at safe altitudes and being especially alert to wire hazards during all airport operations.

Wires generally are not marked as hazards on sectional charts. Rather, those transmission lines that are depicted are there more as an aid to navigation than as a hazard alert. Obstructions lower than 200 feet above ground level are not shown on sectional charts. If you are aware of a wire that is an obstruction at an airport, you should notify your local FAA office. It might be possible for the wire to be moved or buried. At the least, certain operating restrictions can be imposed, such as altering the standard traffic pattern or displacing thresholds. It also might be possible for the wires to be identified as a hazard in facilities directories.

Another remedy, at least for daylight hours, it is to string bright orange spheres—often called Tana balls (after a major manufacturer of the wire markers)—along the uppermost wire to alert pilots to the presence of the wire.

Finally, it is clear that a discussion of the dangers of wire strikes should be a part of every pilot training syllabus. Wire strikes are entirely preventable, and for that reason are even more tragic when they occur.

Child restraint systems

It's an alarming fact, but nonetheless true. Very little consideration has been given to the safety of infants and children aboard general aviation aircraft or, for that matter, aboard commercial carriers.

Aviation accidents often inflict unimaginable pain and suffering, and are all the more tragic when children are involved—especially when serious injury or death could have been avoided had the pilot-in-command ensured that small occupants were restrained in their seats.

But therein lies the problem. Most pilots do not know the best procedures for properly securing young passengers. Only casual reference is made in the Federal Aviation Regulations about restraining children. FARs note that children younger than age two may be held in the lap of an adult during takeoff and landing. Older children must, during takeoff and landing, occupy their own seats and use their seatbelts.

Adults should never buckle a seatbelt around themselves and the child. This practice will almost certainly inflict injury to at least the child in the event of a serious incident or accident.

The practice of lap-holding small children is questionable for other reasons, too. In the event of a low-gravity impact, when the weight of a child multiplies in relation to the forces exerted, the child could be physically impossible to hold. There is also the so-called "jackknife" effect, whereby the upper torso of the adult bends forward over the seatbelt and crushes the child.

Aircraft seats are not designed for children. Children can unfasten their seatbelts, unbeknownst to adult occupants, or wriggle out of them. Worse, in certain instances, they could be strangled, crushed, or otherwise injured by the very seatbelt intended to help protect them.

Pilots are pretty much on their own, then, to provide the best occupant protection for children they can. A proven, practical method of safeguarding children in an aircraft is to secure them in a safety seat, similar in design to those used in automobiles.

However, not just any seat will do. Use of seats not approved by the FAA is potentially dangerous. If, for example, the seat should shatter, be crushed by a forward-falling seat back, or otherwise fail, it could, itself, be the cause of occupant injury or death.

Safety seats used in aircraft must meet the requirements of FAA Technical Standard Order C-100. The TSO incorporates the toughest engineering and safety requirements of automobile safety seats, and goes even further. Generally, the TSO addresses considerations unique to the flight environment, such as vertical acceleration and turbulence. It also requires proper placarding regarding the seats' installation and use.

One such safety seat designed for use in aircraft and given FAA approval is Cosco-Peterson's 78 Safe-T-Seat™ designed for use by infants and children weighing less than 40 pounds or shorter than 40 inches.

The seat is of a molded-shell construction, with a padded seat cover for added protection and comfort and a tubular steel frame designed to withstand crash forces. A five-point, web-type harness with a quick-release buckle holds the child in place. The device is attached to the aircraft seat by the standard FAA-approved seatbelt. For infants, it should be used in the rear-facing position, and for toddlers, in the forward-facing position.

Shoulder harnesses

Shoulder harnesses can substantially reduce injury in case of an accident. Experts estimate that serious injuries and fatalities would be reduced 35 percent if everyone wore shoulder harnesses in aircraft. Ironically, only 23 percent of those involved in fatal/serious-injury accidents in a recent year had their shoulder harness secured, according to the NTSB.

Shoulder harnesses are standard equipment in front seats of all general aviation aircraft built since 1978. They had been installed or made available at every seat in some aircraft long before that. Unfortunately, pilots often treat installed shoulder harnesses as optional equipment. Pilots who wear seatbelts (even to taxi) sometimes omit fastening their shoulder harness.

Remember, shoulder harnesses are valuable extra protection for you and your passengers. Every general aircraft built for personal or business use after December 31, 1984, is equipped with shoulder harnesses as standard equipment at every forward-facing passenger seat. That is how much importance industry places on shoulder harnesses.

Anyone can have an accident, no matter how conscientious a pilot or driver you are. The big difference between cars and planes is that planes travel faster. Thus, it is even more important that airplane occupants be restrained because a shoulder harness will lessen occupant head and chest injuries. Of course, the pilot is responsible under FAR 91.14 to brief passengers on the use of seatbelts. However, you should also urge your passengers to use their shoulder harnesses. If your aircraft is not equipped with shoulder harnesses, consider having them installed. They are one of the most cost-effective safety devices you can buy for your aircraft. Information on them is available in FAA Advisory Circular AC 43.13-2.

Wear the seatbelt as low as possible across your hips. Be sure it is tight enough to stay that way in case of trouble. If you loosen your seatbelt during cruise, be sure to "cinch up" before approach and landing.

Single-strap shoulder harnesses should be snug (but not tight) across your chest. While inertial reel belts should be snug, fixed belts should be adjusted so that you are able to fit your fist between the shoulder harness and your chest at the tightest point.

Even though you and your passengers are secured by seatbelts and shoulder harnesses, you are still not totally prepared for flight unless you properly restrain baggage before flight. It is simply too late to restrain baggage in flight during an emergency. Do it properly before takeoffs.

Seatbelts and shoulder harnesses will not work as intended if they are not in good shape. Frayed belts, twisted shoulder harnesses, and worn buckles just will not do the job. Be sure all belts and shoulder harnesses are in good shape. They will not last for the life of your aircraft. Consider replacing them from time to time.

Key terms

Dead reckoning
Circle of uncertainty
Single-line approach
Military training routes (MTRs)

Review questions

1. Why has dead reckoning largely become a lost art?
   How can it be a valuable aid to navigation?
   Describe the process of dead reckoning using winds aloft forecasts to determine true heading and groundspeed.
   What is the circle of uncertainty?
   Give an example of how one line of position (LOP) can be advanced to a second LOP to establish a fix.
   What is the single-line approach?
   Explain how this approach can be used by flying a radial or using a prominent landfall.

2. Which aircraft tend to have a higher incidence of fuel selector-related accidents?
   Why are some fuel selectors so complicated?
   What are the FAA certification standards for fuel selector valves?

3. What is the single-vacuum system?
   Why are many pilots unable to fly using a partial panel?
   How can impending failure of gyroscopic instruments be identified?
   Can airplanes be flown safely with loss of one or more gyroscopic instruments?

4. Describe some of the unique hazards of night flying.

   What should be included in a thorough preflight preparation for a night flight?

   What are some considerations that should be taken while en route and in preparation for landing?

5. What are the two basic types of military training routes (MTRs)?

   What information is needed by a pilot when his or her route intersects an MTR?

6. Where do most wire strikes occur?

   What are some of the reasons for wire strikes?

   How can wire-strike accidents be avoided?

7. What are some of the problems associated with conventional methods of restraining small children aboard aircraft?

   Should a typical safety seat designed for automobiles be used aboard aircraft?

   Why?

   What is a pilot's responsibility under FAR 91.14?

Ground operations and maintenance

Outline

Learning objectives

When you have finished this chapter, you should be able to:

△ List some of the precautions that should be taken while taxiing.

△ Describe several causes of propeller accidents.

△ Discuss the factors that must be considered in properly securing an aircraft.

△ Define gust locks and rudder locks.

△ Identify the types of maintenance that an owner-pilot can perform in accordance with FAR Part 43.

△ Summarize the items included in a typical general aviation airplane inspection checklist.

△ Describe the purpose and categories of airworthiness directives.

△ Discuss some of the causes and effects of exhaust system failures.

△ Discuss some of the precautions that should be taken to avoid fuel contamination.

△ List the recommended procedures during preflight to prevent fuel contamination.

Taxiing accidents

Learning to taxi an aircraft is one of the first operations a student pilot is taught. Unfortunately, we often forget some of the earliest lessons learned. A surprising number of accidents or incidents occur annually during taxi operations. Taxiing appears to be such an elementary operation that pilots become complacent and inattentive to ground control of the aircraft. Operating on the ground during higher than normal or gusty wind conditions or in close proximity to large and turbine-powered aircraft can be particularly hazardous for small general aviation aircraft. Taxiing off the side of runways and taxiways, running into potholes, striking runway marker lights, reflectors, etc., usually cause damage to landing gear and propellers, and also might result in an upset of the aircraft. Collisions with other taxiing or parked aircraft happen all too often. Explaining such mishaps to investigating authorities and an insurance company can be embarrassing because excuses for taxi accidents are seldom acceptable.

The following precautions should be taken while taxiing:

1. Taxi slowly enough that the aircraft will stop instantly when the brakes are applied or the aircraft will stop on its own when the throttles are closed.

2. Check your brakes before moving more than the length of the aircraft.

3. Keep a sharp lookout outside of the cockpit. This is not the time to be studying maps, running cockpit checklists, or copying ATC clearances.

4. If the clearance between objects looks too narrow, it probably is. Stop. Shut down and take a look or have someone on the ground guide you through. Always have a guide on the ground to assist you when it is necessary to taxi in congested areas.

5. Avoid taxiing behind or too closely to large and turbine-powered aircraft and be careful while taxiing under high-wind or gusty-wind conditions.

Propeller accidents

Hand-propping accidents, like taxiing accidents, just should not happen, but they do. Every year, too many persons ignore safety precautions and try to hand-start aircraft engines without having a qualified person at the controls. Every year many of these aircraft get away and collide with other aircraft or obstructions in their path. Regardless of what the aircraft runs into, the results will be the same: costly repairs. Hand-propping accidents also might result in serious or fatal injuries. Few people who have been struck by a turning propeller have escaped with minor injuries.

No one should attempt to start an aircraft engine without a qualified person at the cockpit controls. The person turning the propeller should be properly trained in the technique of hand-cranking. If you have in mind to try hand-propping by yourself, Don't. If you must hand-prop, get qualified help to position the engine controls and switches during the starting procedure. If hand-propping can be avoided, Do.

Another type of accident that happens too frequently occurs when enplaning or deplaning: passengers walk or run into spinning propellers or helicopter tail rotors. People not accustomed to being around aircraft might fail to see the rotating propeller and inadvertently step into the blade arc. Few survive. The engines should be shut down when enplaning and deplaning passengers unless there are qualified persons on the ramp capable of controlling pedestrian traffic to and from the aircraft.

Tying down your aircraft

Pilots who have encountered a sudden gust of wind just before touchdown know full well how truly vulnerable an airplane can be to strong wind conditions. An airplane sitting on the ground is susceptible to many of the same potentially destructive forces. Each year, numerous aircraft are damaged by windstorms because their owners are negligent, fail to heed adverse weather forecasts, or use improper tie-down procedures.

Sometimes, though, forecast conditions are so threatening that even the best tie-down procedures won't be effective. In these situations, the best protection against windstorm damage is to fly the aircraft out of the impending storm area—provided, of course, that you have sufficient warning time. The next best protective measure is to secure the aircraft in a stormproof hangar, or other suitable shelter.

These two optimum measures of protecting your aircraft against windstorm damage might not always be practical in your case. The remaining alternative is to ensure that the aircraft is tied down securely.

When securing your airplane, it is considered good practice to fasten all doors and windows properly, thereby preventing or minimizing damage inside the aircraft. An aircraft that rides through a storm with a window open might well have serious water damage to electrical systems and avionics equipment.

Engine openings (intake and cowling) should be covered to prevent entry of foreign matter. Pitot-static tubes also should be covered to prevent damage or entry of foreign matter.

In general, pilots should be prepared for the worst conceivable windstorm conditions: pouring rain, gusty winds from 30 mph and up, intermittent sheets of water blowing across runways, ramps, and parking areas, and lack of hangar facilities. With such conditions possible at nearly every airport in the country, owners should plan in advance by reading their aircraft manufacturer's charts and graphs denoting aircraft weights and relative wind velocities that would make varied tie-down procedures necessary for certain weather emergencies.

Any aircraft parking area should be equipped with three-point tie-downs. Aircraft should be tied down at the end of each flight to preclude damage from sudden storms, such as summertime squall lines. Depending upon the locations of fixed parking area mooring points, aircraft should be headed into the wind, or as nearly as possible.

There is more to properly securing an aircraft than many operators might realize. So let's review the whole subject, beginning with the parking area itself.

Tie-down anchors for single-engine aircraft should provide a minimum holding power of about 3000 lbs. each (4000 lbs. each for multi-engine aircraft). While this figure can easily be attained in a hard-surface ramp area of asphalt or concrete, the holding power can be altered or lost completely in rain-soaked, grass tie-down areas.

Most pilots will have to make do with whatever anchors are provided. However, if you have a doubt about the strength or security of the anchor, you should report it to the fixed-base operator. What purpose is served by otherwise properly tying down an aircraft only to have the anchor break free?

Tie-down ropes are just as crucial as the anchors. Ropes also should be capable of resisting a pull of about 3000 lbs. each (4000 lbs. for twins).

Ropes suitable for use as tie-downs fall into two basic classes: manila, and synthetic fiber, including nylon, Dacron, and yellow polypropylene.

Manila ropes are susceptible to rotting and attack by fungus. Also, their strength deteriorates with age, and they're susceptible to shrinkage when wet. They should be inspected periodically.

Nylon or Dacron ropes are preferred over manila rope because of their superior strength and durability. The problem with synthetic rope is the tendency for knots to loosen and slip. Extra care is required when using synthetic ropes, and knots that do not slip should be used.

Whatever the strength of the rope, if you don't tie a good knot, you've lost the battle. Common bowline or square knots give the best results and security.

When tying the knot, leave from 1 to 2 inches of slack. This slack allows the aircraft to move on its gear without tugging the anchors. It also prevents undue stress on the aircraft.

To obtain 3000 lbs. of tensile strength, manila rope requires a diameter of $1/2$ to $5/8$ inch, while nylon and Dacron need only $3/8$-inch and yellow polypropylene requires $1/2$-inch diameter. Incidentally, twisted Dacron or polypropylene is stronger than braided.

Chains are superior to rope of any kind. Never wrap chain, or rope for that matter, around a lift strut, landing gear strut, or the fuselage. When the aircraft rocks in the wind, surface metal could become damaged.

Just as important as tying the aircraft down properly is to install all control locks of the type and in the manner recommended by the manufacturer. Control or gust locks are provided on most aircraft to prevent the ailerons from slamming from stop to stop and the elevator from banging up and down. Rudder locks also are recommended on some aircraft. Make certain, though, that any control locks you use have red "Remove Before Flight" streamers so they're not overlooked during preflight.

If your aircraft has no aileron locks, you can secure the ailerons with the seatbelt. Wrap the belt around the control wheel or stick and put the control full back or nearly so. Then tighten the belt to a firm, snug setting.

Although it might seem natural to leave the brakes set during tie-down, check your pilot's operating handbook. Some aircraft do not have thermal expansion capability in the brake system. If it's hot outside, the brake fluid might expand to the point where O-rings and seals could be blown out of the wheel cylinders. Regardless of whether the brakes are engaged, put chocks around each main and, in the case of tricycle-type aircraft, the nosegear tire.

Commercially available portable tie-downs are highly recommended for trips to airports or landings strips that might not have permanent tie-downs available to transient aircraft.

Most portable tie-down kits have large, corkscrew-type stakes that require insertion into the ground by a twisting clockwise motion. A strong metal bar should be a part of this kit (although seldom included) for use in turning the anchor into the ground. Remember, portable tie-downs are not intended for use as permanent anchors.

In many parts of the country, severe weather warnings call for more extraordinary tie-down measures. The FAA has published an advisory circular—AC 20-35B—that details these tie-down methods.

Finally, there might be occasions when all the best tie-down procedures available aren't enough to do the job. If the weather is truly threatening to aircraft, as in the case of tornadoes or hurricanes, fly the aircraft out of the impending storm area, well in advance, if at all possible. Although that might seem to be a rather extraordinary action, the time and costs involved would be far less than the cost of the damage that could be caused by a severe storm.

Developing good tie-down habits does not require a great deal of a pilot's energies. However, in terms of the protection given an aircraft by being properly secured, the time and energy that is spent is well worth it.

Maintaining your aircraft

One of the most frequently cited types of accidents is engine failure or malfunction. Many of these accidents can be avoided through proper inspection and maintenance. As an owner-pilot, FAR Part 43 allows you to perform certain types of inspections and maintenance on your airplane. The following is a partial list of the things you can do. Appendix A of FAR Part 43 includes a more comprehensive list.

1. Repair or change ties and tubes.
2. Clean, grease, or replace landing-gear wheel bearings.
3. Add air or oil to landing-gear shock struts.
4. Replace defective safety wire and cotter keys.
5. Lubricate items not requiring disassembly (other than removal of nonstructural items such as cover plates, cowling, or fairings).
6. Replenish hydraulic fluid.
7. Refinish the exterior or interior of the aircraft (excluding balanced control surfaces) when removal or disassembly of any primary structure or operating system is not required.
8. Replace side windows and safety belts.

9. Replace seats or seat parts with approved replacement parts.
10. Replace bulbs, reflectors, and lenses of position and landing lights.
11. Replace cowling if removal of the propeller is not required.
12. Replace, clean, or set spark plug clearances.
13. Replace hose connections, except hydraulic connections.
14. Replace prefabricated fuel lines.
15. Replace the battery and check fluid level and specific gravity.

Although this work is allowed by FAR, each individual should make a self analysis as to whether or not he or she has the ability to perform the work satisfactorily.

If you do accomplish any of this work, you must make an entry in the appropriate logbook. The entry shall contain the following:

1. A description of the work performed (or references to data that is acceptable to the Administrator).
2. Date of completion.
3. Name of the person performing the work.
4. Signature, certificate number, and kind of certificate held by the person performing the work.

The signature constitutes approval for return to service only for work performed.

Inspection checklist

As a pilot, you can use the following checklist to conduct an inspection of a typical general aviation airplane.

Propeller—Inspect:

1. Spinner and back plate for cracks or looseness.
2. Blades for nicks or cracks.
3. Hub for grease or oil leaks.
4. Bolts for security and "safetying."

Engine:

1. Preflight engine.
2. Runup engine to warmup and check:
   • Magnetos for rpm drop and ground-out.
   • Mixture and throttle controls for operation and ease of movement.

- Propeller control for operation and ease of movement.
- Engine idle for proper rpm.
- Carburetor heat or alternate air.
- Alternator output under a load (landing light, etc., in the "on" position).
- Vacuum system (if installed) for output.
- Temperatures (CHT, oil, etc.) within proper operating range.
- Engine and electric fuel pumps for fuel flow or fuel pressure.
- Fuel selector, in all positions, for free and proper operation.

3. Remove engine cowling. Clean and inspect for cracks, loose fasteners, or damage.

4. Check engine oil for quantity and condition. Have oil and oil filter changed at 50-hour intervals by an FAA certified mechanic.

5. Inspect oil temperature "sensing" unit for leaks, security, and broken wires.

6. Inspect oil lines and fittings for condition, leaks and security, and evidence of chafing.

7. Inspect oil cooler for condition (damage, dirt and air blockage), security leaks, and winterization plate (if applicable).

8. Clean engine.

9. Remove, clean, and inspect spark plugs for wear. Regap and reinstall plugs, moving "top to bottom" and "bottom to top" of cylinders. Be sure to gap and torque plugs to manufacturer's specifications.

10. Inspect magnetos for security, cracks, and broken wires or insulation.

11. Inspect ignition harness for chafing, cracked insulation, and cleanliness.

12. Check cylinders for loose or missing nuts and screws, cracks around cylinder hold-down studs, and broken cooling fins.

13. Check rocker box covers for evidence of oil leaks and loose nuts or screws.

14. Remove air filter and tap gently to remove dirt particles.

15. Replace air filter.

16. Inspect all air-inlet ducts for condition (no air leaks, holes, etc.).

17. Inspect intake seals for leaks (fuel stains) and clamps for security.

18. Check the condition of priming lines and fittings for leaks (fuel stains) and clamps for security.

19. Inspect the condition of exhaust stacks, connections, clamps, gaskets, muffler, and heat box for cracks, security, condition, and leaks.

20. Inspect the condition of fuel lines for leaks (fuel stains) and security.
21. Drain at least one pint of fuel into a transparent container from the fuel filter and from the fuel tank sump to check for water or dirt contamination.
22. Visually inspect the vacuum pump and lines for missing nuts, cracked pump flanges, and security.
23. Inspect crankcase breather tubes and clamps for obstructions and security.
24. Inspect the crankcase for cracks, leaks, and missing nuts.
25. Inspect engine mounts for cracks or loose mountings.
26. Inspect engine baffles for cracks, security, and foreign objects.
27. Inspect wiring for security, looseness, broken wires, and the condition of insulation.
28. Inspect the firewall and firewall seals.
29. Inspect the generator or alternator belt for proper tension and fraying.
30. Inspect the generator (or alternator) and starter for security and safety of nuts and bolts.
31. Inspect the brake fluid for level and proper type.
32. Lubricate engine controls: propeller, mixture, throttle.
33. Inspect the alternate air source "door" or carburetor heat to ensure when the "door" is closed it has a good seal. Check "door" operation.
34. Reinstall the engine cowling.

Cabin—Inspect:

1. The cabin door, latch, and hinges for operation and worn door seals.
2. Upholstery for tears.
3. Seats, seatbelts, and adjustment hardware.
4. The trim operation for function and ease of movement.
5. Rudder pedals and toe brakes for operation and security.
6. The parking brake.
7. Control wheels, column, pulleys, and cables for security, operation, and ease of movement.
8. Lights for operation.
9. The heater and defroster controls for operation and ducts for condition and security.
10. Air vents for general condition and operation.

11. Plexiglas® in windshield, doors, and side windows for cracks, leaks, and crazing.

12. Instruments and lines for proper operation and security.

Fuselage and Empennage—Inspect:

1. The baggage door, latch, and hinges for security and operation, and the baggage door seal for wear.

2. The battery for water, corrosion, and security of cables.

3. Antenna mounts and electrical wiring for security and corrosion.

4. The hydraulic system for leaks, security, and fluid level.

5. ELT for security, switch position, and battery condition and age.

6. The rotating beacon for security and operation.

7. The stabilizer and control surfaces, hinges, linkages, trim tabs, cables, and balance weights for condition, cracks, frayed cables, loose rivets, etc.

8. Control hinges for appropriate lubrication.

9. Static parts for obstructions.

Wings—Inspect:

1. Wingtips for cracks, loose rivets, and security.

2. Position lights for operation.

3. Aileron and flap hinges and actuators for cleanliness and lubrication.

4. Aileron balance weights for cracks and security.

5. Fuel tanks, caps and vents, and placards for quantity and type of fuel.

6. The pitot or pitot-static for security and obstruction.

Landing Gear—Inspect:

1. The strut extension.

2. Scissors and nosegear shimmy damper for leaks and loose or missing bolts.

3. Wheels and tires for cracks, cuts, wear, and pressure.

4. Hydraulic lines for leaks and security.

5. The gear structure for cracks, loose or missing bolts, and security.

6. The retracting mechanism and gear door for loose or missing bolts and for abnormal wear.

7. Brakes for wear, security, and hydraulic leaks.

Functional Check Flight (FCF)—Check:

1. Brakes for proper operation during taxi.
2. The engine and propeller for power, smoothness, etc., during runup.
3. Engine instruments for proper reading.
4. Power output (on takeoff run).
5. Flight instruments.
6. The gear retraction and extension for proper operation and warning system.
7. The electrical system (lights; alternator output).
8. Flap operation.
9. Trim functions.
10. Avionics equipment for proper operation (including a VOR or VOT check for all VOR receivers).
11. The operation of the heater, defroster, ventilation and air conditioner.

General Items:

1. Ensure that all applicable airworthiness directives (ADs) have been met and properly recorded in the aircraft records.
2. Comply with applicable service bulletins and service letters.
3. See that the FAA-approved *Flight Manual* or *Pilot's Operating Handbook (POH)* is aboard and that all required placards are properly installed.
4. See that the Certificate of Airworthiness and aircraft registration are displayed and that the FCC license is aboard.
5. Verify that all FAA-required tests involving the transponder, the VOR, and the static system have been made and entered in the appropriate aircraft records.

Summary

It pays to take good care of your engine. Good maintenance is not cheap, but poor performance can be disastrously expensive. If you are unqualified or unable to do a particular needed job, depend on competent and certificated mechanics and use approved parts.

You can save money and have better understanding of your airplane if you participate in the maintenance yourself. If you do some of your own maintenance, do it properly. Make sure you complete the job you started.

Money, time, and effort spent on maintenance pays off with your airplane having a higher resale value. Remember, a well-cared-for airplane is a safe airplane if flown by a competent and proficient pilot. Maintain both your airplane and yourself in top-notch condition.

Airworthiness directives

Airworthiness directives (ADs) are required by law. One of the safety functions charged to the FAA is to require correction of unsafe conditions disclosed in any product, be it an aircraft, engine, propeller, or accessory. The medium used to provide notice and to require correction of the unsafe condition is the AD. The AD prescribes the conditions and limitations, including inspection, under which the product may continue to be operated.

ADs are published in the *Federal Register* and are generally mailed to the registered owner of the aircraft make and model affected. When an emergency condition exists, telegrams might be sent.

Depending on the seriousness of the unsafe condition, ADs are published in one of the following categories:

1. *Notice of Proposed Rulemaking*   An NPRM is issued when there is no emergency affecting air safety. Comments are invited from the public, and the notice may be changed or withdrawn. When an NPRM is adopted as a final rule, it is published in the *Federal Register* and sent to registered aircraft owners.

2. *Immediate Adopted Rule*   This is an AD of an urgent nature where prompt action is essential. It is issued without notice (NPRM) and is made effective less than 30 days after publication in the *Federal Register*.

3. *Emergency AD*   This type of AD is issued when an immediate action is required to correct an unsafe condition. Emergency ADs are distributed to the registered owners of the make and model affected, either by telegram or priority mail and are effective upon receipt.

On occasion, ADs are issued that apply to engines, propellers, and accessories (fuel pumps, magnetos, etc.). When the product can be identified as being installed on a specific make and model aircraft, AD distribution will be made to the registered owner.

There are times, however, when a determination cannot be made and direct distribution to the registered owner is impossible. For this reason, owners and pilots should subscribe to AD summary publications, available either from the federal government or a commercial source.

Each AD has an applicability statement specifying the product and, if applicable, the aircraft category to which it applies. ADs that are not specifically limited will apply to all models set forth in the applicability statement, regardless of category.

Some aircraft owners and operators are of the opinion that ADs are not applicable to aircraft certificated in certain categories, such as experimental or restricted. This is not true; if an AD does not specifically exempt a category, then the AD will apply to that category.

No person may operate a product to which an AD applies, unless it is operated in accordance with the requirements of the AD. It is understood that to *operate* does not apply only to the person who causes or authorizes the product to be used, such as the owner or lessee.

Compliance with emergency ADs could be a problem in the case of leased aircraft. The FAA has no other means available to make notification, other than the registered owner. For this reason, it is important that the owner make the information available to the operators of the aircraft in the most expeditious manner possible.

Compliance times specified in ADs are established from a safety standpoint and can be stated in numerous ways. Some ADs are of such a serious nature they might require compliance before further flight. Others might express compliance time in terms of a specific number of hours of operation, such as "compliance required within the next 50 hours time in service." Or compliance times might be expressed in terms of landings, such as "within the next 10 landings after the effective date of the AD."

When a direct relationship between airworthiness and calendar time is identified, a calendar date might be the limiting factor for compliance. Note also that because of the nature of the unsafe conditions, not all ADs have a one-time compliance, and repetitive inspections at periodic intervals after initial compliance might be required.

In some instances, owners are able to substantiate longer inspection intervals on the basis of accumulated service experience with their particular maintenance practices. In order to provide flexibility under these conditions, a statement might be included in the AD to permit reasonable adjustments in the intervals specified to allow compliance at an established inspection period of the owner.

The Federal Aviation Regulations require the person performing an annual inspection to provide the owner with a list of discrepancies, including noncompliance with ADs. The list and the entries should aid the owners and operators in meeting their responsibilities regarding AD compliance and recording. However, according to another FAR section, the owner or operator is primarily responsible for having ADs complied with and is responsible for ensuring that the appropriate entries are made in the aircraft maintenance records.

Finally, the FARs require each registered owner or operator to keep records of the current status of applicable ADs, including, for each, the method of compliance, the AD number and the amendment date. If the AD involves recurring action, the time and, if applicable, the date when the next action is required must be recorded.

Exhaust system failures

Some pilots probably do not give much thought to the exhaust systems of the aircraft they fly. However, accident statistics indicate that failure of this important aircraft component can result in disastrous consequences.

The upward trend in aircraft exhaust system failures over the past ten years is cause for serious concern among aviation safety experts. A review of accident/incident reports filed with the FAA indicates there have been numerous fatalities and injuries to pilots and passengers as a result of powerplant exhaust system failures.

Probable-cause factors have included occupants' incapacitation as a result of carbon monoxide poisoning, engine malfunctions or failures, engine nacelle compartment fires, or a combination of all three.

About half of exhaust system failures occur in the exhaust gas-to-air heat exchanger, resulting in carbon monoxide gas entering the cabin through the aircraft heater. The presence of exhaust gases in the cabin may affect the general efficiency of the pilot by causing impaired mental alertness, judgment, and reasoning, all of which contribute to or cause this type of accident. Far worse, of course, the odorless, colorless gas formed by the incomplete combustion of gasoline and other carbon-containing materials can kill unsuspecting victims.

One in every five exhaust system failures occurred in the exhaust stacks, manifolds, and tailpipes, introducing carbon monoxide gas, smoke, or fire into the aircraft cabin area.

With the same frequency, engine partial power loss and power failure resulted from internal muffler failure. Sheet metal baffles and/or defusers usually break off inside the muffler and completely or partially block the escape of exhaust gases from the engine cylinders. The severity of the power loss is proportional to the extent of the blockage.

A primary reason for most exhaust system failures is inadequate and infrequent inspections and lack of routine and preventive maintenance between inspections. Exhaust systems deteriorate because of engine operating temperatures, vibration that causes metal fatigue in areas of stress concentration, wear at joints and connections, engine backfiring, and unburned fuel in the muffler. All these conditions begin to take effect during the first hour of engine operation, and deterioration progresses through the lifespan of the exhaust system components.

Indications of cracked or leaking fatigue failures usually occur in any area of the system; however, the following are found to be the most likely problem areas:

- Exhaust manifold and stack fatigue failures usually occur at welded or clamp joints (e.g., exhaust stack flange, stack to manifold cross pipes, or muffler connections).

- Muffler and heat-exchanger failures usually occur on the inner wall surface. A proper inspection can be made only when the outer heat shield is removed. This inspection should be accomplished as recommended by the manufacturer or by a properly certified mechanic or repair station.

The owner/operator of an aircraft has the primary responsibility, as noted in the Federal Aviation Regulations, to ensure that, between required inspections, defects are repaired as prescribed in FAR Part 43. In the interest of safety, daily preflight inspections, including a thorough visual external inspection of the exhaust system, should be made.

Because of the design of some aircraft cowlings, an engine exhaust system might not be easily inspected as required. It is necessary, therefore, for these cowlings to be removed at frequent intervals and a detailed check performed.

Manufacturers' service bulletins, information letters, and maintenance manuals recommend when maintenance inspections should be performed. Persons doing these checks should have this information available to them. Use of a high-intensity light and telescoping, hinge-handle mirror is recommended to facilitate a good inspection/check.

Visually inspect the following external components of the exhaust system:

1. Muffler and heat exchanger for general condition and leaks.
2. Leaking exhaust stack gaskets (blown gaskets).
3. Loose or broken clamp connections, attachments, and stacks.
4. Cracked or broken stacks and tailpipes.
5. Dented stacks.
6. Cracks adjacent to welded areas and stack bends.
7. Thinning of joint areas due to vibrational wear.
8. Metal pitting due to internal erosion by combustion products.
9. Turbo supercharger (if installed).

In addition, carefully inspect the firewall seal(s) to ensure that the exhaust gases will not enter the cabin area. The engine compartment also should be free of combustible material and oil to reduce the possibility of a fire hazard.

Exhaust leaks and/or cracks are indicated by a gray-white or sooty-black streak or discoloration of the heat interchanger jacket. An excessive engine rpm drop noted during application of carburetor heat is also an indication of a cracked or leaking heat exchanger.

Any time exhaust fumes are detected in the cabin, immediately shut off the cabin heat control, open a fresh air vent, and land as soon as practical. Repair, replacement, and inspection must be recorded as provided by the FARs.

In the final analysis, it is the responsibility of the pilot to detect and correct any safety hazard that lurks in an aircraft exhaust system. The place to deal with those problems is on the ground—during a thorough preflight inspection—and not in the air.

Fuel contamination

Each year, numerous aircraft are inadvertently filled with fuel of the wrong octane or fuel contaminated by water, sand, rust, or fuel additives. When this situation is discovered during preflight, fuel tanks often must be drained before flight. Costly damage can occur. On some occasions, aircraft accidents are caused by improper or contaminated fuel. All of these incidents and accidents are preventable.

Close attention to compatibility of fuel and aircraft, along with faithful adherence to good housekeeping, is necessary to prevent possible disaster, as well as costly contamination. At all times, however, be certain to refer to the pilot's operating handbook for the aircraft you are flying to be absolutely certain of the proper fuel type(s) that can be used.

A review of accidents attributed to fuel problems reveals that many power failures were due to the use of improper fuel or careless servicing. The latter category includes fueling aircraft from poorly filtered tanks, particularly small tanks or drums; improper mixing of fuel additives; improper preflight action by the pilot; and storing of aircraft with partially filled tanks (which invites condensation and water contamination). The frequency of improper fueling will diminish if operators and personnel refueling aircraft maintain vigilance. The FARs require that aircraft fuel filler openings be marked to show the word FUEL and the minimum fuel grade or designation for the engine(s). In order that these markings retain their effectiveness, regulations also require that they be kept fresh and clean.

It is equally important that tank vehicles be most conspicuously marked to show the type of fuel carried. Likewise, tank vehicle hose lines should be marked.

Never allow a fuel grade lower than that specified for normal operation to be used. Some manufacturers will permit the next highest grade to be used for specific periods. Again, always check your POH.

Never use automotive fuel. The use of auto gas in aircraft is not recommended by aircraft manufacturers for a variety of reasons. The practice might void certain warranties and insurance. Although automobile fuels might be labeled "80 octane and higher," the FAA and the aircraft/engine manufacturers warn pilots that automobile gasoline must not be used in aircraft engines. The FAA advises that the octane numbers for automobile gasoline are not valid for aviation use because different methods are used to rate aviation gasoline. Thus, engine damage could be caused by pre-ignition and detonation. Since automobile gasoline has a much higher vapor pressure, the FAA says that bubbles could form in the fuel lines of aircraft operated at high altitudes and/or high temperatures. Vapor lock in flight could cause an engine failure.

Additives in automotive fuels, according to the FAA, are not compatible with aircraft engines, and could cause corrosion and valve failure. The FAA also notes that automotive gasoline has a shorter storage life than aviation gasoline, so it could become gummy and/or lose some of its octane rating while stored in an aircraft's tank.

Spark plug fouling

In most cases spark plug fouling can be reduced or eliminated by simply applying proven operating techniques. For example, low operating temperatures coupled with rich fuel mixtures result in incomplete vaporization of the tetraethyl lead in the combustion chamber, causing lead fouling of the spark plugs. Maintaining proper cylinder-head temperatures will minimize plug fouling problems.

Be certain that maintenance personnel have installed the spark plugs recommended for the particular engine installation. Have the carburetor idle mixture checked and adjusted. Use recommended leaning techniques in cruise condition at all altitudes. Avoid low-power letdowns, descend with power, and avoid over-rich conditions. Carburetors and fuel injectors are normally set slightly rich in the close throttle position, so it is best to carry a slight amount of power on landing approaches, rather than approach with closed throttle. Keep the cylinder temperatures in the normal range during operation.

After flight or ground operations, before shutdown, advance the throttle to about 1800 rpm for 15 to 20 seconds to clear the plugs and combustion chambers, retard the throttle to about 1200 rpm, and shut the engine off immediately with the mixture control. You should not have plug fouling or misfiring on your next startup.

As long as you make sure the aircraft is serviced with the proper fuel, check the sumps for contaminants, operate the engine according to the aircraft owners manual, and have the spark plugs serviced as recommended, you should not have plug fouling problems.

Turbine fuel

Occasionally, aircraft are inadvertently serviced with the wrong type of fuel, and in most instances it is because of misleading signs. For example, certain turbo-supercharged reciprocating powered aircraft have paint designs with the word TURBO conspicuously displayed on the vertical stabilizer or on the engine nacelle. Line service personnel assumed this to mean turbo-jet and filled the tanks with jet fuel. Another incident involved an air carrier type aircraft that was originally equipped with reciprocating engines, which most operators converted to turbo-props. The service personnel assumed the aircraft was a converted model when it wasn't.

Reciprocating engines may run briefly on jet fuel, but detonation and overheating will soon cause power failure. So, beware of getting jet fuel when you need avgas. Avgas is no substitute for jet fuel, either. The engine failure caused by running the turbine engine on the wrong fuel might not be as sudden, but prolonged operation on gasoline will severely damage the engine by the lead content and differing combustion ranges of the fuel. Time limitations for use of avgas in turbine engines are listed in the airplane or rotorcraft flight manual.

Preflight

If the wrong type of fuel is ever used, consult your certified aircraft and power-plant mechanic before operating the aircraft. It could be that the fuel can be burned under certain operating conditions. In other instances, it might have to be drained from the tanks, lines, and fuel system completely.

Always try to remain with your aircraft as it's being refueled. By doing so, you can personally ensure that the proper fuel is being pumped on board. After refueling, check the color again. Remember, the truck or tank you are refueling from might have the wrong kind of fuel in it. Reseat the filler cap securely. Don't trust the linesman to do it for you. When your aircraft is being filled in less than optimum conditions, such as during a snowfall or a day when wind might kick up dust and dirt, be especially cautious.

During preflight, visually drain and inspect all fuel samples in accordance with the aircraft manufacturer's recommended procedure. Generally, water and other contaminants will settle to the bottom of the fuel tank where the drains and sumps are located. Be suspicious of drains that don't drain properly; they might be partially obstructed. The following procedures are recommended:

1. Use only the fuel recommended by the engine and aircraft manufacturer.
2. Do not use fuel additives that have not been approved by the FAA. Follow mixing instructions carefully and to the letter.
3. If feasible, keep fuel tanks full. Water condenses on the walls of partially filled tanks and enters the fuel system.
4. Filter all fuel entering the tank.
5. Drain fuel sumps regularly.
6. Periodically inspect and clean the fuel strainer (screens) and occasionally have the carburetor bowl flushed as recommended by the aircraft manufacturer.

The damage and accidents caused by improper fuel grade or contaminated fuel are almost always avoidable. Proper preflight inspection and general maintenance can greatly reduce the problem of fuel contamination.

Key terms

Tie-down anchors
Tie-down roper
Control or gust locks
Rudder locks

Airworthiness Directives (ADs)
Notice of Proposed Rule Making (NPRM)
Immediate Adopted Rule
Emergency AD

Review questions

1. What are some common sense precautions that should be taken while taxiing?
    Describe several causes of propeller accidents.

2. Describe several good practices when securing your airplane.
    Describe the various types of tie-down ropes, including the advantages and
    disadvantages of each.
    What are *control* or *gust locks* and *rudder locks*?
    Should the brakes be set during tie-down? Explain.
    Can portable tie-downs be used as permanent anchors?

3. As an owner-pilot, what are some of the things you can do to maintain your
    aircraft?
    Describe some of the items included in an inspection checklist of a typical gen-
    eral aviation airplane.

4. What are airworthiness directives (ADs)?
    Describe the three categories of ADs.
    Do ADs apply to lessees of aircraft?

5. Where do most of the exhaust system failures occur?
    What is the primary cause?
    Which external components of the exhaust system should be visually
    inspected?

6. How can fuel become contaminated?
    Can grades of fuel lower than the recommended kind be used on occasion?
    Automobile fuels? Additives to automobile fuels? Explain.
    How can spark plug fouling be reduced or eliminated?
    List some precautions that can be taken during preflight to avoid fuel contami-
    nation.

Study guide

This study guide is designed to assist you in learning the material covered in the text. It contains close to 400 objective questions, including multiple choice, true-false, matching, and fill-in. Answers to all these questions are located at the end of each section.

Chapter 1 General aviation safety analysis
Multiple Choice   Circle the letter that corresponds to the best answer.

1. The general aviation aircraft accident rate during the 1980s:

  a. was not particularly good.
  b. rose between 1980 and 1985 and then fell for the remainder of the decade.
  c. fell throughout the decade.
  d. remained about the same throughout the decade.

2. A serious injury includes all of the following, except:

  a. hospitalization for more than 48 hours.
  b. death within 60 days.
  c. injury to any internal organ.
  d. second- or third-degree burns.

3. Most general aviation aircraft accidents result in:

   a. no injuries.
   b. fatalities.
   c. serious injuries.
   d. minor injuries.

4. Which of the following kinds of flying has the lowest accident rate?

   a. Business
   b. Corporate/Executive
   c. Aerial Application
   d. Instructional

5. The second most common broad cause/factor of all fatal accidents in 1987 was:

   a. the pilot.
   b. weather.
   c. systems failure.
   d. runway condition.

6. According to accident statistics, the most hazardous phase of flight is:

   a. takeoff.
   b. cruise.
   c. approach.
   d. landing.

7. Which of the following statements concerning recurrency training is correct?

   a. To carry passengers, a pilot must have completed at least six takeoffs and landings in the preceding 90 days.
   b. Instrument-rated pilots must log at least six hours of instrument time every three months to stay current.
   c. Flight instructors are given wide discretion over the content, scope, and direction of instrument competency checks.
   d. None of the above.

8. The FAA minimum requirement of three takeoffs and landings in the past 90 days:

   a. is appropriate for all single-engine aircraft.
   b. is recognized as a bare minimum for single-engine fixed-gear aircraft.

c. does not apply to single-engine retractable gear aircraft.
d. applies to all aircraft operated by private pilots.

9. Accident Prevention Program Managers (APPMs):

a. investigate general aviation aircraft accidents.
b. conduct safety clinics and aircraft seminars.
c. issue airworthiness directives.
d. do all of the above.

10. The Accident Prevention Program is based on the fact that general aviation accidents can be prevented or the accident rate reduced:

a. by recommending more regulations.
b. through increased training requirements.
c. through airman education.
d. by restricting airspace to qualified pilots.

11. APPMs do all of the following, except:

a. work closely with aviation organizations to identify potential safety problems.
b. manage the FAA's Remedial Training Program.
c. conduct aviation safety seminars.
d. perform safety inspections at flight schools and maintenance training facilities.

True/False   Circle "T" if the statement is true; "F," if it is false.

T   F   1. A fatal accident results in death within 30 days.

T   F   2. Single-engine airplanes were involved in over 80 percent of the general aviation accidents in 1987.

T   F   3. The fatal accident rate for instructional flying is higher than personal and business flying.

T   F   4. In 1987, the pilot was found to be a broad cause/factor in over 80 percent of all accidents.

T   F   5. During the 1990s, more attention will be directed toward airframes and powerplants and less on human factors.

T   F   6. Human factors include such things as judgment, risk assessment, decision making, and stress reduction.

T   F   7. It has been established that the pilot has very little impact on weather-related accidents.

T   F   8. The biggest percent of landing accidents occur during touch-down.

T   F   9. The initial climb is the most hazardous portion of takeoff.

T   F   10. The FARs are more concerned with the initial training than recurrency or proficiency training.

T   F   11. Proficiency in using avionics equipment has not been given a great priority in recurrency training.

T   F   12. More than 50 percent of all general aviation accidents occur on or within 5 miles of airports.

T   F   13. The average age of the general aviation aircraft fleet is actually decreasing with the introduction of so many foreign models in recent years.

T   F   14. Accident Prevention Program Managers (APPMs) are volunteer counselors located throughout the country.

T   F   15. Accident Prevention Counselors are paid by the FAA for the hours in which they conduct seminars and workshops.

Chapter 1   Answers
Multiple Choice

1. c	6. d	11. d
2. b	7. c	
3. a	8. b	
4. b	9. b	
5. b	10. c	

True/False

1. T	6. T	11. T
2. T	7. F	12. T
3. F	8. F	13. F
4. T	9. T	14. F
5. F	10. T	15. F

Chapter 2   Physiological factors

Multiple Choice   Circle the letter that corresponds to the best answer.

1. The best advice for a pilot with a cold or flu is to:
   a. fly at higher altitudes where pressure on the eustachian tube in the ear is lower.
   b. rely on cold remedies and prescriptions by physicians only.
   c. use ear plugs.
   d. stay on the ground.

2. Some of the dangers of taking medication while flying include:

   a. nausea and vertigo.
   b. the unknown effect of high altitude or G forces on such medications.
   c. the violation of FARs.
   d. all of the above.

3. The shortage of oxygen in the body can result in:

   a. emphysema.
   b. hypoglycemia.
   c. hypoxia.
   d. circadian rhythm.

4. Oxygen deficiency can result in all of the following symptoms, except:
   a. drowsiness.
   b. false sense of security.
   c. nausea.
   d. dull headache.

5. Hyperventilation can cause:

   a. liver and kidney problems.
   b. a concentration of glucose in the bloodstream.
   c. a sense of euphoria.
   d. blurring of vision.

6. Which of the following statements is correct?

   a. FAR Parts 121 and 135 require the flightcrew to use supplementary oxygen at cabin altitudes above 10,000 feet.
   b. Above an altitude of 40,000 feet, oxygen must be delivered under "positive pressure."
   c. FAR Part 91 requires supplementary oxygen at altitudes above 8000 feet.
   d. *a* and *b* are correct.

7. The most commonly used oxygen system in piston-engine general aviation aircraft is the:

   a. ambient flow system.
   b. continuous flow system.
   c. demand system.
   d. pressure demand system.

8. Carbon monoxide:

   a. is easily detected because of its distinctive odor.
   b. affects the brain and body tissue.
   c. can be eliminated from the body after 5 to 10 minutes' exposure to fresh air.
   d. cannot be detected through the use of technology.

9. A pilot's inability to correctly perceive his position, attitude, and motion relative to the center of the earth is referred to as:

   a. acute skill fatigue.
   b. hypoglycemia.
   c. spatial disorientation.
   d. psychological stress.

10. Which of the following actions would not be appropriate in the event of motion sickness?

    a. Close up the air vents.
    b. Loosen clothing.
    c. Use supplemental oxygen.
    d. Keep the eyes on a point outside the airplane.

11. All of the following can assist in avoiding spatial disorientation, except:

    a. becoming familiar with unique geographical conditions in the areas to be flown.
    b. maintain visual flight when flying at night.
    c. check weather forecasts before departure.
    d. rely on instruments unless the natural horizon or surface reference is clearly visible.

12. The most immediate harmful effect of tobacco smoking is:

    a. carbon monoxide.
    b. nicotine.

c. tar.

d. stress.

13. The effects of a hangover can be alleviated by all of the following, except:

    a. eating a well-balanced meal.

    b. consuming large quantities of nonalcoholic fluids.

    c. breathing 100 percent oxygen.

    d. sleep.

14. Which of the following drugs is a stimulant?

    a. Antihistamines.

    b. Amphetamines.

    c. Barbiturates.

    d. Tranquilizers.

15. Antihistamines present in most common-cold compounds can cause:

    a. prolonged periods of wakefulness.

    b. hypoglycemia.

    c. a sense of euphoria.

    d. drowsiness.

16. Missing meals or substituting a quick snack and coffee for a balanced meal can lead to:

    a. hypoxia.

    b. hypoglycemia.

    c. hyperventilation.

    d. a hangover.

17. Acute skill fatigue can be caused by:

    a. obesity.

    b. caffeine and amphetamines.

    c. monotony and psychological stress.

    d. too much sleep.

True/False   Circle "T" if the statement is true; "F," if it is false.

T   F   1. A common cold is really no problem for pilots, provided they are taking proper medication.

T   F   2. Infection of the inner ear by a flu virus can cause vertigo.

T   F   3.   Two drugs taken at the same time occasionally cancel each other or render each other more potent.

T   F   4.   Oxygen starvation is generally lessened the longer a pilot remains at a given altitude, or at a higher altitude.

T   F   5.   A pilot actually can feel more confident in his or her flying ability while experiencing hypoxia.

T   F   6.   FAR Part 91 states that exposure to altitudes above 10,000 feet up to and including 12,500 feet for periods of more than 45 minutes duration require supplementary oxygen.

T   F   7.   Most pressurized aircraft have cabin altitudes equivalent to sea-level pressure.

T   F   8.   The continuous-flow oxygen system provides flightcrew members protection at altitudes above 40,000 feet.

T   F   9.   Aviation and medical oxygen systems are basically the same.

T   F   10.   Passengers with significant circulatory or lung problems might need to use supplemental oxygen at lower altitudes.

T   F   11.   Aircraft heaters are a common source of carbon monoxide poisoning.

T   F   12.   There are several types of relatively inexpensive carbon monoxide detectors available on the market.

T   F   13.   Spatial disorientation to a pilot means simply the inability to tell "which way is up."

T   F   14.   Pilots who are susceptible to airsickness should take preventive drugs, which are available over the counter or by prescription.

T   F   15.   Marital, financial, personal problems, tobacco smoking, and alcohol can cause stress but are not significant factors affecting safety.

T   F   16.   Cigarette smoking causes a relative deprivation of oxygen to the heart muscle and contributes to circulatory problems.

T   F   17. Walking, drinking black coffee, or taking a cold shower can help eliminate alcohol from the body.

T   F   18. Mild intoxication is present when the blood alcohol level is 0.15 to 0.20 percent.

T   F   19. The effect of a hangover probably constitutes a more significant flight safety hazard than does the mild intoxication state of alcohol ingestion.

T   F   20. Codeine is a cough suppressant found in many common cough syrups.

T   F   21. Antihistamines delay the onset of fatigue, resulting in the popular name "pep pill."

T   F   22. Hypoglycemia is caused by consuming large amounts of caffeine.

T   F   23. Physical fitness is the same as muscle conditioning.

T   F   24. *Circadian rhythm* refers to an internal "biological clock."

Matching Select the letter on the right that corresponds to the description on the left.

_____ 1. Vertigo

_____ 2. Hypoxia

_____ 3. Hyperventilation

_____ 4. Hypoglycemia

_____ 5. Motion sickness

_____ 6. Circadian rhythm

_____ 7. Acute skill fatigue

_____ 8. Tranquilizers

_____ 9. Psychological stress

_____ 10. Amphetamines

a. Relieves tension and anxiety

b. Timing of biological functions

c. Sense of balance is disturbed

d. Produces an elevation of mood and a feeling of well-being

e. Mental confusion and difficulty in concentrating

f. Spatial disorientation

g. Abnormal breathing

h. Lack of glucose in the bloodstream

i. Loss of strength, coordination, or attention to details

j. Oxygen starvation

Chapter 2   Answers
Multiple Choice

1. d	6. d	11. b	16.b
2. d	7. b	12. a	17.c
3. c	8. b	13. c	
4. c	9. c	14. b	
5. d	10. a	15. d	

True/False

1. F	6. F	11. T	16. T	21. F
2. T	7. F	12. T	17. F	22. F
3. T	8. F	13. T	18. F	23. F
4. F	9. F	14. F	19. T	24. T
5. T	10. T	15. F	20. T	

Matching

1. f	6. b
2. j	7. i
3. g	8. a
4. h	9. e
5. c	10. d

Chapter 3   Flight planning

Multiple Choice   Circle the letter that corresponds to the best answer.

1. Density altitude is affected by all of the following factors, except:

    a. altitude.
    b. humidity.
    c. temperature.
    d. wind direction and speed.

2. An increase in density altitude results in:

    a. decreased landing roll distance.
    b. decreased true airspeed on approach and landing.
    c. reduced rate of climb.
    d. decreased takeoff distance.

3. Which of the following statements is correct?

    a. The published performance criteria in the pilot's operating handbook is generally based on standard atmospheric conditions at sea level.
    b. Density altitude effects are always confined to mountain areas.
    c. Humidity is considered a major factor in density altitude.
    d. An increase in density altitude decreases landing roll distance.

4. The product of the weight of an item multiplied by its arm, expressed in inch-pound is called:

    a. datum line.
    b. center of gravity.
    c. moment.
    d. useful load.

5. An aircraft's empty weight includes all of the following, except:

    a. special equipment
    b. hydraulic fluid.
    c. drainable oil.
    d. undrainable (residual) oil.

6. Balance refers to:

    a. a location in the aircraft identified by a number designating its distance in inches from the datum.
    b. the location of the c.g. along the longitudinal axis of the aircraft.
    c. an imaginary vertical plane or line from which all measurements of arm are taken.
    d. the distance between the forward and aft c.g. limits.

7. The actual location of the c.g. is determined by a number of factors under the control of the pilot. They include:

    a. placement of baggage and cargo.
    b. assignment of seats to passengers according to each individual's weight.
    c. fuel load.
    d. all of the above.

8. Which of the following statements is not correct?

 a. The loaded c.g. is determined by dividing the total moment by total weight.
 b. Useful load includes the weight of the baggage, usable fuel, and drainable oil.
 c. The weight and balance of your aircraft should be checked monthly.
 d. The loaded c.g. should be within the fore and aft c.g. limits—shown in the aircraft flight manual.

9. Suppose you have fuel to fly for three hours at 160 kts true airspeed. The trip is 300 nm and the headwind is forecast to be 70 kts. Your fuel reserve is:

 a. 15 min.
 b. 30 min.
 c. 45 min.
 d. 60 min.

10. A 90-degree crosswind will:

 a. increase the takeoff distance.
 b. decrease the takeoff distance.
 c. have a negligible effect on takeoff distance.
 d. have an indeterminable effect on takeoff distance.

11. Pilot operating handbooks for light aircraft include takeoff and landing runway length required using a new airplane flown by a(n):

 a. average pilot under average conditions.
 b. average pilot under good conditions.
 c. competent pilot under average conditions.
 d. competent pilot under good conditions.

12. If power loss occurs just after liftoff:

 a. try to return to the airport.
 b. raise the nose to gain altitude.
 c. lower the nose to maintain proper airspeed then land as straight ahead as possible.
 d. select an open field in which to land or possibly make a 180-degree turn to the airport.

True/False   Circle "T" if the statement is true; "F," if it is false.

T F 1. The pilot owner's manual must be carried aboard the aircraft according to federal regulations.

T F 2. Knowing your own capabilities is just as important as knowing the capabilities of your aircraft.

T F 3. High-density altitude and high humidity are often directly related.

T F 4. Density altitude is basically the same as pressure altitude.

T F 5. At airports of higher elevations, high temperatures can make operations particularly hazardous during midday hours.

T F 6. A pilot's first reference for aircraft performance information is the Koch Chart.

T F 7. Weight and balance should be checked by the pilot at least once every six months.

T F 8. All general aviation aircraft are designed so that all seats can be occupied, a full load of baggage can be carried, along with full fuel, and remain within approved weight and balance center of gravity limits.

T F 9. The distance between the forward and aft c.g. limits is called the *datum line*.

T F 10. There are forward and aft limits beyond which the c.g. should not be located for flight.

T F 11. The weight and balance information for each aircraft must be amended when repairs or alterations have been made that affect a change in the aircraft empty weight or c.g. location.

T F 12. Aircraft stability decreases as the c.g. moves aft.

T F 13. The slower the airplane, the more difficult it is to calculate time en route.

T F 14. Range charts are based on still air.

T F 15. Suppose you have fuel to fly for three hours under day, VFR conditions at 160 kts true airspeed. The trip is 400 nm and the headwind is forecast to be 10 kts. This will leave a fuel reserve of 20 minutes.

T F 16. A headwind will increase your overall takeoff distance.

T F 17. Ground effect makes it possible to lift off at too high a pitch angle, or too soon with a heavy load.

T F 18. Taking off too soon, at possibly too steep an attitude, might cause a stall.

T F 19. To be on the safe side on takeoff, triple the published length of runway needed to climb to 50 feet.

T F 20. If you experience a power loss after sufficient altitude has been gained, always complete a 180-degree turn and return to the airport from which you departed.

Fill-in   Complete the following sentence.

1. The aircraft performance characteristics adversely affected by overweight are:

a. _____   f. _____

b. _____   g. _____

c. _____   h. _____

d. _____   i. _____

e. _____   j. _____

Chapter 3   Answers
Multiple Choice

1. d	6. b	11. d
2. c	7. d	12. c
3. a	8. c	
4. c	9. b	
5. c	10. c	

True/False

1. T	6. F	11. T	16. F
2. T	7. F	12. T	17. T
3. F	8. F	13. T	18. T
4. F	9. F	14. T	19. F
5. T	10. T	15. T	20. F

Fill-in

1. a. increased takeoff speed
    b. increased takeoff runway length
    c. rate of climb
    d. maximum altitude capability
    e. operational range
    f. maneuverability
    g. controllability
    h. stall speed
    i. approach speed
    j. landing distance

Chapter 4   Weather briefings and icing

Multiple Choice   Circle the letter that corresponds to the best answer.

1. In order to complete a preflight weather briefing, you should inform the briefer of your:

    a. qualifications; e.g., student, private, commercial, and whether instrument rated.
    b. flying hours during the past 90 days.
    c. home airport.
    d. flying hours under instrument conditions.

2. A Standard Preflight Briefing includes all of the following, except:

    a. adverse conditions.
    b. NOTAMs.
    c. synopsis.
    d. barometric pressure.

3. Adverse conditions in a Standard Preflight Briefing would include such things as:

    a. winds aloft and temperature.
    b. NOTAMs.
    c. low ceilings and icing.
    d. PIREPs.

4. _____ are issued for specific airports and generally cover a 5-nautical-mile radius from the center of the runway complex.

   a. Area Forecasts
   b. Center Weather Advisory
   c. Terminal Forecasts
   d. SIGMETs

5. Terminal forecasts include all of the following, except:

   a. expected ceilings.
   b. air traffic advisories.
   c. cloud heights.
   d. obstructions to vision.

6. Winds and temperatures aloft forecasts:

   a. contain upper air velocity and temperature forecasts for some 160 locations in 48 states.
   b. cover a 5-nautical-mile radius from the center of the runway complex.
   c. are specific aviation weather observations taken at designated reporting sites throughout the United States.
   d. cover a broad geographical area, giving general descriptions of weather conditions.

7. SIGMETS:

   a. concern weather of less severity than AIRMETS.
   b. provide in-flight weather advisories.
   c. warn of severe and extreme weather conditions.
   d. are issued for specific airports.

8. A good PIREP should include all of the following, except:

   a. visibility restrictions.
   b. turbulence and icing.
   c. outside air temperature.
   d. all of the above.

9. The average number of thunderstorm days per year is greatest in which part of the country?

   a. Northeast.
   b. Southeast.
   c. Midwest.
   d. Southwest.

10. When rain droplets can no longer be supported by the updraft within a cumulus cloud, this marks the beginning of the:

    a. cumulus stage.
    b. mature stage.
    c. dissipating stage.
    d. high-moisture stage.

11. Windshear:

    a. is a change in wind speed and/or direction over a short distance.
    b. is a tremendous updraft during a thunderstorm.
    c. results out of limited-state thunderstorms.
    d. marks the beginning of the mature stage of a thunderstorm.

12. The most hazardous form of windshear is generally encountered in:

    a. frontal activity.
    b. thunderstorms.
    c. temperature inversions.
    d. surface obstructions.

13. Flying in snow, sleet, rain, or clouds is conducive to the formation of:

    a. impact induction ice.
    b. fuel ice.
    c. throttle ice.
    d. fuselage ice.

14. Fuel icing:

    a. primarily occurs while flying in snow, sleet, or rain.
    b. generally occurs with temperatures above 70°.
    c. generally occurs with relative humidity above 80 percent.
    d. is formed at or near a partially closed throttle.

15. Which of the following statements concerning carburetor heat is not correct?

    a. Carburetor heat should be applied before throttling back for descent.
    b. Carburetor heat should be on the pretakeoff checklist to test its effectiveness.
    c. Carburetor heat should be applied for full-power operations such as takeoffs and emergency go-arounds.
    d. If the relative humidity is above 50 percent and the temperature is below 70°F, apply carburetor heat immediately before takeoff.

True/False   Circle "T" is the statement is true; "F," if it is false.

T   F   1. *TIBS* is the acronym for Traffic Information Broadcast System.

T   F   2. So that your preflight weather briefing can be tailored to your needs, you should give the briefer your proposed route, but not necessarily your altitude.

T   F   3. A Standard Preflight Briefing includes current NOTAMs.

T   F   4. An Abbreviated Briefing might be called for when you need only one or two specific items.

T   F   5. You should request an Outlook Briefing whenever your proposed time of departure is 24 or more hours from the time of the briefing.

T   F   6. An in-flight briefing can be obtained by tuning to Flight Watch on 122.0 MHz below FL 180.

T   F   7. It is best to allow more margin for weather at night.

T   F   8. MVFR CIG HK means ceiling 3000 to 5000 feet height and smoke.

T   F   9. Sequence weather reports are 6-hour aviation forecasts plus a 1-hour categorical outlook giving general descriptions of cloud cover and weather conditions.

T   F   10. Terminal forecasts are issued six times a day based on the time zone in which the forecast office is located.

T   F   11. AIRMETS concern weather of less severity than Convective SIGMETS.

T   F   12. The best way to get PIREPs into the system is via Flight Watch.

T   F   13. The main feature of the cumulus cloud that will develop into a thunderstorm is the predominate updraft.

T   F   14. Most cumulus clouds become thunderstorms.

T   F   15. A steady-state thunderstorm cell often contains hail.

T   F   16. Hail and violent turbulence can be encountered within 20 miles of very strong thunderstorms.

T   F   17. Windshear is associated with weather fronts moving at a speed of at least 10 kts.

T   F   18. Gusty winds and downdrafts are associated with windshear arising out of thunderstorms.

T   F   19. Horizontal windshears generally have the most serious effect on aircraft.

T   F   20. Windshear is most critical when encountered at low altitudes.

T   F   21. Most carburetor or induction icing accidents occur during climbout.

T   F   22. Visible moisture in the air is necessary to cause fuel icing.

Fill-In   Complete the following sentences.

1. A Standard Preflight Weather Briefing includes the following elements:

   a. _____   e. _____

   b. _____   f. _____

   c. _____   g. _____

   d. _____

2. The four common sources of low-level windshear are:

   a. _____   c. _____

   b. _____   d. _____

Chapter 4 Answers
Multiple Choice

1. a	6. a	11. a
2. d	7. c	12. b
3. c	8. d	13. a
4. c	9. b	14. c
5. b	10. b	15. c

True/False

1. F	6. T	11. T	16. T	21. T
2. F	7. T	12. T	17. F	22. F
3. T	8. F	13. T	18. T	
4. T	9. F	14. F	19. F	
5. F	10. F	15. T	20. T	

Fill-In

1. a. Adverse conditions
   b. Synopsis
   c. Current conditions
   d. Enroute forecast
   e. Destination forecast
   f. Winds aloft
   g. Notice to Airmen (NOTAMs)

2. a. Frontal activity
   b. Thunderstorms
   c. Temperature inversions
   d. Surface obstructions

Chapter 5   Winter weather operations

Multiple Choice   Circle the letter that corresponds to the best answer.

1. Icing will occur in flight when:

   a. the air temperature is below freezing.
   b. some liquid water is present.
   c. the sizes of the droplets are large enough to strike an aircraft component.
   d. all of the above.

2. Which of the following statements is not correct?

   a. There is a lower rate of ice accretion per unit area on blunt objects with a large radius of curvature.
   b. Ice will build up twice as fast in cumulus clouds.
   c. The rate of ice accumulation increases as penetration airspeed increases.
   d. Ice accretion amount or size is primarily a function of aircraft speed and humidity in the air.

3. _____ is most likely to form when descending from subfreezing air into a warm, moist layer.

   a. Rime ice.
   b. Clear ice.
   c. Frost.
   d. Glaze ice.

4. The following classifications are used when reporting ice accumulation:

   a. Trace, Light, and Heavy.
   b. Light, Moderate, and Heavy.
   c. Trace, Light, Moderate, and Severe.
   d. Trace, Moderate, Severe, and Heavy.

5. Structural icing increases:

   a. draft and lift.
   b. weight and fuel consumption.
   c. stall speed and angle of attack.
   d. stability and control.

6. All of the following are precautions during winter weather operations, except:

   a. use a thinner oil or one of the multiviscosity oils.
   b. preheat the engine whenever the temperature is 10°F or below.
   c. make sure your battery cells are topped off with distilled water.
   d. check for water in your fuel tanks due to snow and ice melting around fuel filler caps.

7. Which of the following statements is correct?

   a. Fueling your aircraft should take place as soon as possible after landing.
   b. If fuel does not drain freely from sumps, a line or sump is obstructed by sediment or ice.
   c. Low temperatures can change the viscosity of engine oil.
   d. All of the above.

8. All of the following recommendations are appropriate for taxiing on ice and snow, except:

   a. stop gradually to avoid locking of tires.
   b. use maximum controllable power to avoid skidding.
   c. increase distances between aircraft.
   d. all of the above are appropriate.

9. Takeoff in snow, slush, or standing water:

   a. should be avoided under all circumstances.
   b. is permissible provided the wet snow or slush is no more than 3 or 4 inches.
   c. increases drag as velocity increases.
   d. has no significant effect on the ground roll provided full power is used.

10. Which of the following statements is correct?

   a. A whiteout condition calls for an immediate shift to instrument flight.
   b. Never use carburetor heat on takeoff in very cold weather.
   c. Ice collected during climb will increase the rate of climb and range.
   d. None of the above statements is correct.

11. Carbon monoxide poisoning:

   a. usually can be detected during preflight inspection.
   b. is distinguishable because of its distinctive odor.
   c. generally presents no symptoms until the victim passes out.
   d. generally causes sluggishness and a headache.

12. Viscous hydroplaning:

   a. occurs when the standing fluid is not displaced from under the tire at a rate fast enough to allow the tire to make contact with the runway.
   b. occurs primarily at lower landing speeds.
   c. is the normal slipperiness or lubricating effect that occurs on a wet surface.
   d. results when the aircraft is either partially or totally supported by the fluid pressure between the tire and the pavement.

13. Following a flight in cold weather, it is recommended that:

   a. engine oil be removed.
   b. the carburetor be partially filled with fuel.
   c. the fuel tanks be topped off.
   d. engine oil be diluted with kerosene.

14. In the event of a crash landing:

   a. stay away from the aircraft until all gasoline fumes are gone.
   b. take care of injuries first.
   c. take time to analyze the pros and cons of each decision before proceeding.
   d. all of the above.

True/False   Circle "T" if the statement is true; "F," if it is false.

T   F   1. Aircraft structural icing normally involves liquid moisture and subfreezing temperatures.

T   F   2. Under the same temperature conditions, ice will build up twice as fast in cumulus clouds.

T   F   3. Generally, there is a lower rate of ice accretion per unit area for objects like antenna masts, pitot tubes, and wiper blades.

T   F   4. Ice accretion actually has little effect on aerodynamic performance if the aircraft is flown properly under such conditions.

T   F   5. The accumulation of frost on the upper wing surface is much less hazardous than the accumulation of ice.

T   F   6. Clear ice is frequently encountered in areas of freezing rain in temperature regions slightly below freezing.

T   F   7. Ice deposits of up to 1/2 inch on the leading edge on most airfoils have little effect on lift and stall speed.

T   F   8. Manufacturers generally can predict their product's performance in temperature extremes but offer few precautions to be taken to prevent premature failures.

T   F   9. Defective hoses and loose fittings are among the most common causes of maintenance-related accidents.

T   F   10. Cabin heaters should be checked to eliminate the possibility of carbon monoxide entering the cabin.

T   F   11. Wheel pants should be removed from fixed-gear aircraft during winter months.

T   F   12. When preheating an aircraft, place the heat ducting so it will blow hot air directly on parts of the aircraft.

T   F   13. In moderately cold weather, there is a tendency to overprime engines, resulting in poor compression.

T   F   14. *Slush drag* refers to the combination of frost and clear ice forming on the upper wing surfaces.

T   F   15. Because ice accumulation greatly increases stalling speed, airspeed should be increased during approach and landing.

T   F   16. In general, carburetor ice will form in temperatures between 32° and 80°F when the relative humidity is 50 percent or more.

T   F   17. Ice fog is similar to blowing snow.

T   F   18. In order to avoid hydroplaning, it is best to land at a slightly faster speed so that control of the aircraft will not be lost.

T   F   19. Shorter takeoff runs can be expected in deep powder snow because there is less chance of surface friction.

T   F   20. One method of keeping skis from freezing to the snow is to taxi the aircraft up onto poles placed across and under the skis.

Fill-In   Complete the following sentences.

1. After a flight in cold weather, you should do the following things:

   a. _____

   b. _____

   c. _____

   d. _____

   e. _____

   f. _____

2. A survival kit should include the following items:

   a. _____   d. _____

   b. _____   e. _____

   c. _____   f. _____

Chapter 5   Answers
Multiple Choice

1. d	6. c	11. d
2. d	7. d	12. c
3. c	8. b	13. c
4. c	9. c	14. d
5. b	10. a	

True/False

1. T	6. T	11. T	16. T
2. T	7. F	12. F	17. F
3. F	8. F	13. T	18. F
4. F	9. T	14. F	19. F
5. F	10. T	15. T	20. T

Fill-In

1. a. Fill the fuel tanks.
   b. Put on engine covers and pilot covers.
   c. Put on rotor or wing covers.
   d. Put on control locks or tied controls.
   e. Dilute the engine oil if the aircraft is equipped with an oil dilution system.
   f. Run the carburetor dry.

2. a. Metal container with a lid.　　　　d. Shelters.
   b. Life support tools.　　　　　　　　e. Life support kit.
   c. First aid kit.　　　　　　　　　　　f. Food and energy package.

Chapter 6　Takeoffs and landings

Multiple Choice　Circle the letter that corresponds to the best answer.

1. Slow-flight maneuvers:

   a. should be practiced at a low enough altitude to ensure a safe landing.
   b. should be practiced with a flight instructor aboard.
   c. merely attempt to demonstrate how slowly an airplane can be flown.
   d. are generally flown at minimum controllable airspeed, which is a set figure for every aircraft.

2. When the engine fails on a light single-engine aircraft during takeoff:

   a. attempt to get back to the airport.
   b. look through an arc of about 60 degrees left and right of the aircraft heading and select the best available landing area.
   c. concentrate on restarting the engine.
   d. raise the nose and trim into the glide at optimum speed.

3. Vortices:

   a. are generated from the moment aircraft leave the ground.

b. are governed by the weight, speed, and shape of the wing of the aircraft generating it.

c. often create wind velocities up to 130 kts.

d. all of the above.

4. If the engine fails after takeoff and below 400 feet, the following steps are recommended:

a. Depress the nose, make a sharp turn back to the runway, and turn off the fuel and mags.

b. Select the best available landing area, raise the nose to gain altitude, and turn off the fuel and mags.

c. Depress the nose, select the best available landing area, and turn off the fuel and mags.

d. Make a gentle turn back to the airport, turn off the fuel and mags, and depress the nose.

5. Which of the following statements concerning vortices is not correct?

a. The vortex flow field of large aircraft covers an area about two wingspans wide and one wingspan deep.

b. Vortices from large aircraft sink at a rate of 400 to 500 feet per minute.

c. Stay below a heavy jet's final approach path to avoid vortices.

d. Vortex strength diminishes with time and distance behind the generating aircraft.

6. Airport Advisory Service (AAS) is a service provided by an FSS located on an airport that:

a. does not have a control tower.

b. has a control tower that is temporarily closed.

c. has a control tower that is operated on a part-time basis.

d. all of the above.

7. Unicoms:

a. are located at private-use airports.

b. may provide weather information and recommended runway.

c. supplement information provided by the control tower.

d. are federally owned and controlled.

8. All of the following are causes of undershooting the runway, except:

a. flying too wide a pattern on downwind.

b. making a late turn to the base leg.

    c. flying too narrow a pattern on downwind.

    d. easing the nose up without adding power on final approach.

9. Which of the following recommendations apply with respect to correct landing approach speed?

    a. On downwind, fly no slower than two times the calibrated stall speed for your airplane.

    b. On downwind, fly no faster than the top of the flap operating range.

    c. Maintain an airspeed no lower than two times stall speed after turning final.

    d. On final approach, let your airspeed decay to stall speed as you near the runway.

10. This publication provides VASI glide angle information for standard VASIs for each runway where they are installed.

    a. *Airman's Information Manual.*

    b. *Aeronautical Information Publication.*

    c. *Airport/Facility Directory.*

    d. *Airport Information Guide.*

11. Which of the following statements is not correct?

    a. Fuel flaps should be used for all normal landings.

    b. Never let your airspeed decay below the targeted airspeed for each segment of the approach.

    c. Reducing power during approach will make the glide path shallower.

    d. One way of slowing down during final approach is to lower your landing gear.

12. The aim point on the runway:

    a. that appears to be moving toward you when you are established on final means you will probably undershoot that point.

    b. is the actual touchdown point.

    c. that appears to be constant in your windshield means you are right on target.

    d. that appears to be moving away from you is a sure sign of overshooting that point.

13. All of the following are causes of hard landings, except:

    a. not looking out ahead of the airplane and losing perspective relative to the ground.

    b. distractions.

    c. excess airspeed combined with poor flare technique.

    d. not enough elevator (or stabilator) trim, resulting in a nose-low contact with the runway.

14. To avoid the bounced landing (porpoising):

    a. always trim the airplane for a stabilized approach.

    b. keep your wings level.

    c. add power and reduce your angle of attack.

    d. none of the above.

15. A ground loop is a(n):

    a. hard landing.

    b. bounced landing.

    d. cross-control stall.

    d. uncontrolled turn.

16. Directional control accidents can be reduced by:

    a. avoiding wheelbarrowing by holding back-pressure on the controls during rollout.

    b. maintaining speed before taxiing clear of the active runway.

    c. keeping your flight path and longitudinal axis parallel to the runway centerline.

    d. *a* and *c*.

17. The most important factor in achieving landing precision is:

    a. airspeed control.

    b. landing weight.

    c. wind.

    d. density altitude.

18. If you land with a touchdown speed of 60 kts and a tailwind of 15 kts, the actual speed at touchdown (assuming no-wind landing rollout of 1000 feet) is _____ percent greater than normal, and you will need approximately _____ feet of extra runway for rollout.

    a. 15; 1000

    b. 25; 1500

    c. 15; 1500

    d. 25; 2000

19. Which of the following statements is correct?

    a. The lower end of the white arc on the airspeed indicator is Vso for all landing weights.
    b. Airplanes manufactured before the mid-1970s had their airspeed-indicator color-coded speed-range arcs marked in calibrated airspeeds, and shown in miles per hour.
    c. A tailwind under 20 kts has little effect on landing roll-out distance.
    d. A headwind under 20 kts has little effect on landing roll-out distance.

20. Which of the following factors is a relatively minor factor in landing rollout at most airports?

    a. Wind gusts.
    b. Density altitude.
    c. Runway slope.
    d. Runway surface.

21. Add about _____ percent to the landing rollout for each additional 1000 feet of density altitude.

    a. 5
    b. 10
    c. 15
    d. 20

22. The safest way to increase braking effectiveness is to:

    a. retract the flaps.
    b. hold the wheel or stick full back as brakes are applied.
    c. apply brakes as soon after touchdown as possible.
    d. wait until you approach a turnoff taxiway.

23. In executing a proper go-around procedure:

    a. accelerate to your best rate of climb, communicate with tower or Unicom, retract gear, and stay slightly to the right side of the runway as you climb out.
    b. retract the gear, adjust cowl flaps, communicate with tower or Unicom, and accelerate to your best rate of climb.
    c. communicate with tower or Unicom, retract the gear, adjust cowl flaps, and watch for departing traffic.
    d. retract the gear, accelerate to your best rate of climb, adjust your track over the ground to stay slightly to the right side of the runway, and communicate with tower or Unicom.

24. Which of the following statements concerning night flying is not correct?

    a. A long, low final is to be avoided at all costs.
    b. Take advantage of VASI guidance where available.
    c. Atmospherics can change colors, light intensities, and depth perception.
    d. Only attempt a landing at an unlighted airport with extreme caution.

True/False   Circle "T" if the statement is true, "F," if it is false.

T   F   1. Most general aviation aircraft accidents occur during takeoffs and landings.

T   F   2. The minimum controllable airspeed for the aircraft you are flying is a set figure.

T   F   3. When the first indication of a stall is felt during slow flight, reduce the angle of attack and reduce power.

T   F   4. When the engine fails after takeoff and below 400 feet, resist the temptation to turn back to the field.

T   F   5. If there is any hint of abnormality in engine performance during the early part of the takeoff run, abort the takeoff.

T   F   6. It is a rare instance when an encounter with wake turbulence would cause in-flight structural damage.

T   F   7. For VFR departures behind heavy jet aircraft, controllers are required to use at least a two-minute separation interval.

T   F   8. When flying into an airport without an operating tower, there is only one way to obtain airport-traffic information and that is through the Unicom operator.

T   F   9. The appropriate CTAF frequency can be obtained by contacting any FSS.

T   F   10. *Unicoms* are federal air/ground radio communication stations that provide airport information at private airports.

T   F   11. You should call the Unicom station approximately 50 miles from the airport and give your location relative to the airport.

T   F   12. The "self-announce" system is primarily used at large, public-use airports.

T   F   13. Of the many factors that must be considered prior to landing, wind direction and speed are two of the most important.

T   F   14. The vast majority of gear-up landings are caused by systems failure.

T   F   15. You can set up a proper and constant distance from the runway for all airports by placing the runway centerline at a specific point on the leading edge of the wing.

T   F   16. A fundamental key to flying a stabilized approach is the interrelationship of pitch and power.

T   F   17. Adding more power during final approach will make the glide path steeper.

T   F   18. Selecting an aim point on the runway is a great aid in making good, safe landings.

T   F   19. Cross-control stalls can be avoided by good planning, including a properly flown pattern and proper airspeeds.

T   F   20. The *sterile cockpit concept* means always trim the airplane for a stabilized approach in order to avoid unnecessary over-controlling.

T   F   21. A go-around might be the answer in some cases of porpoising.

T   F   22. In the case of a left crosswind on landing, the left wing must be lowered into the wind and this control input countered with right rudder.

T   F   23. Wind is the most important factor in achieving landing precision.

T   F   24. The lower end of the white arc on the airspeed indicator is the Vso for all landing weights.

T   F   25. Most airplanes built after the mid-1970s had their airspeed indicators marked in indicated airspeed.

T   F   26. In the case of a headwind greater than 10 percent of the normal touchdown speed, the rule of thumb is 0.9 minus (the headwind component divided by the normal touchdown speed) times the no-wind landing roll-out distance, which equals the new, estimated landing rollout.

T   F   27. Density altitude has a greater effect on landing rollout than takeoff distances.

T   F   28. Grass is generally a much more effective braking surface than dry concrete.

T   F   29. A properly executed go-around is one of the best accident avoidance procedures.

T   F   30. Like instrument flying, proficiency is a key factor in night flying.

Fill-In   Complete the following sentence.

1. List eight factors that affect landing roll:

a. _____   e. _____

b. _____   f. _____

c. _____   g. _____

d. _____   h. _____

Chapter 6   Answers
Multiple Choice

1. b	6. d	11. c	16. d	21. a
2. b	7. b	12. c	17. a	22. b
3. d	8. c	13. d	18. b	23. d
4. c	9. b	14. a	19. b	24. d
5. c	10. c	15. d	20. c	

True/False

1.	T	11.	F	21.	T
2.	F	12.	F	22.	T
3.	F	13.	T	23.	F
4.	T	14.	F	24.	F
5.	T	15.	T	25.	T
6.	T	16.	T	26.	T
7.	T	17.	F	27.	F
8.	F	18.	T	28.	F
9.	T	19.	T	29.	T
10.	F	20.	F	30.	T

Fill-In

1. a. Airspeed control
   b. Landing weight
   c. Wind
   d. Wind gusts

   e. Runway slope
   f. Density altitude
   g. Runway surface
   h. Runway length

Chapter 7   Midair collisions

Multiple Choice   Circle the letter that corresponds to the best answer.

1. All of the following factors present problems to air traffic controllers in maintaining safe separation among aircraft, except:

   a. general aviation aircraft are much slower than air carrier aircraft.
   b. some operations of general aviation aircraft are not under positive control of ATC.
   c. less experienced pilots fly general aviation aircraft.
   d. not all general aviation aircraft are equipped to provide as much information about their location to ATC as is provided by air carrier aircraft.

2. The greater the speed disparity in a traffic mix:

   a. the greater number of aircraft can be landed in a given period of time.
   b. the easier it is for controllers to ensure adequate spacing.
   c. the greater the traffic congestion and controller workload.
   d. none of the above.

3. The Positive Control Area consists of certain airspace within the United States that begins at:

   a. 10,000 feet MSL.
   b. 14,500 feet MSL.
   c. 18,000 feet MSL.
   d. 30,000 feet MSL.

4. If you fly in uncontrolled airspace above 1200 feet AGL, but below 10,000 feet MSL, you must have:

   a. at least 1 mile visibility.
   b. at least 1 mile visibility and fly no closer than 500 feet below, 1000 feet above, and at least 2000 feet horizontally from any clouds.
   c. at least 5 miles visibility and remain 1000 feet above and below the clouds, as well as 1 mile horizontally.
   d. at least 1 mile visibility and fly no closer than 1000 feet below, 500 feet above, and at least 1000 feet horizontally from any clouds.

5. Airspace that surrounds certain airports and extends from the surface up to the Continental Control Area are called:

   a. *transition areas.*
   b. *positive control areas.*
   c. *terminal control areas.*
   d. *control zones.*

6. A plus or circle symbol appearing on a controller's radarscope:

   a. can be safely ignored by a busy controller.
   b. is generated by an aircraft equipped with a transponder but no encoding altimeter.
   c. indicate nonparticipating VFR aircraft.
   d. provide little information that is useful for traffic advisories or separation.

7. The services a pilot receives within the ARSA include:

   a. traffic advisories for both IFR and VFR aircraft.
   b. weather advisories for IFR aircraft.
   c. Fixed Base Operator services.
   d. all of the above.

8. Which of the following statements is not correct?

   a. Pilots of both controlled and uncontrolled aircraft have the legal responsibility for traffic separation by visual means.
   b. A square or asterisk radar symbol can be safely ignored by a busy controller.
   c. The vague smudges on the radarscope are generated by aircraft without any transponder equipment.
   d. Air traffic control computers that are currently in use are capable of tracking an unlimited number of targets simultaneously.

9. TCASI:

   a. is designed for general aviation use and includes only traffic advisories.
   b. allows the transponder to be addressed individually and enables data to be passed between ground radars and airplanes and between airplanes.
   c. must be aboard all airliners with more than 30 seats by December 31, 1992.
   d. emits a "squitter" signal that contains a unique code, or address.

10. Nearly all midair collisions occur:

    a. during daylight hours and in IFR conditions.
    b. during daylight hours and in VFR conditions.
    c. in uncontrolled airspace 20 miles from any airport.
    d. in controlled airspace within 1 mile from an airport.

11. Which of the following statements is correct?

    a. The eye is vulnerable to the vagaries of the mind. In other words, we see and identify only what the mind lets us see.
    b. The problem of focusing is more common at lower altitudes, causing *empty-field myopia*.
    c. To accept what we see, we only need to receive cues from one eye, which is referred to as *binocular vision*.
    d. Although our eyes accept light rays from an arc of nearly 270 degrees, they are limited to a relatively narrow area (approximately 180 degrees) in which they can actually focus and classify an object.

12. Lighting affects our vision stimuli in a number of ways, including:

    a. glare, particularly on a sunny day over a cloud deck or during flight directly into the sun.
    b. a well-lit object will have a high degree of contrast and easy to detect.

   c. trying to find an airplane over a cluttered background.

   d. all of the above.

13. All of the following are proper scanning techniques, except:

   a. concentrate on the areas most critical to you at any given time.

   b. try to look everywhere possible.

   c. in the traffic pattern, clear yourself before every turn.

   d. on descent and climbout, make gentle S-turns to see if anyone is in your way.

14. The block system of scanning:

   a. normally gives you about 25 blocks in your scan area.

   b. includes a sweeping motion from right to left.

   c. includes a series of eye fixations at different points in space with each fix or block 10-15 degrees wide.

   d. none of the above.

15. An instrument panel scan should start with the:

   a. attitude indicator.

   b. altimeter.

   c. airspeed indicator.

   d. directional gyro.

16. A collision avoidance checklist includes all of the following, except:

   a. your eyesight, mental and physical condition.

   b. avoid crowded airspace en route, such as directly over a VOR.

   c. adhering to standard operating procedures.

   d. all of the above.

True/False   Circle "T" if the statement is true, "F," if it is false.

T   F   1. In recent years, most midair collisions have involved two general aviation aircraft.

T   F   2. Reports of near midair collisions between air carriers and general aviation aircraft have actually decreased in recent years.

T   F   3. A slow aircraft mixed in the approach stream of faster aircraft requires a large, empty space behind it.

T   F   4. Weather minimums is one factor that determines whether airspace is controlled or not.

T   F   5. The areas of uncontrolled airspace in the United States are expanding as a result of fewer Flight Service Stations.

T   F   6. The maximum altitude you may fly and remain in uncontrolled airspace is 18,000 feet MSL.

T   F   7. The Continental Control Area covers the entire 48 contiguous states, Alaska, and the District of Columbia from 14,500 feet MSL on up.

T   F   8. Transition areas beginning at 700 feet above the surface are shown on Sectional maps in the magenta (red) color.

T   F   9. ARSAs are blocks of airspace surrounding the busiest airports throughout the United States.

T   F   10. Aircraft equipment requirements to operate into Group II TCA include Mode C transponders.

T   F   11. One of the primary reasons for establishing ARSAs was to reduce near misses and midair collisions.

T   F   12. A basic transponder fixes the geographical position and altitude of an aircraft on the controller's radar.

T   F   13. Air traffic controllers must issue advisories to controlled aircraft about nonparticipating traffic observed on the radar that may pose a threat of collision.

T   F   14. All airliners with more than 30 seats must be equipped with TCAS II in order to fly in the United States after December 31, 1993.

T   F   15. The TCAS II computer tracks and lists every transponder it detects within a bubble of airspace measuring a minimum of 15 nautical miles.

T   F   16. In most midair collisions, at least one of the pilots involved could have seen the other in time to avoid contact.

T   F   17. It has been estimated that 80 percent of our total information intake is through the eyes.

T   F   18. One function of the eye that is a source of constant problems to a pilot is the time required to refocus on near and far objects.

T   F   19. The distance of an aircraft on a collision course will remain seemingly motionless and then suddenly bloom into a huge mass. This is known as *binocular vision*.

T   F   20. Proper scanning calls for looking behind and below at least once during final approach.

T   F   21. In normal flight, you can generally avoid the threat of a midair collision by scanning an area 60 degrees to the left and to the right of your center visual area.

T   F   22. The amount of time spent scanning depends on the workload inside the cockpit and density of traffic outside.

T   F   23. Instrument scanning is not necessary if you limit your flying to VFR conditions.

T   F   24. It is a good idea to skim over the attitude indicator each time you move on to a new instrument, since this is your chief control instrument.

T   F   25. All planes have blind spots.

Fill-In   Complete the following sentence.

1. A collision-avoidance checklist includes:

a. _____

b. _____

c. _____

d. _____

e. _____

f. _____

g. _____

h. _____

i. _____

Chapter 7   Answers
Multiple Choice

1. c	6. b	11. a	16. d
2. c	7. a	12. d	
3. c	8. d	13. b	
4. b	9. a	14. c	
5. d	10. b	15. a	

True/False

1. T	6. F	11. T	16. T	21. T
2. F	7. T	12. F	17. T	22. T
3. T	8. T	13. F	18. T	23. F
4. T	9. F	14. T	19. F	24. T
5. F	10. F	15. T	20. T	25. T

Fill-In

1. a. Check yourself.
   b. Plan your flight ahead of time.
   c. Clean windows.
   d. Adhere to standard operating procedures.
   e. Avoid crowds.
   f. Compensate for design.
   g. Equip for safety.
   h. Talk and listen.
   i. Scan.

Chapter 8   Miscellaneous in-flight hazards

Multiple Choice   Circle the letter that corresponds to the best answer.

1. Which of the following statements regarding dead reckoning navigation is not correct?

   a. Dead reckoning can be used in conjunction with VOR to arrive at a running fix.
   b. Dead reckoning can be combined with radio navigation to determine an approximate position.

c. *Crabbing*, or turning into the wind, results in some loss of groundspeed, but this can be ignored when the crab angle is less than 10 degrees.

d. A rule of thumb states that 90 percent of the time the maximum dead reckoning error (per hour of flight) is 10 miles plus 10 percent of the estimated distance flown during that hour.

2. Which of the following aircraft has a lower incidence of fuel selector-related incidents?

   a. Beech Bonanza.
   b. Beech Travel Air.
   c. Cessna 150.
   d. Piper Comanche.

3. Fuel selectors:

   a. on some models require you to go through the OFF position when changing tanks.
   b. are similar for all aircraft because of FAA certification standards.
   c. must be located "so that the pilot can reach it upon entering the aircraft."
   d. none of the above.

4. The loss of a pneumatic system:

   a. represents close to 10 percent of the total general aviation accidents in recent years.
   b. is an emergency, but generally never life-threatening.
   c. with no backup system or backup instruments can make flying under IFR conditions virtually impossible.
   d. *a* and *c* are correct statements.

5. The attitude and heading gyroscopic instruments in most single-engine airplanes are powered by a _____ system.

   a. pressure.
   b. vacuum.
   c. electrical.
   d. hydraulic.

6. A slow decrease in gauge indication may indicate a:

   a. dirty filter.
   b. pump failure.
   c. collapsed line.
   d. none of the above.

7. Impending failure of gyroscopic instruments might appear in any of the following ways, except:

    a. a heading indicator that shows excessive drift.
    b. sluggish response by turn indicators.
    c. noise.
    d. attitude indicators showing no deviation from level flight when the aircraft is, in fact, straight and level.

8. Night flying is generally safer for all of the following reasons, except:

    a. radio traffic is sparse.
    b. judgment of the landing approach and flare is easier.
    c. there is less traffic.
    d. the air is usually smoother and cooler.

9. All of the following are good tips while night flying, except:

    a. plan a more generous fuel reserve.
    b. select high cruising altitudes.
    c. select the most direct route to your destination.
    d. keep panel lights as dim as possible.

10. The final approach to landing at night should be made:

    a. at a steeper angle than a daylight approach.
    b. at a shallower angle than a daylight approach.
    c. at about the same angle as a daylight approach.
    d. by focusing your attention on the area immediately in front of the airplane.

11. Military training routes:

    a. below 1500 feet AGL are identified by three-digit numbers.
    b. above 1500 feet AGL are identified by four-digit numbers.
    c. vary in width.
    d. all of the above.

12. Most wire-strikes are caused by:

    a. poor night vision.
    b. undershooting the approach.
    c. performing aerobatics.
    d. distraction in the cockpit.

13. Which of the following statements are correct?

    a. Wires are generally marked as hazards on sectional charts.
    b. Nearly four out of ten wire-strike accidents involve takeoffs from soft and wet sod airstrips.
    c. Close to 25 percent of wire-strike accidents involve an aircraft over its gross takeoff weight.
    d. None of the above statements is correct.

14. Presently:

    a. safety seats used in aircraft must meet FAR Part 141 standards.
    b. the FAA recommends that children under 40 lbs. should be held in an adult's lap with a seatbelt secure around both persons.
    c. there are few aircraft safety seats designed for use by infants and small children.
    d. the FAA recommends the use of any automobile safety seat for infants aboard aircraft.

15. Shoulder harnesses in aircraft:

    a. could significantly reduce serious injuries and fatalities in aircraft.
    b. have been standard equipment in front seats of all general aviation aircraft since 1978.
    c. should be worn snug across your chest.
    d. all of the above.

True/False   Circle "T" if the statement is true; "F," if it is false.

T   F   1. Dead reckoning is a relatively simple procedure that can be combined with radio navigation to determine approximate position at all times.

T   F   2. If more than one wind condition is encountered en route, they may be arithmetically averaged if wind directions do not vary by more than 90 degrees and wind speeds are within 15 kts of each other.

T   F   3. Dead reckoning is more reliable than VOR navigation.

T   F   4. Dead reckoning can be used in conjunction with VOR to arrive at a running fix.

T   F   5. Some aircraft have been shown to have a higher incidence of fuel selector-related accidents.

T   F   6. Fuel-selector valves are fairly standardized throughout the industry.

T   F   7. Switching fuel tanks at low altitudes is permissible except while on final approach.

T   F   8. It is not legal to fly aircraft without dual power sources for gyroscopic instruments.

T   F   9. Pneumatic systems, like other mechanical systems, can malfunction suddenly or slowly.

T   F   10. Most pilots are trained to fly on a "partial panel," and consequently, there is generally no problem in deciding when to make that decision.

T   F   11. The heading indicator should be accurately set to some magnetic reference, such as a properly calibrated magnetic compass, just before takeoff.

T   F   12. In the event of instruments becoming inoperative or giving false readings, it is best to cover them while attempting to fly on a partial panel.

T   F   13. Generally, night flying is more pleasant than daytime flight because clouds and bad weather are easier to detect.

T   F   14. At night, it is best to select lower cruising altitudes so that you can see land forms better.

T   F   15. During night flights, the panel lights should be as bright as possible, so as to avoid misinterpreted readings.

T   F   16. While flying at 12,000 feet at night without supplemental oxygen, a person's vision is only about one-half of that normally experienced at sea level.

T   F   17. Focusing your attention on the area immediately in front of the airplane during a night landing is the best practice.

T   F   18. FSS briefers normally will inform a pilot about MTRs along the intended route.

T   F   19. Pilots should contact FSS stations within 100 nm of a particular MTR to obtain current information on route usage in their vicinity.

T   F   20. Most wire-strike accidents occur in the general vicinity of an airport familiar to the pilot.

T   F   21. Many wire-strike accidents occur after flying low over a lake or river.

T   F   22. Obstructions lower than 200 feet AGL are not shown on sectional charts.

T   F   23. The FARs are quite explicit regarding child-restraint systems.

T   F   24. Safety seats used in aircraft must meet the requirements of FAA Technical Standard Order C-100.

T   F   25. All pilots are responsible under FARs to brief passengers on the use of seatbelts.

Chapter 8   Answers

Multiple Choice

1. d	6. a	11. c
2. c	7. d	12. b
3. a	8. b	13. d
4. c	9. c	14. c
5. b	10. a	15. d

True/False

1. T	6. F	11. T	16. T	21. T
2. T	7. F	12. T	17. F	22. T
3. F	8. F	13. F	18. F	23. F
4. T	9. T	14. F	19. T	24. T
5. T	10. F	15. F	20. T	25. T

Chapter 9   Ground operation and maintenance

Multiple Choice   Circle the letter that corresponds to the best answer.

1. All of the following precautions should be taken while taxiing, except:

   a. you should avoid studying maps, running cockpit checklists, or copying ATC clearances.

b. taxi fast enough so that you will not be a hazard to other taxiing aircraft.

c. always have a guide to assist you when taxiing in congested areas.

d. check your brakes before moving more than the length of the aircraft.

2. When securing your airplane, it is good practice to:

a. fasten all doors and windows properly.

b. cover all engine openings.

c. lock all control surfaces.

d. all of the above.

3. Tie-down anchors for single-engine aircraft should provide a minimum holding power of about:

a. 1,000 lbs.

b. 3,000 lbs.

c. 6,000 lbs.

d. 12,500 lbs.

4. The problem with nylon or Dacron ropes is their:

a. tendency to loosen and slip.

b. lesser strength and durability compared to manila ropes.

c. susceptibility to attract fungus.

d. tendency to deteriorate after 3 to 5 years.

5. Which of the following statements is correct?

a. Portable tie-downs can be used as permanent anchors if they are checked periodically.

b. Ailerons can be secured by wrapping the seatbelt around the control wheel or stick and putting the control full back or nearly so.

c. Chocks are not necessary when brakes are set and the aircraft is properly tied down.

d. None of the above statements is correct.

6. As an owner you may perform certain types of maintenance on your airplane, including all of the following, except:

a. clean, grease, or replace landing gear wheel bearings.

b. replace defective safety wire and cotter keys.

c. replace hydraulic connections.

d. replace the battery and check fluid levels and specific gravity.

7. A typical engine inspection by an aircraft owner might include all of the following, except:

 a. remove, clean, and inspect spark plugs for wear.
 b. check brake fluid for level and proper type.
 c. replace the air filter.
 d. replace the generator or alternator belt for proper tension and fraying.

8. This type of AD is issued by telegram when an immediate action is required to correct an unsafe condition:

 a. service bulletin.
 b. emergency AD.
 c. immediate adopted rule.
 d. notice of proposed rulemaking.

9. Airworthiness Directives:

 a. are not applicable to aircraft certificated in certain categories, such as experimental or restricted.
 b. all require immediate compliance.
 c. are sent directly to the operator, including owners, lessors, and lessees.
 d. none of the above.

10. Which of the following statements is not correct?

 a. About one-half of exhaust system failures occur in the exhaust gas-to-air heat exchanger.
 b. The presence of exhaust gases in the cabin might affect the general efficiency of the pilot.
 c. Most exhaust system failures occur in the exhaust stacks, manifolds, and tailpipes.
 d. Two primary reasons for most exhaust system failures are inadequate and infrequent inspections and lack of routine and preventive maintenance between inspections.

11. Fuel contamination can result from:

 a. poorly filtered tanks.
 b. improper mixing of fuel additives.
 c. improper preflight action by the pilot.
 d. all of the above.

12. The FARs:

   a. require that aircraft fuel filler openings be marked to show the word FUEL and the minimum fuel grade or designation for the engines.
   b. allow a fuel grade lower than that specified under certain circumstances.
   d. permit the use of automotive fuel only when avgas is unavailable.
   d. caution owners and operators of aircraft regarding the use of automobile additives for aviation engines.

13. Spark plug fouling can be reduced by:

   a. maintaining proper cylinder-head temperatures.
   b. avoiding low-power letdowns.
   c. avoiding over-rich conditions.
   d. all of the above.

14. Which of the following statements is correct?

   a. Reciprocating engines may use jet fuel, but avgas cannot be substituted for jet fuel.
   b. Generally water and other contaminants will stay suspended in a tank so partial draining of the fuel tank is generally not sufficient.
   c. All fuel entering a tank should be filtered.
   d. *b* and *c* are correct.

True/False Circle "T" if the statement is true; "F," if it is false.

T   F   1. Taxi slow enough that the aircraft will stop instantly when the brakes are applied.

T   F   2. Hand-propping an aircraft can be performed by an individual without assistance if the wheels are properly chocked and the controls are locked.

T   F   3. Engines should be shut down when enplaning and deplaning passengers unless there are qualified persons on the ramp capable of controlling pedestrian traffic.

T   F   4. It is preferable to tie down aircraft headed into the wind.

T   F   5. Tie-down ropes should be capable of resisting a pull of about 3000 lbs. for single-engine aircraft.

T   F   6. Manila ropes are less susceptible to rotting and attack by fungus than nylon ropes.

T   F   7. When tying down an aircraft, do not leave any slack in the line.

T   F   8. Chains are superior to rope of any kind when tying down aircraft.

T   F   9. As an owner-pilot, FAR Part 43 allows you to perform certain types of inspections and maintenance on your airplane.

T   F   10. As an owner-pilot, FAR Part 43 allows you to replace a propeller.

T   F   11. Upon completion of maintenance by an owner-pilot, a description of the work performed must be made in the appropriate logbook.

T   F   12. A typical cabin inspection might include checking rudder pedals and toe brakes for operation and security.

T   F   13. An airworthiness certificate prescribes the conditions and limitations, including inspection, under which a product may continue to be operated.

T   F   14. An NPRM is issued when prompt action is essential.

T   F   15. Compliance times specified in ADs vary considerably.

T   F   16. FARs do not require the person performing an annual inspection to provide the owner with a list of discrepancies, including noncompliance with ADs.

T   F   17. Exhaust manifold and stack fatigue failures usually occur at welded or clamp joints.

T   F   18. Anytime exhaust fumes are detected in the cabin, immediately shut off the engine and look for a place to land.

T   F   19. Storing aircraft with partially filled tanks can lead to fuel contamination.

T   F   20. When using automotive fuel in aircraft, special attention must be given to the octane numbers.

T   F   21. After flight or ground operations, before engine shutdown, advance the throttle to about 1800 rpm for 15 to 20 seconds.

T   F   22. The damage and accidents by improper fuel grade or contaminated fuel are almost always avoidable.

Chapter 9 Answers

Multiple Choice

1. b	6. c	11. d
2. d	7. d	12. a
3. b	8. b	13. d
4. a	9. d	14. c
5. b	10. c	

True/False

1. T	6. F	11. T	16. F	21. T
2. F	7. F	12. T	17. T	22. T
3. T	8. T	13. T	18. F	
4. T	9. T	14. F	19. T	
5. T	10. F	15. T	20. F	

Index